THE

DEEP AND

THE PAST

THE DEEP AND THE PAST

BY

DAVID · B · ERICSON

&

GOESTA WOLLIN

New York: Alfred A. Knopf

1964

L. C. catalog card number: 64–17698

THIS IS A BORZOI BOOK,
PUBLISHED BY ALFRED A. KNOPF, INC.

FIRST EDITION

This book is for

JANET *and* KAREN

ACKNOWLEDGMENTS

This book is based primarily on our studies of cores of deep-sea sediment and the results of our studies, which have first been published in scientific journals. However, in order to tell our story, we have drawn on the work of many scientists. It is impossible to thank them all adequately for the great debt we owe them. With the exception of the relatively few men and women mentioned here, in the body of the book, and in the bibliography, this debt, of necessity, cannot be acknowledged. How many scientists have made a valuable contribution is indicated by the fact that James Geikie, when he wrote his book *The Great Ice Age,* around 1870, had to abandon his plan of preparing a complete bibliography: it would have required a volume in itself. Today, after almost a hundred years—during which the output of literature on the Pleistocene has accelerated vastly—such a task would be almost impossible.

We are deeply indebted to Maurice Ewing, Director of the Lamont Geological Observatory, Columbia University, for the privilege of working on the cores that were obtained through his vigorous leadership, and for his generous support of the work and his active participation in it. Maurice Ewing's enthusiastic interest and his advice and collaboration in all phases of the study of the cores have been invaluable sources of encouragement and stimulation, for which we are deeply grateful.

The studies that led to this book began at the Woods Hole Oceanographic Institution just after World War II. With the founding of the Lamont Geological Observatory in 1949, the work was transferred to the Observatory at Palisades, New York. The scientific parties and crews of each of the more than forty deep-sea expeditions involved in the gathering of data contributed directly or indirectly to this book. To these seagoing scientists and mariners, too numerous to mention, we are extremely grateful.

The great majority of the cores we studied were obtained during deep-sea expeditions sponsored by the Office of Naval Research. The study of the cores was supported by the National Science

Foundation. Thanks are extended to William E. Benson and Richard G. Bader of the National Science Foundation for their helpful suggestions and many courtesies.

We are greatly indebted to Janet Wollin, Matilda Flannery, Nancy Anderson, Julie Ryder, and Ann Riley for able assistance in the laboratory investigations and in the preparation of the illustrations and the manuscript.

We express our sincere appreciation to J. Lamar Worzel, John E. Nafe, Bruce C. Heezen, W. Arnold Finck, John I. Ewing, Charles L. Drake, Gordon Hamilton, Allen W. H. Bé, Kia K. Wang, William Sackett, Charles T. Fray, Manik Talwani, Marie Tharp, Howard Wehner, Angelo Ludas, John T. Stanley, Harold Siroonian, and the other members of the staff of the Lamont Geological Observatory whose contributions made this book possible. Among former members of the Lamont staff, Albert Bally, William Wiles, Ivan Tolstoy, Walter Beckmann, and Robert Menzies deserve our particular thanks for assistance in obtaining and studying the cores.

To J. Laurence Kulp, Wallace S. Broecker, and Hans Suess we owe thanks for radiocarbon age determinations. We are particularly grateful to William Sackett for the protactinium method of dating.

We are also indebted to Carleton S. Coon, who read the manuscript of this book and gave us much valuable advice, particularly regarding the history of early man.

We are grateful, too, to a great number of scientists from all over the world for valuable advice and stimulating discussion of the problems of research in the depths of the sea. We are particularly indebted to Gustaf Arrhenius, M. N. Bramlette, Walter Bucher, A. P. Crary, Cesare Emiliani, C. O'D. Iselin, Fritz Koczy, Ph. H. Kuenen, Börje Kullenberg, Frances L. Parker, Hans Pettersson, Fred B Phleger, Roger R. Revelle, William Riedel, Francis P. Shepard, and John D. H. Wiseman.

We also wish to express our thanks to Angus Cameron, editor of Alfred A. Knopf, Inc., for counsel, guidance, and very important suggestions regarding the organization of the book. Our association with Mr. Cameron has been most enjoyable and instructive.

D. B. E. AND G. W.

Palisades, New York / April 1964

CONTENTS

PLATES

FIGURES

THE
DEEP AND
THE PAST

1

THE IMPORTANCE OF THE

PLEISTOCENE RECORD

A MOMENTOUS event in organic evolution, the emergence of man, occurred during the Pleistocene, the geological epoch of the ice ages. Only once before in the history of the earth had an event of comparable importance taken place; that was when life first originated out of inorganic matter.

Man is the product of the selective pressure of the brutal climatic changes of this latest epoch of earth history on a group of unspecialized primates. The Pleistocene is the great backdrop of time for man. If the ice ages and the topographical changes of the Pleistocene had not begun about one and a half million years ago, it is probable that our species would have failed to develop, for the evolution of man is intimately related to the glacial and interglacial ages of the Pleistocene Epoch. The growth of continental glaciers compelled proto-men and early men to migrate and favored the splitting up of populations into small groups. The Pleistocene was above all a time of restless change. As the continental glaciers grew, they absorbed water from the oceans, causing a lowering of sea level and the opening of new routes and land connections. Migration along these new routes reunited tribes that had formerly been separated. The reaction when they met, we may be sure, was fierce intertribal fighting and intertribal loving, for such paradoxical behavior is deeply engrained in man's nature. And no doubt with good reason. Intertribal fighting intensified selection, and intertribal mating led to the recombination of advantageous genes, which in turn increased the probability that these genes would survive and eventually become dominant in the gene pool of the population. Had early man not been a wrangling, libidinous scoundrel, it is doubtful that he could ever have made his way to his present evolutionary pinnacle.

Fundamentally, man is an accident, the culmination of a series of highly improbable coincidences. Among the millions of species of animals that have existed since the beginning of life, man is unique. Of all the fantastic evolutionary adaptions to peculiar environments, man's has brought him an unparalleled degree of awareness of his environment and of his place in it. What did proto-man have that no other animal has ever had? Apparently through chance accumulation of genes, he possessed a combination of traits that interacted in such a way as to reinforce one another in the course of natural selection and thereby led to an acceleration of the development of his brain. Foremost was the primate hand, which could transform the smallest spark of ingenuity in the brain into tangible means of surviving. Eventually this led to the invention and use of tools and weapons, which intensified the interaction between manual and mental dexterity. The effect was like that of a fire which creates its own draft. With increased intelligence came the use of symbols, language, new methods of child care. This last made possible the slower maturation necessary for the development of a highly complex brain and nervous system. The human type of mother-child relationship and language probably emerged at the time that the large-brained, fully bipedal hominids of the second glacial age began to make their fine tools, use fire, and perfect their hunting methods. Under the selective pressure of the more complex social life, the brain evolved further, until the stage of human evolution typified by *Homo sapiens* was reached during the last interglacial age. Man came to full development during the last ice age.

Evolution, or genetic change within populations of men, has not ceased in spite of the fact that we have attained a highly complex culture. There still are, and always will be, important innate differences between individual men; and selection, whether "natural" or otherwise, continues, insofar as some types leave many more descendants than others. Where the evolutionary process is taking mankind is the most vital question bearing on man's future as a species, and the answer is closely related to man's understanding of his past. In order to replace the blind force of natural selection by conscious direction, man needs greater knowledge of his nature, evolution, and the fossil record of his birth and changes.

The publication of Charles Darwin's *Origin of Species* in 1859 gave the first great stimulus to the search for documentation of the fossil record of man's ancestry. This search has brought in considerable evidence about the main stages of man's development during the Pleistocene. In the past few years Louis and Mary Leakey have made discoveries of fascinating interest at Olduvai Gorge in Tanganyika. Recently they have found evidence that a primitive species of the genus *Homo,* to which modern man belongs, was making stone tools about 1,750,000 years ago.

The questions that have most aroused man's curiosity are how old he is and at what rate he developed. The timing of man's beginnings and the rate of man's change in the past are crucial to the theory of evolution and to many related branches of science.

In the past, most human and near-human fossils were fitted into a time succession elaborated from the sequence of sedimentary deposits within which the fossils occurred. At best, this provided only a relative chronology. One point, however, seemed quite certain: man had evolved during the climatic changes of the Pleistocene. But attempts to assign ages in years to the stages of man's evolutionary rise amounted to little more than conjecture, usually influenced by some favorite theory of the cause of glaciations. The divergence of estimates of the duration of the Pleistocene, which ranged from 300,000 to about 1,000,000 years, testifies to the uncertainties involved.

Now, through the study of deep-sea sediments, we have discovered the first complete record of the Pleistocene, the epoch which brought forth both ice and man. Our time scale dates the beginning of the Pleistocene at about 1,500,000 years ago. This date will necessitate a revision of the basic time scale of prehistoric events and particularly the rate of human development, past and future. We can now put the chronology of human evolution in order.

By our chronology we date the second ice age, during which the early men called *Pithecanthropus* appeared, as between 1,205,-000 and 1,060,000 years ago, and the last interglacial, when *Homo sapiens* appeared, between 340,000 and 115,000 years ago. This time scale is in disagreement with a widely accepted chronology based on the ratio between oxygen isotopes in cores of sediment from the Atlantic and the Caribbean. According to it, the second ice age took place between 200,000 and 170,000 years ago and the last interglacial between 100,000 and 65,000 years ago. This greatly shortened timetable has met with skepticism among a few students of human evolution; they regard the implied rate of man's evolution as improbably rapid. Our chronology stretches out the span of the evolution of man and allows time for the slow accumulation of small changes which Darwin assumed to be the basis of evolution.

Geochronology, the science of dating the past, generally draws the methods for its main objective, the development of time scales, from geology, botany, zoology, physics, and chemistry. These disciplines will be influenced indirectly by the discovery of the complete record of the Pleistocene. Though the new time scale will be most important in the study of the evolution of man, it will also have application in such fields as biological evolution in general, prehistoric archaeology, the study of the succession of mammals during the Pleistocene and of the rates of erosion and mountain building and other geological processes. The significance of the time scale for organic evolution cannot be overestimated. The animal assemblages of the Pleistocene have provided scientists with an opportunity to follow the development of species and relate the stages to the climatic changes of the epoch. This kind of evidence indicates that the most rapid development occurred among the Pleistocene elephants of Europe. By applying the generally accepted chronologies of the Pleistocene to the speciation of these elephants, it has been estimated that the minimum time required for the divergence of two distinct species from a common ancestor was about 500,000 years. According to our time scale, however, the minimum time is more nearly 1,400,000 years.

In 1947 we turned to the deep sea in search of the complete record of the Pleistocene. From time to time we have reported the progress of our work in scientific journals, often in collaboration with fellow scientists at the Lamont Geological Observatory of Columbia University. In October 1964 we, together with Dr. Maurice Ewing, director of Lamont, published the first report on the discovery of the complete stratigraphical, chronological, and climatic record of the Pleistocene. The report is a brief summary of the main result of our studies of Lamont's unique collection of cores of deep-sea sediment from all the oceans. By far the largest in the world, the collection contains more than three thousand cores, obtained in forty-four expeditions.

Two thirds of the surface of the earth is covered by the 300 million cubic miles of water we call the oceans. The abundance of life on the continents is meager in comparison with that in the oceans. Even the lushest of tropical regions cannot compete with the oceans in the number of organisms and the diversity of forms within any given area.

Beneath the oceans lie the clues to many fundamental questions regarding the origin of the earth and its great features, the continents, the evolution of life, and the climatic history and chronology of the Pleistocene. For millions of years a mantle of sediment has been accumulating on the floor of the sea, particle by particle, slowly settling from the surface like a perpetual fall of snow. The "snow flakes" are of many kinds: minute particles of mineral matter wafted from the continents by winds and ocean currents, flakes of volcanic ash that settle after volcanic eruptions, the tiny shells and skeletons of countless millions of sea creatures, and the ashes of burnt-out meteorites and cosmic dust from outer space.

This sediment is much more than mere mud. To the geologist it tells a thrilling story of dramatic and catastrophic events in the history of the earth: the outpourings of volcanoes, advances and retreats of great ice sheets on the continents, the burning dryness of desert conditions, the destructive effect of floods and past climatic changes.

In what environment the first chemical reaction that could be called life took place we do not know; most probably it happened in a shallow sea. All we can say with certainty is that the earliest traces of life occur in ancient marine sediments. Our ancestral home was in the seas and oceans. And although our ancestors came ashore hundreds of millions of years ago, we and all other life on the continents are dependent for existence upon the oceans; they are the primary source of rain, without which the continents would be deserts. Probably it is not mere coincidence that in our solar system it is the "watery planet" on which intelligence has reached a high enough level to begin the probing of outer space.

In studying the time sequence of ancient sedimentary rocks exposed on the continents, early geologists recognized four major divisions, which they called Primary, Secondary, Tertiary, and Quaternary. The terms *Primary* and *Secondary* have fallen into disuse, largely because it is now known that the "Primary" rocks are not really primary. Instead, we now use the terms *Paleozoic* and *Mesozoic,* and the time intervals represented by the series of rocks are known as the Paleozoic and Mesozoic eras. For Tertiary and Quaternary the term *Cenozoic* has been substituted; the time equivalent of the rocks is known as the Cenozoic Era. Originally the Cenozoic Era was subdivided into six periods. Starting with the oldest, these are the Paleocene, the Eocene, the Oligocene, the Miocene, the Pliocene, and the Pleistocene. The last is equivalent to the Quaternary Era of earlier geologists. Since we now know that the Cenozoic Era was no longer in duration than some of the shorter periods, or subdivisions, of the earlier eras, it is customary to regard the Cenozoic as including only one period, the Cenozoic, and to classify its subdivisions as epochs. Accordingly, the Quaternary Era becomes the Pleistocene Epoch. Or, by all reason, it should. Actually, however, the term *Quaternary* is still in use; this is sometimes defended by the argument that the Quaternary includes both Pleistocene and so-called Recent time. But there is no valid reason to believe that the Pleistocene Epoch has come to an end. We agree with R. F. Flint that we are living in the Pleistocene. Moreover, the derivation of the word *Pleistocene*—which means "most recent" in Greek—makes a distinction between Pleistocene and Recent time illogical; can the Recent be more recent than the "Most Recent"?

The Pleistocene has been a battleground for scientists since it was named more than a hundred years ago. A complete record of it will help solve many problems, among them that most tantalizing of all geological problems, the cause of the ice ages. One of the chief reasons for the great controversy regarding the Pleistocene is probably its close connection with the evolution of man, for truly man is the child of the Pleistocene.

The record of the Pleistocene on the continents is like a tattered old book from which many pages, even entire chapters, are missing. This is due partly to the destruction of the evidence of earlier glaciations by more recent advances of the continental glaciers, but largely it is due to erosion, the ceaseless removal of unconsolidated sediments by rainfall, streams, and rivers which little by little transfer all deposits on the continents to the oceans. As the record on the continents is nearly illegible, we turned to the oceans, the universal, age-old archive where we might hope to find the data missing from the continental record.

Ancient peoples must have felt the universality and permanence of the oceans; this seems to be reflected in the conception of an encompassing ocean bounding the habitable world, an idea which recurs in many of the myths that explain creation. The Babylonians looked on the world as a vast round mountain rising from the midst of a universal sheet of water. In the Hebrew scriptures, at the word of God the waters were gathered together in one place and

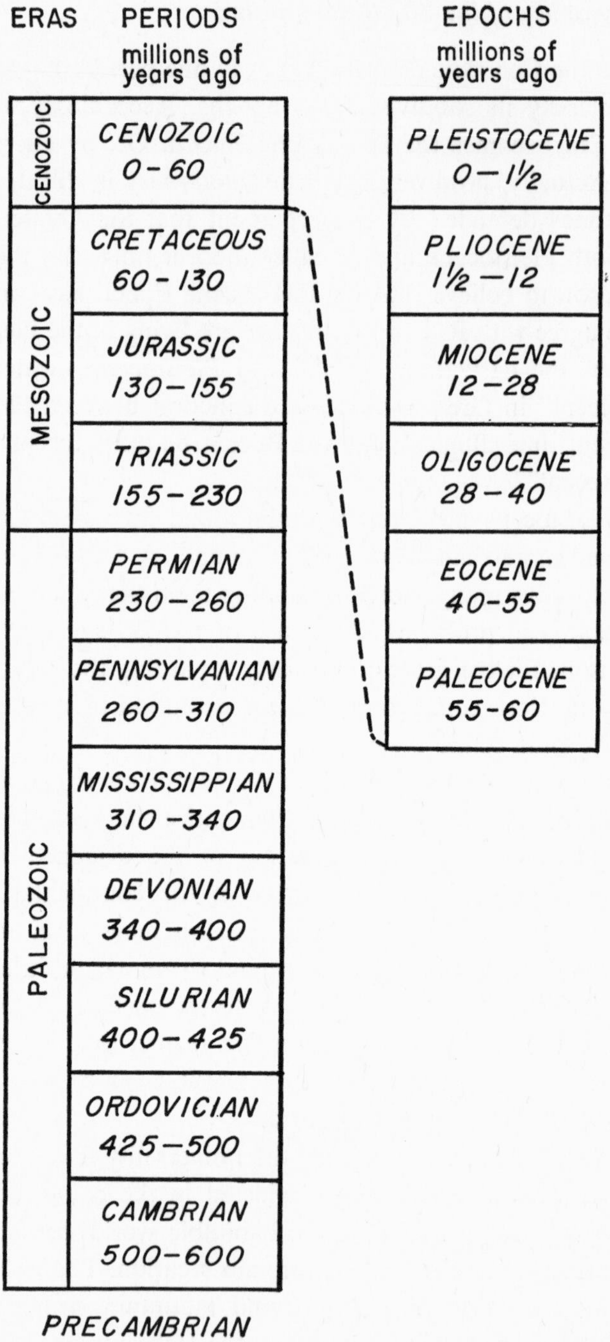

ERAS	PERIODS millions of years ago		EPOCHS millions of years ago
CENOZOIC	CENOZOIC 0-60		PLEISTOCENE 0-1½
MESOZOIC	CRETACEOUS 60-130		PLIOCENE 1½-12
	JURASSIC 130-155		MIOCENE 12-28
	TRIASSIC 155-230		OLIGOCENE 28-40
PALEOZOIC	PERMIAN 230-260		EOCENE 40-55
	PENNSYLVANIAN 260-310		PALEOCENE 55-60
	MISSISSIPPIAN 310-340		
	DEVONIAN 340-400		
	SILURIAN 400-425		
	ORDOVICIAN 425-500		
	CAMBRIAN 500-600		

PRECAMBRIAN

FIGURE 1 *Geologic time chart beginning with the Cambrian Period, in which easily recognizable fossils first made an appearance. On right, an expanded time scale of the Cenozoic Era.*

the dry land appeared. The Ionian geographers thought of the circular disc of the habitable world as surrounded by a mighty stream called Oceanus, the name of the primeval god, father of gods and men, and thus the bond between heaven and earth.

If poetic license is permissible in the expression of a scientific fact, we may truly say that Oceanus is the father of man and gods. Without water, life as we know it would be impossible; without the abundant water of the oceans, it is most unlikely that our planet could have provided sufficient diversity of climate and scope of environment to permit organic evolution to reach the level of complexity that culminates in the human brain and nervous system. And without the imaginings of men, where would the gods be?

About one hundred years ago scientists made two giant strides toward an understanding of man's past environment and origin; these were general acceptance of the theory of continental glaciation during the Pleistocene Epoch, and recognition that during that epoch man had evolved from some lower primate. Since then, geologists and anthropologists have sought some way to measure the duration of the Pleistocene in order to determine the rate of the physical and cultural evolution of man. They have searched for evidence concerning the duration of the individual ice ages and the interglacial times of mild climate which separated them; such information might have a bearing upon the cause or causes of these extraordinary climatic changes. And they have asked whether the start of the ice ages was sudden and drastic or gradual, and whether its deep chill was felt throughout the world or only here and there.

The glacial theory, like many other scientific theories of note, occurred to several people at roughly the same time, if not in quite the same form. The idea that glaciers were formerly far more extensive than at present dates from the nineteenth century. It was first expressed in detail by a Swiss civil engineer, Ignaz Venetz-Sitten, who in 1821 read a paper before the Helvetic Society at Lucerne in which he argued that the glaciers of the Alps had at some former time been expanded on an enormous scale. Three years later, Jens Esmark, in Norway, reached a similar conclusion concerning the glaciers in the mountains of Norway.

The concept of a great ice period caused by climatic changes and marked by a vast sheet of ice extending from the North Pole to the Alps and to central Asia was developed in 1837 by J. L. R. Agassiz, a young Swiss zoologist. In his general concept, Agassiz was anticipated by a German professor in the Academy of Forestry at Dreissigacker named A. Bernhardi, who in 1832 suggested that glacier ice from the region of the North Pole had once extended as far south as Germany. However, no one in Germany seems to have paid serious attention to this idea until 1875, when Otto Torell, a Swedish geologist, brought to Berlin overwhelming evidence that Bernhardi had been right and that to him belonged the distinction of having first recognized the existence of the ice ages. Yet Agassiz came to be regarded as the founder of the glacial theory. In 1846 he came to America, and as professor of natural history at Harvard, he brought about the wide acceptance in America of that bold and novel theory, one of the most far-reaching and fertile in geology.

In the 1850's evidence was recovered both in Britain and in the Alps that the spread of glaciers over great areas of low lands was not a single event but had been repeated. Gradually, data were accumulated indicating that within the limits of the Pleistocene Epoch there had been several distinct ages when glaciers covered about a third of the land area of the world. These ages had been separated by warmer, interglacial times when temperatures were at least as high as they are today. The concept of repeated glaciations grew up with the glacial theory itself.

Today it is generally accepted that the relatively short span of the Pleistocene brought greater changes to the face of the earth than any that had occurred during the previous seventy million years of the Cenozoic Era. The present boundaries between land and sea were established; the earth attained the relief it has now; much of the world's scenery was fashioned; and the physical and cultural evolution of man took place.

The continental glaciers were powerful modifiers of the land surface. All glaciated regions bear unmistakable evidence of their effect on topographical features; over large areas the old rocks are bared of soil and subsoil and have been ground by the moving glaciers into rounded, smoothed forms. The soil, the product of millions of years of weathering and chemical decay, was removed from vast areas and piled up and concentrated in others, filling old valleys, diverting rivers from their courses, and creating lakes of great size by damming old outlets. Innumerable lakelets were also formed in depressions along the margin of the ice and in depressions left on the land surface as the ice retreated.

Because of the nature of the depositional process, the easily accessible deposits left on the continents by former glaciers provide only a discontinuous record at best. To compound the difficulty, what remains of the record is badly garbled. Each succeeding ice sheet as it spread over the land tended to destroy the evidence of earlier glaciations. Furthermore, the important interglacial ages only too often are represented by nothing more than a weathered zone on the surface of the glacial debris left by glaciers of the preceding ice age. Elsewhere the interglacial ages may be represented by layers of soil or peat, but because of intervals of nondeposition or even erosion, such layers cannot be relied upon to contain complete records. In many cases it is clear that they represent no more than a small part of the total time of the interglacial during which they were deposited.

As earth history goes, we are living in a time of exceptionally rapid change, a time of geological unrest. Our epoch, the Pleistocene, is characterized by emergent continents and deep ocean basins, by long ranges of lofty mountains too young to have been worn down by erosion. It is also marked by great diversity of climate from place to place and by drastic changes of climate over relatively short periods of time. During most of geological time the continents were low in relation to sea level, so low that vast areas of the continents were periodically flooded by shallow seas, which must have teemed with life. We know this because the sediments they left are full of fossil shells and sometimes include huge coral reefs. Some of these sediments contain quantities of petroleum, further evidence of organic productivity on a vast scale. The climate during most of geological time seems to have been mild and remarkably uniform throughout the world, in contrast with the well-defined climatic zones of the present day. Probably this uniformity was a consequence of low continents, many broad seaways, and few or no mountains.

Yet the record of the rocks contains unmistakable evidence of relatively brief intervals of time during which the face of the earth must have been much as it is now. One of these intervals occurred more than 600 million years ago, before the appearance of animals with hard parts that were durable enough to become recognizable fossils. As nearly as geologists can tell from bits of evidence in rocks scattered all over the world, this ancient time, like the Pleistocene, was marked by emergent continents and high mountains. Of fascinating interest is the abundant and unmistakable evidence of glaciation on an enormous scale, probably exceeding that of the Pleistocene. From this ancient evidence we can reassure ourselves that the glaciations of the Pleistocene are not symptoms of old age. Accordingly, we reject all theories that relate the ice ages to exhaustion of the reserve of energy of the earth or the sun. On the contrary, the exceptional mountain-building activity of the Pleistocene shows that Mother Earth is as full of life and energy as she was 600 million years ago.

One other interval of geological time has left clearly legible evidence of large-scale glaciation. Sediments deposited at the close of the division of geological time known as the Permian Period, about 230 million years ago, include deposits of heterogeneous rock detritus in every way similar to the ice-transported deposits of the Pleistocene, except that the clayey matrix containing striated pebbles and boulders has become hard rock. Convincing evidence that these deposits are truly glacial is provided in some places by beautifully polished, grooved and striated surfaces of basement rock beneath the consolidated detritus. Such surfaces are formed by the powerful grinding of slowly moving glaciers with cobbles and boulders frozen into their lower surfaces. As with the earlier glaciation, the evidence from late Permian rocks in many parts of the world indicates that in general the degree of topographical relief during the glaciation was similar to that of the Pleistocene; it seems to have been a time of emergent continents and high mountains. This evidence, together with the theoretical influence of topography upon climate, has led many geologists to surmise that emergent continents, high mountains, and oceans and seas restricted to deep basins are a necessary condition for the spread of continental glaciers. However, these topographical features cannot have been the sole cause of the glaciers. No appreciable topographical change occurred at the end of the last ice age, yet the continental glaciers melted. The interglacial ages provide an additional argument against the theory that topographical relief was the sole cause of the ice ages; there is no suggestion of evidence that the continents were lower or the mountains less high during the interglacials than during the ice ages. But the probability is that topography plays an important part. Epochs of repeated glaciations very likely result from the coincidence of certain topographical conditions with some other independent factor that is characteristically cyclical.

Since the Pleistocene is our epoch, we would like to know more about it. What caused the climatic changes? Why were the ice ages separated by long intervals during which the climate was warm or warmer than it is now? Have the ice ages come to an end, or are we living in an interglacial age, with another ice age to follow? If we could work out a satisfactory chronology of climatic events during the Pleistocene, we would have a rough chronology of the physical and cultural development of man. The stages of development of primitive man have been tied into the sequence of climatic changes by archaeologists in collaboration with Pleistocene geologists. We have a fair idea of the sequence of events, but a reliable time scale has been lacking.

As we have pointed out, each interval of time between the glaciations is recorded by a zone of weathering, a chemical alteration of the upper part of the detritus deposited by the preceding glacier. In weathering, the most important chemical changes are the solution of carbonates and the oxidation of iron-bearing minerals. Oxidation commonly leads to a change in color from the gray of the original deposit to shades of rusty brown in the weathered zone. Weathering proceeds downward from the surface; the thickness of a weathered zone, which may reach several meters, gives a rough indication of the length of time during which the deposit was exposed to chemical alteration. This evidence suggests that the intervals of mild climate separating the ice ages were long, probably much longer than the ice ages themselves, but because of disagreement regarding rates of weathering, estimates of the durations of the interglacials vary by many tens of thousands of years. For the durations of the ice ages the evidence on the continents is even less satisfactory.

With the development of devices capable of taking cores of sediment from great depths in the oceans, a new approach to the problems of the Pleistocene opened. If deep-sea sediments consisted only of mineral particles, it is doubtful that they would serve our purpose. Fortunately, however, a large part, often the major part, of these sediments consists of the microscopic shells of protozoa, the foraminifera, which spend at least a part of their life cycle floating about in the surface waters. Certain species are sensitive to temperature, and accordingly are restricted geographically to certain climatic zones. The extremely slow but continuous rain of these shells upon the ocean floor provides an ideal recording mechanism. As the millennia roll by and climatic changes occur, the populations of species sensitive to temperature shift from latitude to latitude. The complete record of these shifts is there, word by word, page after page; like a forgotten language, it can be deciphered, if one has the patience of a cryptographer and the inquisitiveness of a detective.

When in 1947 we began the study of deep-sea sediment in order to find a record of the Pleistocene, we, like other scientists concerned with the problem, believed that a complete record could be found in almost any single core from some point well out in the Atlantic. This belief was based on the classic notion that the deep ocean basins were regions of utter and perpetual calm, a conception that had its origin in theory rather than in direct observation. A series of deep-sea expeditions undertaken before 1947 had explored the ocean floor, but the emphasis had been for the most part on charting the areal distribution of the classic types of sediment.

Well-organized scientific exploration of the oceans began with the circumglobal voyage of H. M. S. *Challenger* between 1872 and 1876 under the scientific direction of Sir Wyville Thomson and the naval command of Sir George Nares. This epoch-making expedition gave us the first wide and general view of the physical and biological conditions in the oceans. The bottom sampling was done with dredges and a short tube attached to a sounding weight. The tube was only about thirty centimeters long, but it could easily have yielded cores showing stratification, and in one case it actually did so. However, no importance was attached to the evidence. At about the same time a German expedition on the S. M. S. *Gazelle* explored the South Atlantic, the Indian, and the South Pacific oceans, and the U. S. S. *Tuscarora* explored the North Pacific. It has been rightly stated that at no time since the days of Columbus and Magellan had so much knowledge of the surface of our planet been gathered as in the eighth decade of the nineteenth century.

Many other deep-sea expeditions followed, and by 1947 there had been more than ninety. However, most of these had concentrated on physical oceanography, marine biology, terrestrial magnetism, or on applied aspects such as fishery problems. The geology of the ocean basins had been more or less neglected. This should not be surprising; to take samples deep below the sediment surface requires heavy, specialized equipment and a powerful winch, and takes a great deal of time. And it was not thought that anything of value would be found to repay the considerable effort required.

Much interest was aroused by the pioneer work of Wolfgang Schott on the cores of sediment collected in the equatorial Atlantic by the German research ship *Meteor*. With this, it became apparent that deep-sea sediment is not uniform with depth but is zoned. A new approach to the problem of Pleistocene climates had been found.

Between 1925 and 1927 the *Meteor* took a series of short cores about a hundred and twenty centimeters long in the equatorial

Atlantic. The coring apparatus was of the simplest kind, a tube with a glass liner and a lead weight to drive it into the sediment. When a core had been taken, the glass liner containing the core was removed and the ends sealed. Thus, the cores were brought back to the laboratory in perfect condition. After the cruise, Schott made a careful study of the different kinds of shells of foraminifera in samples from different levels in the cores. He found that most of the cores consisted of two layers. An upper layer about twenty-five centimeters thick contained the shells of a species of foraminifera which flourishes now in the equatorial Atlantic. In the lower layer, certain typical equatorial species were absent; instead, there were evidences of species now abundant only in middle and high latitudes. Schott surmised that the lower layer had been deposited during the last ice age. This meant that about twenty-five centimeters of sediment had accumulated in this part of the Atlantic since the climatic change which caused the continental glaciers to recede. In 1927 it was generally believed that the climatic change had taken place about twenty thousand years ago. Thanks to radiocarbon dating, we now know that the change occurred only eleven thousand years ago and that therefore the rate of sediment accumulation in the deep Atlantic is somewhat faster than previously supposed.

In the following years, many cores were taken in the North Atlantic and the Caribbean with the Piggot coring tube. This ingenious corer, designed by C. S. Piggot, consisted of a tube and a short gun. When the apparatus was just above the sediment surface, a triggering device fired the gun and shot the tube into the sediment. Later, H. C. Stetson and H. J. Hvorslev at the Woods Hole Oceanographic Institution designed a simpler but equally effective corer which was in fact a reversion to the type of corer used on the *Meteor*, but on a much larger scale.

Several suites of cores had been taken with these corers before 1947. The foraminifera in the cores taken with the Piggot device were studied by J. A. Cushman and L. G. Henbest; those taken by Stetson were studied by F. B Phleger. The consensus of these scientists was that a single ice age was recorded within the section of sediment cored, but there was reason to suppose that cores from just about anywhere on the deep ocean floor, if they were long enough, would provide a continuous record of the climatic events of the Pleistocene.

With this kind of encouragement, it seemed to us in 1947 that it would be relatively easy to work out the chronology of the Pleistocene through the study of cores of deep-sea sediments. All we had to do was take long enough cores—that is, cores about thirteen or fourteen meters long.

2

PROBING THE OCEAN FLOOR

THE early conception of the bottom of the ocean as a naked abyss was replaced after the deep-sea explorations of the nineteenth century by an image of a universal veil of sediment. This was based on the reasonable theory that almost the only kind of material that could reach the deep-sea basins far from land was very fine mineral matter and the shells of single-celled microscopic organisms that had lived near the surface of the ocean. These particles, the essential ingredients of deep-sea sediment, would settle down from above, regardless of the topography of the bottom. Therefore, it was reasoned, a great and uniform thickness of sediment must cover all parts of the ocean floor. More thorough sampling of the sea floor soon showed that the calcareous shells of single-celled organisms were dissolved at great depths. Since the shells make up a considerable portion of the sediment at depths less than three thousand meters, it was evident that the rate of sediment accumulation at such depths was a good deal faster than at greater depths. The blanket of sediment, therefore, should be somewhat thicker on rises than on the floors of deep basins. But, except for this qualifying discovery, the many samples of sediment collected during the nineteenth century tended to support the theory of a universal blanket of sediment. In view of recent discoveries, this may seem strange. The explanation lies in the older methods of sampling; until the *Meteor* expedition in 1925, the only sampling devices in use penetrated only the upper thirty centimeters of sediment. As it happens, the upper twenty-five or thirty centimeters of sediment had, in fact, accumulated very much as the early oceanographers thought. The theory of continental glaciation in the Pleistocene had come into good standing by the late nineteenth century, but the early oceanographers failed to realize how profound an effect the climatic changes of the Pleistocene had had upon oceanic sedimentation.

The cores of sediment raised during our first deep-sea expedition in 1947 left no doubt that much more had been going on in the ocean basins than the early oceanographers dreamt of. What we found out about sediments during the expedition of 1947 changed the direction of our study of the climatic history of the Pleistocene; and the mishaps of the expedition gave us a taste of the difficulties that confront oceanographers and marine geologists.

Only the big winch on the research ship *Atlantis*, a steel-hulled auxiliary ketch, was capable of lowering and raising the large coring tube. The hydrographic winch could lower a lighter wire to the same depth, but it lacked the lifting power to handle the coring tube. We had been out only a few days and had hardly begun to take cores when trouble developed. The big winch was braked electrically; as the cable ran out, the braking device generated a torrent of electricity that was controlled by a series of resistance coils. And even at this early stage the coils were in poor condition, and some were in dangerous condition. If, in the course of lowering the coring tube, one of these coils should burn out, the braking device would fail, with disastrous consequences. Accordingly, the chief scientist radioed to Woods Hole to have a set of coils sent to our next port, which was to be Mindello on the Island of São Vicente in the Cape Verde Archipelago. But what of the long

stretch of interesting ocean between us and Mindello? Oughtn't
we to continue to core for a little longer? The chief engineer ad-
vised us against it, but he did not forbid it. This put the responsi-
bility on the chief scientist, who had not had much experience with
resistance coils. During the debate of the problem among the
scientists, the psychology of the chief engineer came in for no little
analysis. Wasn't he overcautious? Perhaps he had ulterior motives
for not wanting to run the winch. The upshot was that we took a
few more cores, and then the chief engineer put his foot down.
At about this time we noticed that the cable on the main winch
showed an unhealthy amount of corrosion. How would this affect
the expedition later on?

In the meantime, other operations were going forward according
to plan. Every quarter of an hour a stick of dynamite was thrown
overboard with enough fuse to ensure that it would explode at a
safe distance astern. The sound waves reflected from the bottom and
from the layers of sediment and rock beneath were picked up and
recorded on a strip of photographic paper. Day and night the echo
sounder drew a continuous profile of the bottom. Thanks to the
hydrographic winch designed for lowering strings of bronze bottles
with thermometers—known as Nansen bottles—we were able to
take short cores, thirty or forty centimeters long, with a miniature
coring tube. By means of the same winch we towed small nets of
silk gauze to catch the microscopic life at various depths, particularly
the foraminifera, so that we might learn as much as possible about
the habits of these creatures and be in a position to use the shells
of their ancestors as indicators of past conditions in the oceans.
Every half hour the bathythermograph was lowered to a depth of
several hundred meters. This ingenious instrument draws on a
smoked glass slide a curve of variation in temperature with depth.
At other times the Nansen bottles were lowered to obtain samples of
water to determine salinity and temperatures at various depths all
the way to the bottom. Thus the days and nights passed, but we
did not take longer cores, and finally the *Atlantis* dropped anchor
in Mindello harbor.

At Mindello we learned that the resistance coils were in Dakar and that there was no plane to bring them to Mindello. Rather than trust them to a local sailing packet, Captain Adrian Lane decided to take the *Atlantis* to Dakar. But she needed diesel oil, and that was not to be had on the islands, not any more. Once a diesel generator had supplied the town with light, but it had ceased to function some time before our coming. Bunker oil was to be had; like the well-known Mr. Hobson, we chose it. Since the deep-keeled *Atlantis* could not get in to the town dock, the drums of oil were lightered out to her, hoisted on deck, and emptied one by one into her tanks.

For the geologists on board the delay was not without compensations. Darwin had visited the Cape Verdes in 1832 during his voyage on the *Beagle*, and we were eager to set foot on these islands, whose desolate aspect had so strongly impressed him. The harbor is the partially breached crater of an enormous extinct volcano. All about the *Atlantis* lay cliffs of naked black lava and dark gray beds of volcanic ash. The somber, almost sinister effect was relieved only slightly by the white houses of the town and a few dunes of calcareous sand on a flat area south of the town.

Each day while the fuel came on board we went ashore and tramped about in the searing heat. Our most interesting discovery was evidence of changes in sea level. There was a conspicuous wave-cut bench about two meters above present sea level which could be found wherever a cliff came right down to the water. And to the south of Mindello in the vicinity of the calcareous sand dunes, we found a soft calcareous sandstone whose surface was awash at low tide. The steeply inclined bedding of this deposit showed clearly that it must once have been part of a sand dune now submerged by rising sea level. Darwin in his account of the island of St. Jago fails to mention similar evidence of change of sea level. Since he was not one to overlook anything as significant as a wave-cut bench, we are inclined to think that this is a peculiarity of São Vicente and due therefore to local uplift of the island. Darwin could easily have missed the soft sandstone, if he went ashore and departed at high tide; or for some reason of topography it may not occur where he landed. Very probably the sandstone had its origin during the last ice age, when sea level all over the world was lower by about two hundred meters because of the withdrawal of water from the oceans to form the vast continental glaciers.

When we returned from these excursions, we usually stopped at a *venda* in town where we could enjoy a boiled chicken and some bottles of *vinho verde*. By the time we had finished the last bottle, the tropical night was upon us. The darkness of the streets and waterfront was like black velvet, broken only by the white eyeballs and rows of almost luminous teeth of our black friends who thronged the landing.

Just as the geology of the island was becoming most fascinating, the fueling ended and we had to leave for Dakar. Soon after we cleared the harbor, it began to snow—black snow, of course. The exhaust from the engine led into a small stack which stood just about amidships, pouring a cloud of flakes of greasy soot. As it was a calm day, most of it fell on deck. The chief engineer was in despair and vowed that never again would a single drum of bunker oil come on board the *Atlantis*.

Just outside the harbor we passed the beautiful schooner *Effie M. Morrissey,* still heavily sheathed as protection against the ice through which she had so often fought under the command of Captain Bob Bartlett, of Arctic fame. Now she had become a Cape Verde packet. Her engine had been taken out, and as we passed alongside she was standing motionless, with all sail set, in a glassy calm. But her Portuguese owner loved her; she was as spick and span and brightly varnished as a yacht.

At Dakar we found the resistance coils, and after taking on good diesel fuel, we headed west. Southwest of the Cape Verde Islands we hove to and lowered the coring apparatus in 4,500 meters of water, but before the corer reached bottom, the wire rope broke. The corrosion we had noticed earlier had gone deeper than we realized. Under a tension of more than four thousand pounds, the end whipped back with enough force to kill. Fortunately, the deck was clear at the time. What hurt was the loss of the two and a half miles of wire and the coring apparatus.

The next day while we were making the most of the trade wind the mainsail ripped badly, not because of the force of the wind, but because it was an old piece of canvas no longer fit to be at sea. And we had no other; the new mainsail was at Woods Hole. The same evening Fred Kent, one of the seamen, fell ill with abdominal pains so severe that he could not eat or sleep. We did not have a doctor on board, and Captain Lane did what he could; he gave Kent morphine and altered course for Barbados, the nearest land, though four days away.

No experienced oceanographer questions the validity of Murphy's Law, which states that "if, under a given set of conditions, there is anything that can go wrong, it will." The following night, just after eight bells we were startled by a crash and a strange shudder of the ship, followed by the racing of the engine; the *Atlantis* had lost her propeller! The mizzen, forestaysail, and jib were set, but with no more sail than that, the *Atlantis* could do hardly better than four knots. The mainsail had not been repaired; it had seemed a waste of time to repair a worthless piece of canvas. But now Mattie Hampton, the sailmaker, got his palm, needle, and twine; lights were rigged on deck and the job began. By ten o'clock next morning the crew were able to hoist the mainsail; the rest of the day the *Atlantis* drove along at ten knots and for a time at thirteen. The weather was perfect and the ship was at her best. Her motion as she rose and fell on the long equatorial swells was like the swooping flight of a bird.

But by nightfall the old sail had ripped again from luff to leach. So down it came, and once more Mattie Hampton went to work by lamplight. The remainder of the crossing consisted of alternate sailing and sewing. In the meantime, the condition of the seaman remained about the same. At length Captain Lane brought the *Atlantis* to anchor off Bridgetown, Barbados, without having had to perform his first operation for appendicitis. Seaman Kent was sent ashore, and after a short stay in the Bridgetown hospital, he recovered as mysteriously as he had fallen ill, and took a plane home.

The mainsail was also sent ashore to have all its seams reinforced. It was to be our only means of getting home; Barbados could not provide a new propeller or any way of installing one, even if we had had a spare.

While the sail was ashore, we made the most of the opportunity to explore this geologically unique island in the Atlantic. A large part of the sediment of which the island is composed consists of the siliceous skeletons of microscopic single-celled animals called radiolaria, and uplifted ancient sediments containing abundant radiolaria are unusual. The sediments containing the radiolaria are of Eocene age, which means they were deposited about fifty million years ago, and according to classical geological theory, at great depths, that is, below five thousand meters.

The island was pushed up out of the sea rather recently. A series of terraces of coral rock of Pleistocene age rising to a height of 335 meters provides dramatic proof of this. What bothers marine geologists and geophysicists is not that the uplift occurred, but rather the extent of it as implied by the radiolaria. Uplift above sea level of a block of the sea floor from abyssal depth is difficult to explain if the ocean basins are really underlain by denser rock. However this may be, we are inclined to question the value of the radiolaria as indicating deposition at great depth. In the Pleistocene sediments of the North Atlantic we have not found abundant radiolaria even at the greatest depths, as, for example, in the Puerto Rico trench at almost eight thousand meters. On the other hand, we have found remarkable concentrations in the Pleistocene sections of cores from the Mediterranean and the waters around Antarctica from moderate depths, such as two thousand meters. But these are always associated with abundant particles of volcanic glass, which suggests that the chemistry of the water is more important than its depth in determining the distribution of the siliceous skeletons. It would seem that the radiolaria reproduce in great numbers and construct more durable, less easily dissolved skeletons wherever the water is rich in silica. If so, it may very well be that the abundant radiolaria of Barbados indicate nothing more than a copious local supply of dissolved silica at the time of deposition, perhaps because of nearby outpourings of lava and volcanic waters on the sea floor.

Again we put to sea. As it was getting late in the year, Captain

Lane laid out a straight course for New London, and we held to it as closely as weather permitted. For the most part we had favorable winds, and little tacking was necessary.

Some days after leaving Barbados, while we were sailing in fine weather, "the bottom fell out of the barometer." In spite of the fine weather, Captain Lane had every bit of canvas taken off, and gave orders to double lash and secure all our gear. With the *Atlantis* drifting, we waited for the worst. Toward evening the squall struck with extraordinary suddenness, catching the *Atlantis* full on the beam.

One can easily become accustomed to a long roll; you know that after a few seconds the ship will rise and come back to an even keel. But now, under the impact of the squall, the *Atlantis* heeled to forty-five degrees and stayed there. It was uncanny and not at all pleasant. In seconds the sea became a sheet of white foam, but it remained fairly flat. In less than an hour it was all over, and once again we were under sail.

Shortly before we reached New London, the mainsail ripped hopelessly and for the last time; by then it did not matter much. On a cold clear afternoon we sailed into the harbor under mizzen and staysails. A tug was waiting, ready to tow us to the shipyard; as she passed us a line, we heard for the last time the familiar clatter of the staysail hanks as the big sails came down. Soon we were secure at the dock and tasting the last of the Barbados rum—excellent stuff.

In spite of the many difficulties, this expedition, under the leadership of Dr. Maurice Ewing, yielded results of extraordinary interest and scientific importance. Much had been learned about the topography of the gloom-shrouded peaks, valleys, and ridges of the greatest mountain system on earth, the Mid-Atlantic Ridge. The expedition had taken a large number of measurements of water temperature and salinity and made numerous seismic-reflection records and a profile of the topography of the bottom along a 5,000-mile track across a relatively unexplored part of the Atlantic. Many valuable samples of planktonic life had been collected, and much material of geological and biological interest had been dredged from the floor of the ocean. In spite of the loss of the coring tube, some sediment cores were brought home which eventually helped to revolutionize our ideas about sedimentary processes in the deep ocean basins.

The cores were taken with the free-fall corer developed by H. J. Hvorslev and H. C. Stetson. The corer consisted essentially of a steel tube, six and a third centimeters in diameter and about six meters long. The top of the tube screwed into a torpedo-shaped mass of lead weighing about a thousand pounds. The lower or penetrating end of the tube was fitted with a sharp cutting edge, inside of which was a core-catcher, that is, a ring of springy brass leaves which permitted the sediment to enter the tube but prevented it from sliding out. Before coring, a plastic liner was put into the tube; this was removed with the core. Kinetic energy to drive the tube into the sediment was provided by a free fall of three meters, which was achieved by a triggering device shackled to the end of the main cable. This consisted of a trigger arm or lever pivoted near one end, and a trigger weight hanging by a line attached to the long end of the trigger arm; the coring tube itself hung by a bail hooked into a notch in the short end. The ratio of the lengths of the two parts of the trigger arm were such that the hundred pounds of the trigger weight more than counterbalanced the weight of the coring tube. The length of the line carrying the trigger weight was so adjusted that the weight hung three meters below the lower end of the coring tube. As soon as the trigger weight came to rest on the bottom, the weight of the coring tube, no longer counterbalanced, pulled down the short end of the arm, thereby causing the coring-tube bail to slip out of the notch. This permitted the tube to fall. A slack loop of chain maintained a connection between the coring tube and the main cable. In principle, this kind of a corer works a good deal like an apple corer, but its performance was less satisfactory. The kinetic energy from the free fall was more than enough to drive the full length of the tube into the sediment, but in spite of the length of the tube—six meters —we never got cores much longer than about three meters. Sometimes our hopes were raised when the apparatus came up with mud even on the upper part of the lead weight, but we were invariably disappointed by finding no more than the usual three meters of sediment in the tube. This failure to take longer cores was due to the friction between the entering sediment and the inner surface of the coring tube. As more sediment entered the tube, the frictional resistance increased; after about three meters of sediment had entered the tube, the frictional resistance became so great that the tube and the sediment it contained would push downward into the soft sediment on the sea floor as a solid cylinder. Moreover, the lower parts of cores taken with this kind of corer were distorted because the softer layers of sediment had been squeezed aside.

Because of their shortness, the cores taken during this expedition did not add much to our knowledge of the Pleistocene. But several of the cores turned out to have great significance. One, taken from the top of a seamount[1] about 140 miles northeast of Bermuda, contained two distinct layers. The upper one, which was twenty centimeters thick, was a calcareous sand composed of the shells of large planktonic foraminifera, the shells of planktonic snails, and other calcareous detritus of organic origin, all of them from species now living in the North Atlantic. The lower layer was a white, extremely fine-grained calcareous sediment containing beautifully preserved shells of planktonic foraminifera. Despite the isolated occurrence of this sediment, we were able to fit it into the great sequence of sediments. It had been deposited during what geologists call the Eocene Epoch, or during the dawn of the Recent, the time when the mammals were coming into dominance on the continents.

The foraminifera were our clue to the age. For years, all over the world micropaleontologists have been describing, cataloguing, and noting the occurrences of these minute shells. As a result, it is possible today to assign a sample containing foraminifera to its place in the sedimentary sequence with reasonable assurance.

In addition to the foraminifera, the sediment contained great

---

[1] A seamount is a mountain that rises from the floor of the sea but does not reach the surface. Many isolated seamounts in the Atlantic and Pacific are cone-shaped and are without doubt submarine volcanoes. The Hawaiian Islands are in fact volcanic seamounts, but since their peaks rise above the surface of the ocean, we call them islands.

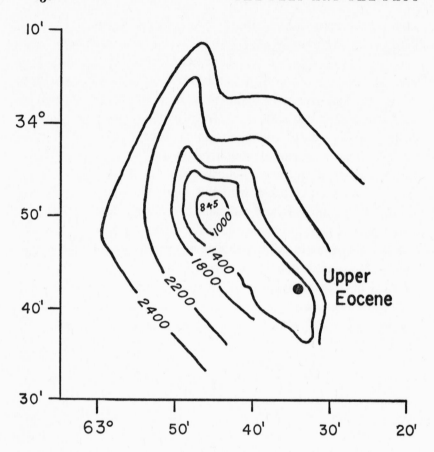

FIGURE 2 *Chart of the Muir Seamount (about 33° 40′ North, 62° 40′ West) 260 kilometers, 140 nautical miles, northeast of the Bermuda Islands, showing where Upper Eocene sediment was cored. The contours are in fathoms.*

quantities of little plates of calcium carbonate about fifteen thou-sandths of a millimeter in diameter. These were secreted by plank-tonic organisms known as Coccolithophoridae and Discoasteridae. All the species of Coccolithophoridae that lived in the oceans of the Upper Eocene are now extinct, but their descendants, having evolved into new species, are very much alive in the Atlantic today. They are single-celled biflagellated organisms. Although they are of great importance as food to filter-feeding organisms, and geo-logically as contributors to calcareous sediments, little is known about their habits and affinities with other organisms. They are among the oldest of living things; their calcareous plates, called coccoliths, have been found in the rocks of the Cambrian Period, which began some 600 million years ago. The Discoasteridae, as their name implies, secreted star-shaped plates about the same size as the coccoliths. They became extinct at the beginning of the Pleistocene Epoch, and consequently we shall probably never know whether they were plants or animals; all we can say with assurance is that they must have lived in or just below the upper layer of water which is penetrated by light. Only there, through photosynthesis on their own part or on the part of other organisms on which they fed, could they have found enough nourishment to permit the great proliferation which is indicated by the astronomical abundance of the little stars in pre-Pleistocene sediments.

The Eocene age of the foraminifera in the lower layer meant that the boundary between the layers represented an unrecorded or lost time interval of about forty million years. Samples of sediment of this age, even somewhat older, had been dredged up and cored before, particularly by H. C. Stetson, but previous occurrences of old sediments had been found along the margins of the continental masses, that is, on the continental slopes. This core was our first sample of an Eocene sediment from a point far out in the Atlantic. Its occurrence there told us that the Atlantic was at least forty million years old. At the same time, the core posed some tantalizing questions. Why was the Pleistocene sediment coarse-grained and the Eocene so fine? We thought the coarseness of the Pleistocene sediment was probably due to a deep current which swept fine particles from the top of the mount. In 1947 this was a rather unorthodox idea; deep circulation in the oceans was supposed to be much too slow to move even fine clay particles. But our guess was correct; since then, many photographs taken on the tops of seamounts have shown ripple marks in coarse sediments, clear evidence that deep currents are much more powerful than was formerly thought.

But then, what of the Eocene Atlantic? Was it relatively stagnant. Possibly, but the abundant planktonic organisms in the Eocene sediment suggested water rich in nutrient salts, and these occur abundantly in the upper layer of water only where there is fairly vigorous upwelling of deep water in which the supply of salts has been renewed by the decay of sinking organic matter and the solution of mineral particles. But upwelling implied deep circulation much as in the North Atlantic of today. This left one alternative: that the seamount had come into existence after the Eocene sediment had been deposited on a broad, featureless plain. If so, the mount could not be an ancient submarine volcano, because extrusion of lava would have destroyed or at least thoroughly altered the Eocene sediment. Instead, the Eocene sediment was as fresh and as little altered as the overlying Pleistocene sediment. This forced us to the conclusion that the mount must have originated as a block of the ocean floor bounded by fractures—or faults, in the language of geologists—and subsequently pushed bodily up above the surrounding floor, perhaps by intrusion of molten rock beneath.

This theory had the further advantage that it provided an explanation for the absence of all the sediment that ought to have been deposited during the forty million years since the Upper Eocene Epoch. In the course of uplift, the mass of soft sediment overlying the Eocene was left unsupported by the rise of the mount. Disturbed by seaquakes accompanying the uplift, the sediment had probably slipped off the sloping top of the mount. When had this taken place? During the Pleistocene, we suspected; otherwise a layer of coarse sediment showing the action of a scouring current should have been present between the Eocene sediment and the uppermost, Recent layer.

Some years later this theory of the origin of the Muir Seamount received strong support. A fairly detailed topographical survey of the mount showed that it did not have the circular plan of a submarine volcano; instead it appeared as an elongated tilted block.

Even more exciting than the Eocene sediment were some layers of fairly coarse, clean sand, largely composed of particles of quartz, in two cores from deep stations about midway between New York and Bermuda. But why not sand in the sea? the reader may ask. Because sand composed of particles of the highly stable mineral quartz is the ultimate residue of the chemical and mechanical disintegration of rocks like granite, and the conditions which lead to disintegration occur only on land. Eventually, streams carry sand to the sea, where waves distribute it along coasts and to some extent seaward on the continental shelves. But the power necessary to carry coarse quartz particles hundreds of miles from land is not ordinarily available in the oceans. Evidently these sand layers recorded extraordinary events, but of what kind?

When we examined the sands more closely, we found evidence of a former sojourn in shallow water. They contained a few shells of species of foraminifera that dwell on the bottom but only on the continental shelves, and also particles of a green mineral called glauconite, which, according to all previous experience, forms only in shallow water.

We knew that a few other samples of similar sands had been found at abyssal depths by earlier investigators and that the marine geologist Karl Andrée had devoted a chapter in his book *Geologie des Meeresbodens,* published in 1920, to a discussion of the occurrence and possible origin of these sands. After reviewing various theories of origin, Andrée fell back on the theory that E. Philippi had developed in 1910. Philippi, who had described the samples of sediment collected by the German South Polar Expedition of 1901–3, held that after the sands had been deposited in shallow water, vast downwarping of the sea floor had taken place and the sands had dropped to abyssal depths. Unfortunately for this theory, a short core from the Romanche Deep in the equatorial Atlantic contained abyssal sediment below a sand layer. This, as Andrée acknowledged, introduced an embarrassing complication; it became necessary to assume that great upwarping had preceded the downwarping.

At the end of the nineteenth century and the beginning of the twentieth, other deep-sea research ships, particularly the *Valdivia* and the *Gauss,* found sands at deep stations far from land. This stimulated additional theorizing. It was suggested that the sands were transported by drifting ice during the ice ages of the Pleistocene, but this failed to explain the characteristically uniform sizes of the sand grains in these mysterious sediments. Deposits of material transported by ice are notoriously unsorted; in other words, particles of every size, from clay to boulders, occur together. Such mixed sediments do occur in regions of high latitude visited by drifting ice. They are common in the waters off Antarctica, and they bear no resemblance whatsoever to deep-sea sands. Furthermore, to suppose that drifting ice had reached equatorial waters even at the height of the ice ages seemed rather farfetched, to put it mildly. Another theory would have it that the sands were evidence of something called "sedimentary vulcanism"; that is, that the sands had been deposited originally at some time long before the Pleistocene Epoch, when the configuration of the North Atlantic basin was quite different, and that subsequently, during the Pleistocene, they had been forced upward as intrusions into the overlying sediments. But this hypothesis failed to explain why the sands invariably occurred as horizontal beds and usually contained perfectly good fossils of Pleistocene age. A more plausible hypothesis appealed to violent winds during the Pleistocene, but, as we shall see later, when more was learned about the occurrences of the sands, this theory also proved to have fatal weaknesses.

Thus, the relatively few cores taken during the cruise of 1947 tended to upset existing preconceptions about the ocean basins. The evidence did not favor the classic static theory which envisioned the ocean basins as regions of awful and perpetual calm since the very beginning of things. For example, to explain the nature of the Eocene sediment we had to suppose that block faulting of the ocean floor had taken place rather recently. Then there were the sand layers. Whatever the correct explanation of their origin, their presence added little luster to the static theory.

One thing was sure: there were to be impediments in our efforts to find a complete record of the climatic events of the Pleistocene Epoch. To attack the problem intelligently, we would have to learn much more about depositional processes; otherwise we stood in danger of being hopelessly misled by extraneous effects quite unrelated to climate. If more than forty million years of sediment accumulation could be missing from one core, how could we be sure that parts might not be missing from others? And how could we detect the absence of such sections in the Pleistocene record, where we would not have the benefit of the striking contrast between Pleistocene and Eocene?

Were we discouraged? On the contrary, the subject became all the more fascinating. In this little-explored realm of the ocean sediments, we were finding now not just one challenge, how to interpret the Pleistocene, but a multiplicity of challenges. Then, for other reason, the future held promise. The National Geographic Society, the Woods Hole Oceanographic Institution, and Columbia University, the three institutions that had sponsored the cruise of 1947, indicated that they would sponsor another one. It also appeared that there had been a revolutionary advance in coring technique. A new device had been developed which was reported to have taken cores as long as twelve meters, and possibly even more! Our next expedition would be equipped with such a coring device.

3

IMPACT OF CURRENTS ON

THE SEDIMENT RECORD

IT WAS the Swedish oceanographer Börje Kullenberg who had developed a new and improved coring device. With only the Stetson corer available, our efforts to get a long record of the Pleistocene had been squarely blocked at three meters. Kullenberg put a piston into a coring tube and thereby revolutionized the art of taking cores. The effect of the piston was to put to work the great hydrostatic pressure at the bottom of the ocean to push the core into the tube against friction. This new instrument promised to provide us with records of Pleistocene events extending back in time three or four times further than the longest cores we had hitherto been able to obtain.

Stimulated by this exciting possibility and by the remarkable cores brought back by the expedition of 1947, Maurice Ewing devised a new version of the piston corer by combining the principles of Kullenberg and Stetson. Ewing's corer had an important advantage over earlier corers. Whereas the tubes of the Stetson and

Kullenberg corers had been especially turned on lathes, like gun barrels, at great expense, the Ewing version used commercial steel pipe. With characteristic foresight, Ewing had a quantity of this relatively cheap tubing put on board the *Atlantis* in preparation for the expedition of 1948. He realized that it was going to be necessary to lower the corer not only in regions of smooth topography but also in regions of rugged relief, where there was serious danger that the tube would break or bend if it hit hard rock. With an ample supply of tubing on board, we could now take chances that would have been out of the question with the older corers.

It was a tense but eagerly awaited moment when we first tested the Ewing corer in 1948. The *Atlantis* lay hove to on the gray mid-ocean swells over the western terraces of the Mid-Atlantic Ridge, the great backbone of the North and South Atlantic which runs roughly north and south, midway between the continents.

We had finished the preparations for the first lowering. The trigger-release mechanism was hanging down from the A-frame, the A-shaped steel structure tilted out over the side of the ship, from which the corer was to be lowered. The upper part of the corer, which held the ten lead discs, each weighing one hundred pounds, and the tail fins rested over the side of the ship in a cradle under the A-frame. The coring tube, twelve meters long and extending aft from the weights, rested on brackets riveted to the side of the ship. We slid the tube forward into a socket in the upper part of the corer and secured it in place with a powerful coupling.

The half-inch, improved plow-steel wire that would lower and raise the coring apparatus ran from the winch in the hold up to the deck amidship, where it passed through a tensionmeter, then along the starboard rail to the A-frame near the mainmast. At the A-frame the wire passed outboard over a large sheave at the apex of the A-frame, down through the trigger-release mechanism, through tail fin, and down through the coring tube. A few inches above the penetrating end of the tube, the wire was fastened to the piston. Just below the piston was the core catcher, which consisted of a ring of springy bronze prongs that would close together after the sediment had entered the tube, thus preventing it from sliding out when the apparatus was hauled up. Finally a hardened-steel cutting edge was attached to the end of the tube.

With the help of a chain hoist hanging from the A-frame, we lifted the upper part of the apparatus out of the cradle, while other members of the coring crew lifted the twelve meters of coring tube off the brackets and lowered it gently into the water with a loop of hemp line around the lower end. Now the apparatus was hanging vertically from the A-frame. In the meantime, the tripping device had been immobilized by a safety pin which prevented the long trigger arm from rising in spite of the fact that the trigger weight had not yet been lowered.

While all this was going on, the *Atlantis* was reacting to a moderate swell with her characteristic long period roll, a motion that has brought acute distress to many a scientist. Had the coring apparatus been hanging quite freely, the lead weights, like a massive sledge hammer, would have struck the side of the *Atlantis* repeatedly. To prevent this, Ewing had thrown a line around the tube just below the weights. By snubbing this line around a cleat on the rail, he subdued the swings of the apparatus enough to avoid the danger of starting some of the rivets of the ship. The hundred-pound trigger weight was lowered over the side, and the triggering device swayed as the wire came taut on the long arm. A last check-up showed that everything was in place. At a word from Ewing a seaman jerked the safety pin out. "Lower away!" cried Ewing as he cast off the snubbing line.

Captain Adrian Lane, at the winch controls, pushed over the lever, and a grinding roar came up from the winch in the hold while the heavy steel wire rattled and slapped as it unreeled. We went to the rail and watched the coring apparatus disappear below the surface of the sea.

Would everything turn out as we hoped? Would the highly complicated gear really work, and make the ocean floor give up some of its secrets? If the wire kinked or fouled, it might break, and we would lose the corer and perhaps thousands of meters of valuable wire. If, by mistake, the corer were hauled up before it hit bottom, we would not get a core; and if the tripping device failed to let the corer fall freely the last three meters, it would not get as long a core as the previous instrument had. Or the tube might hit hard rock and be broken. In oceanography one must always brace oneself against disappointment. This time there seemed to be even more things than usual which might go wrong and prevent us from getting a long core.

We were in water 4,630 meters deep. Since the corer was being lowered at a rate of about ninety meters a minute, it would take almost an hour for the instrument to reach the bottom.

That would be a critical moment. The winch had to be stopped dead just as the reduced strain on the tensionmeter over which the wire was running out indicated that the release had been set into operation. If the winch was not stopped at the right moment, too much wire would be payed out and it would probably kink and foul.

The captain's hand was taut on the control lever. Ewing carefully observed the movements of the brass pointer on the tensionmeter. Since the tension on the wire changed each time the ship rolled, Ewing's job was complicated by the necessity of distinguishing the twitch of the pointer that would indicate the tripping of the corer from the surges caused by rolling. As the meters of wire payed out approached the depth indicated by the sonic depth recorder, Ewing became as intense as a cat with a mouse. Suddenly the pointer flipped back—the tube had hit bottom. "Stop!" called out Ewing. Captain Lane stopped the winch abruptly. There was silence for a moment.

We hoped that all had gone well deep down in the ocean; that the trigger weight had hit bottom first, causing the trigger arm to snap up and release the clamp that held the lead discs and the tube to the wire; that the kinetic energy of the falling lead discs had driven the tube all the way down into the sediment; that the piston inside the tube had been held stationary by the lowering wire, while the coring tube descended, thereby bringing into effect great water pressure to force a column of sediment to fill the tube. But even if all these things had gone well, there still remained the problem of getting the twelve-meter tube out of sediment which, most likely, had been packed down for hundreds of thousands of years.

Hurriedly the captain changed the winch to reverse. The roar from the hold began again. Again our attention was fixed on the tensionmeter. The greenish brass pointer moved slowly over the shining dial. It stopped at six thousand pounds. Then again it flipped back. There was a sudden slacking of the strain on the wire—the tenacious grip of the sticky sediment around the coring tube had been broken; the tube was free, and the long haul-up could begin.

As soon as the instrument was visible under water, Ewing called out: "In sight!" The skipper reduced speed. At Ewing's shout of "Surface!" the skipper reduced speed still more and brought the apparatus up to the A-frame at a snail's pace. At once the snubbing line was thrown around the weights. Another bight of line was passed around the tube and allowed to slide down to the lower part. By pulling aft on this line it was possible to bring the coring tube up into a horizontal position along the rail.

A smear of mud on the outside showed that the tube had successfully penetrated about nine meters of sediment. When the core had been extruded from the tube, we found it to be 945 centimeters long, about three times as long as any we had been able to take before.

Since only a rapid preliminary description of the cores can be made on board ship, this core was promptly marked and packed for future study in the laboratory. The preliminary examination was enough, however, to show that the core did not contain a continuous record of slow accumulation of sediment. Here again we found layers of well-sorted sand interbedded with normal deep-sea sediment, that is, clay with abundant shells of planktonic protozoa, or foraminifera.

Of the more than twenty cores taken during this expedition, few contained an unbroken record of Pleistocene climatic changes. Another core of about the same length contained many sand layers, one of which was more than a hundred and twenty centimeters thick. Others contained numerous thin silt[1] layers and layers of

[1] Geologists define silt as an unconsolidated sediment most of the particles of which are between $\frac{1}{16}$ and $\frac{1}{256}$ millimeter in diameter. Thus, in size of particles, silt is intermediate between clay, which is composed of particles smaller than $\frac{1}{256}$ millimeter, and sand, the particles of which range from $\frac{1}{16}$ to 2 millimeters in diameter.

clay that were quite unlike normal deep-sea sediment both in color and in the absence of shells of foraminifera. Apparently, sediment accumulation according to the classical conception—that is, by an extremely slow and continuous rain of microscopic particles—was the exception rather than the rule.

Since we found the sands and silts so common, why had earlier expeditions not found them more often? They had found them only very rarely; even so, there had been some speculation regarding their origin. Karl Andrée had devoted a chapter to them in his *Geologie des Meeresbodens,* but he had not realized their importance among deep-sea sediments. They had not been found more often because the sampling devices used by the earlier investigators were not designed to penetrate more than about thirty centimeters of sediment. Since the great majority of sands were deposited during the ice ages, the last of which came to an end about 11,000 years ago, most are covered by twenty-five to thirty centimeters of normal deep-sea sediment. Furthermore, clean sand notoriously defies sampling; it will invariably run out of a coring tube unless the bottom of the tube is plugged by entering clay beneath the sand. A few sands occur at the surface or are covered by only two or three centimeters of normal sediment, and it was probably these surface or near-surface sands that the earlier investigators sampled.

In addition to the cores, the expedition was obtaining valuable information about the topography of the ocean floor. The recording echo sounder was drawing a continuous profile of the bottom along the entire track of the expedition. The Hudson Submarine Canyon received a particularly thorough survey. We found that the canyon could be traced with certainty to a distance of about a hundred and fifty nautical miles southeast of the edge of the continental shelf, which meant that the canyon extended much farther and into deeper water than had been known before. Beyond this point, the regional topography took the form of a broad plain gently sloping to the southeast. It was on this plain that the cores containing sand had been taken. This association of coarse, well-sorted sediment with a topographical feature that resembled an alluvial plain extending out beyond the submarine Hudson Canyon strongly suggested a genetic connection between type of sediment and topography.

To test this theory, coordinated coring and topographical surveys were carried out the following year in the region of the Hudson Canyon. These yielded a great deal of new evidence that had an important bearing on submarine erosion and deep-sea sedimentation.

Study of the cores raised in the region of the canyon showed that the sediment on the floor of the canyon was sand and gravel covered by no more than twenty-five centimeters of typical deep-sea sediment. In the gravel of at least one core were numerous fragments and even some whole shells of clams and snails of Pleistocene age. Cores taken on the relatively steep walls of the canyon contained green clay of the Pliocene Epoch, the epoch of the Cenozoic Era that directly preceded the Pleistocene. Pebble-sized balls of this same green clay occurred in the gravels of the bed of the canyon. Cores from the submarine alluvial fan did not contain gravel but did contain silt and sand layers ranging in thickness from mere films to beds more than 550 centimeters thick. Cores from the divides on both sides of the canyon—including points well above the floor of the canyon—contained normal deep-sea sediment representing continuous slow accumulation during the past hundred thousand years.

The gravels and shells of animals typical of shallow water in the bed of the canyon seemed to prove that the canyon had been eroded at a time when the region was above sea level. On the evidence of the thickness of normal deep-sea sediment overlying the gravels, submergence of the region must have taken place no more than about ten thousand years ago. However, this seemingly simple explanation was altogether wrong. The cores from the divides proved beyond a shadow of a doubt that the region had been continuously under deep water for at least a hundred thousand years. Preliminary surveys by sonic sounding of other areas showed that the Hudson Submarine Canyon was not unique. A great canyon extended to abyssal depth off the Congo River of Africa. Other canyons were found off the coast of Portugal, in the Mediterranean, and along the west coast of North America. Evidently the process responsible for their existence had taken place on a global scale.

With the systematic study of the Hudson Submarine Canyon, the Lamont Geological Observatory set a new and important pattern in deep-sea exploration. In earlier exploration, a one-time expedition had been the rule. Upon the ship's return home, she would be decommissioned or put to some other use, and the scientists would scatter to their respective laboratories. Such expeditions often covered vast distances and collected quantities of valuable material and information. As can be expected in the exploratory stage of a science, the data brought home always raised more questions than they answered, but by the time the collections had been studied and working hypotheses had been elaborated, there would no longer be any means of returning to critical regions where the hypotheses could be tested.

After the first North Atlantic expedition of 1947, several circumstances combined to favor a new approach. Random collecting without any provision for follow-up was no longer good enough. Moreover, an adequate vessel was constantly available. This was the *Atlantis* of Woods Hole Oceanographic Institution, an auxiliary ketch designed expressly for oceanographic research. Later the Lamont Geological Observatory acquired the *Vema,* a steel auxiliary three-masted schooner. Like the *Atlantis,* the *Vema* has been kept continuously in commission.

Another factor of importance was the discovery that deep-sea sands were prevalent and might be related to another tantalizing problem, the origin of submarine canyons. The result was a whole series of fascinating hypotheses that could be tested by more closely spaced cores and more detailed charting of the regional topography of the ocean floor.

Subsequent expeditions paid off handsomely—and gave rise to new questions—with the result that more than forty expeditions have been sent out by the Lamont Geological Observatory. These have brought back many hundreds of cores containing sands collected in all the ocean basins. Because of this wealth of material, our conclusions regarding the processes responsible for the occurrence of the sands are based on evidence that has a high degree of statistical validity. The following characteristics of these remarkable sediments have been determined from examination of thousands of layers.

Grading in the size of particles is usually present; by grading we mean gradual decrease in the size of particles from the bottom of any one layer to the top.

The mineral composition of the layers varies greatly from place to place. In the region of the Hudson Submarine Canyon the dominant mineral is quartz, with a sprinkling of felspars, micas, ferromagnesian minerals, glauconite, particles of red and gray shale, limestone, and flint. Usually some of the quartz and felspar grains are stained red by iron oxide. The quartz grains show every gradation of rounding, polishing, and frosting, but the dominant form is angular. In the sands from the region east of Cape Hatteras, particles of coal are sometimes common. Off the Bahamas and the Bermudas, the sands are almost wholly calcareous and often consist largely of fragments of lime secreted by certain species of seaweeds. Off the Cape Verde and Azores Islands the sands are sometimes composed almost entirely of particles of volcanic glass.

These layers are also distinctive in that the bases that rest directly on normal sediment of slow accumulation are sharply defined. On the other hand, the tops of the layers, particularly when they grade upward into clay, are often blurred by the mixing effect of burrowing, mud-eating animals. The absence of disturbance by burrowers is a reliable criterion by which sediments laid down almost instantaneously by turbidity currents may be distinguished from sediments of slow and continuous accumulation. Evidence of burrowing in the form of irregular mottling is almost universally present in slowly accumulated sediments, but, except for the upper few centimeters, burrow mottling is never present in layers deposited by turbidity currents.

In general these beds, in their physical, chemical, and biological nature, are strikingly discordant with the environment in which they occur. We find them in the deepest parts of the oceans, but almost all contain some element of shallow-water origin. This, and the

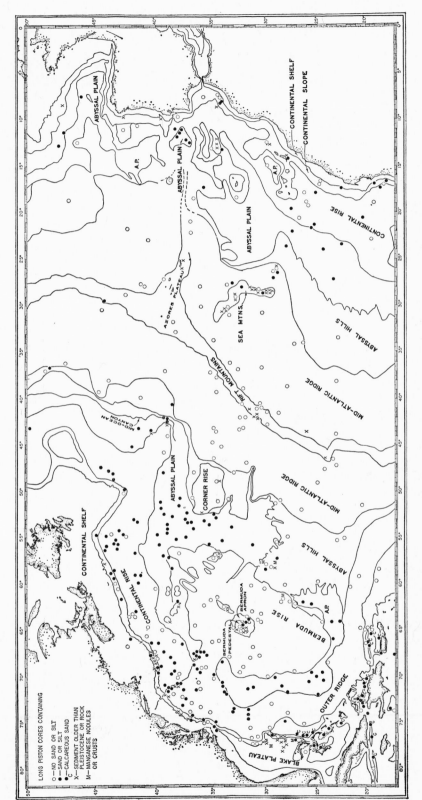

FIGURE 3 Distribution of various kinds of deep-sea sediments in relation to physiographic provinces.

fact that they are composed of coarser particles than normally occur in deep-sea sediments, has led some geologists to insist that they must have been deposited at a time of greatly lowered sea level. However, when these layers are compared with the sediments in cores from the continental shelf, it is evident that the resemblance is only superficial. The layering of the shallow-water deposits is distinctly less regular; grading is only occasionally present; and the fairly large shells that commonly occur in shallow-water sands are absent from deep-sea sands, though they are present in two layers of gravel from the bottom of the Hudson Submarine Canyon.

Perhaps the most significant characteristic of these deposits is their distribution with respect to the topography of the ocean floor. We have found them in submarine canyons, on gently sloping plains upon which submarine canyons open, and in deep basins and trenches. But of the many hundreds of cores containing graded layers, not one comes from the top of an isolated rise. Graded layers of calcareous sand containing the shells of planktonic snails, of shallow-water species of single-celled animals and particles of calcareous algae have been cored in the deepest part of the North Atlantic, at a depth of 7,900 meters in the Puerto Rico Trench. At such great depths, particles of calcium carbonate slowly settling from the surface dissolve before they reach the bottom. In consequence, the normal sediment of the Puerto Rico Trench is a dark brown clay almost devoid of calcium carbonate. Such sediment occurs both below and above the graded layers in these extraordinary cores from the trench. Presumably the sediment of the graded layers was deposited so rapidly that there was no time for solution of the abundant particles of calcium carbonate. Cores from the ridge north of the Puerto Rico Trench offer a striking contrast; they come from depths varying between 4,875 to 5,800 meters, or more than a mile above the bottom of the trench, but they contain only brown clay of the kind which marine geologists regard as typical of the deep ocean basins.

Elsewhere, as in the deep basin of the Gulf of Mexico, differences of depth of no more than about a hundred meters are enough to make the difference between an almost continuous succession of graded layers and uniform abyssal clays containing the shells of planktonic protozoa. The abyssal clays were cored on the tops of several low hills that occur near the center of the nearly level plain of the deepest part of the Gulf. The rate of sediment accumulation on the tops of the hills has been determined by dating samples from the upper parts of the cores by the radiocarbon method. On the basis of the rate of sediment accumulation, the uniformity of the sediment, and the lengths of the cores, we can say with confidence that the depth of water in the Gulf of Mexico has not varied by more than a few hundred feet during the past several hundred thousand years. On the other hand, radiocarbon dating of cores from the surrounding plain, which contain graded layers with material of shallow-water origin, shows that some of these layers were deposited only a few thousand years ago, that is, since the close of the last ice age.

In summary, the problem posed by the occurrence of sands at great depth in the oceans is as follows. Chemical decay of the silicate minerals associated with quartz in granitic rocks must occur in order that the quartz crystals may be released as sand. The conditions and agents necessary for this decay are abundant free oxygen, organic acids produced by plants, and probably bacteria. These are aided by the removal by rain and wind of the residual material that would hinder continuation of the disintegration process. Needless to say, the disintegration of granite, "the rock of ages," is slow, but in the many millions of years of geological time a great deal of quartz sand has been generated. In the oceans, at depths of several thousand meters, however, conditions are quite different. The generation of quartz sand by the disintegration of granitic rocks is ruled out, even if such rocks did occur there. Actually, according to geophysical theory and observation, they don't occur there. Gravity and seismic measurements at sea indicate that the ocean basins are underlain by dense rocks presumably rich in iron, calcium, and magnesium, and poor in silicon dioxide, the chemical substance of the mineral quartz. The rock specimens that have been dredged from the floor of the ocean and the rocks one can see on oceanic islands confirm the evidence from geophysics. These rocks, uniformly, contain so little silicon dioxide that all of it is combined with other substances. There is none left to occur alone as quartz.

But this is not all. The sands in cores from deep stations contain the shells of foraminifera that have never been found living anywhere but in shallow water. This strongly suggests that before reaching abyssal depths the sands passed over the continental shelves. True, some of the sands we have found at great depths are composed largely of particles of calcium carbonate, and here again there is a startling contrast between the place where they now occur and what must have been the environment in which the particles originated. Many of the calcareous particles unmistakably were secreted by a group of marine plants known as calcareous algae, which, like all plants, must have sunlight to grow. By what means, then, have the sands been transported from the continents?

This was a difficult problem. Both the everyday currents of normal oceanic circulation and the variable currents due to tidal forces are too weak by many orders of magnitude to transport the relatively coarse particles of the sands. Moreover, the layering and grading of the sands in the cores clearly pointed to a spasmodic process entirely different from the currents known to oceanographers. And yet the sands had been transported somehow. The guess that their transportation had had a causal connection with the erosion of submarine canyons was difficult to avoid.

In 1930 the United States Coast and Geodetic Survey charted in detail, with an echo sounder, the ocean floor off the northeastern part of the United States. In principle, the method depends upon measuring the time it takes a sound wave from the ship to reach the bottom and return to the ship on being reflected from the bottom. The survey extended out from the coast to a distance of more than a hundred and fifty miles. Now, it had been known for some time that what appeared to be drowned valleys occurred here and there on the continental shelf, particularly off the mouths of large rivers such as the Hudson. There was nothing particularly surprising about this. Most geologists agreed that sea level must have been lowered during the ice ages because of withdrawal of water from the oceans to form the great continental glaciers. A lowering sufficient to uncover the continental shelves seemed reasonable enough from what was known about the extent and probable thickness of the ice sheets of the Pleistocene. However, as the 1930 survey progressed, the astonishing fact emerged that the valleys which crossed the continental shelf could be traced down the continental slopes to depths as great as 3,000 meters. Not only that, but the valleys became great canyons where they plunged down the steeper parts of the continental slope. This new evidence of the great depth to which the canyons descended seriously strained the theory that they had been formed by river erosion at a time of lower sea level.

However, A. C. Veatch and A. P. Smith, who published a report on this survey, still insisted that the canyon must have been cut by stream erosion at a time of greatly lowered sea level. This was very difficult for most geologists to accept; no matter how generously one extended the area of the Pleistocene glaciers, no matter how desperately one thickened them, it was simply not possible to account for so enormous a withdrawal of water. An attempt to relegate the time of erosion to some very early period of earth history also failed. H. C. Stetson in 1936 was able to show by coring and dredging in some of the canyons that most if not all of the erosion had indeed taken place during the Pleistocene, that is, within the last one or two million years.

In 1936 also, Reginald A. Daly, a famous geologist at Harvard University, proposed the theory that the canyons had been eroded underneath the sea by density currents or turbidity currents.

The density of water may be increased in various ways: by cooling it, by dissolving salt in it, or by creating a suspension of fine mineral matter in it. For example, if you dissolve some salt in a tablespoonful of water, add a couple of drops of ink, and pour it into a tilted glass of water, you will see a miniature density current flow down the sloping side of the glass under the clear water. A turbidity current is the same, except that the density of the flowing water is due to mineral particles in suspension.

Sea level was certainly lower during the ice ages. It was probably low enough to expose quantities of unconsolidated sediment on the continental shelves to erosion by waves during storms. Daly thought that the stirring effect of wave erosion would put a great deal of sediment into suspension, thereby generating large volumes of turbid water. But water full of mineral particles in suspension is denser than clear water and therefore could be expected to cascade over the edge of the continental shelf and rush down the continental slope. Daly called his hypothetical streams of turbid water *turbidity currents*. He suggested that they might have sufficient energy to erode submarine canyons. Apparently he did not take into consideration a secondary effect of turbidity currents— the transportation to and deposition at great depths of much material of shallow-water origin. It is rather a pity that he did not predict that anomalous deposits of sands, silts, and gray calcareous clays would be found on abyssal plains off the mouths of submarine canyons; it would have made the task of finding the correct explanation for the sand layers in our cores a good deal easier. But Daly published his brilliant theory too early; like many another good theory before it, scientists received it almost unanimously with contempt and proceeded to think up rafts of other theories to explain submarine canyons, most of them mare's nests of fantastic improbability.

In 1947, while we were finding layers of sand in deep-sea cores, Ph. H. Kuenen, a professor of geology at the University of Groningen in the Netherlands, was experimenting with artificial turbidity currents. He found that they behaved, at least on a small scale, much as Daly had supposed. He also made the important observation that the layers of sediment deposited by his turbidity currents were graded from coarse material at the bottom to fine at the top. This observation provided us with another valuable clue in our search for a satisfactory explanation for the coarse-graded layers that we were finding with such surprising regularity in the deep-sea cores.

We at the Lamont Geological Observatory are now fully convinced that turbidity currents have played an important part in marine sedimentation and probably an equally important role in modifying the bottom topography of the Atlantic and adjacent seas. Cores from the Atlantic and the Gulf of Mexico provide good evidence that turbidity currents were particularly active during the last ice age, which came to an end about 11,000 years ago. This was implied in Daly's theory of the erosion of submarine canyons by turbidity currents, in which lower sea level was attributed to withdrawal of oceanic water to build up the continental ice sheets. Had we nothing but the canyons as evidence, as was the case when Daly published his hypothesis in 1936, we would have no way of knowing when erosion of the canyons had taken place. But we have the graded layers in the cores and can date them by radiocarbon. These layers, which occur beneath an upper layer of sediment containing the normal present-day assemblage of planktonic foraminifera, provide good evidence that turbidity currents occurred with great frequency during the last ice age and that their prevalence came to an abrupt end toward its close.

The fact that Daly's reasoning regarding the timing of the erosion of the canyons has been confirmed from evidence that was not known in his day gives powerful support to the overall theory of turbidity currents and their ability to erode.

For us, the graded layers of material of shallow-water origin introduced a serious complication. Because they clearly were connected with the last ice age, we were particularly anxious to find a satisfactory explanation for them; they might very well give us a lead as to the cause of glaciations. As it turned out, however, they fitted very nicely into Daly's theory and were of no help in the problem of causation. At the same time, their association with lower stands of sea level during the ice ages may someday make them useful as indirect indicators of past climates; they could then act as checks on the conclusions we reached on the basis of the planktonic foraminifera.

As yet, however, these graded layers have not been of much use in this respect. Where they occur abundantly, the section of sediment deposited during the last ice age is too thick to be penetrated with the coring apparatus available today. In the entire Gulf of Mexico, for example, there are only three or four low hills or mounds, near the center of the Gulf, which can be cored with some assurance of obtaining long and continuous records. For the same reason, broad areas of the Caribbean and the Atlantic can be regarded as useless for our purpose. On the other hand, an understanding of the mechanism of sediment deposition by turbidity currents enables us to pick out the topographical features on the sea floor that are most likely to yield good records. Since turbidity currents, like streams on land, are guided by the configuration of the bottom, it is possible to take cores that do not show their influence; for example, on isolated rises, such as the low mounds in the Gulf of Mexico. These mounds rise little more than a hundred meters above the surrounding abyssal plain, but apparently their tops have not been reached by the floods of turbid water that spread so frequently over the plain during the last ice age. We know this from the striking contrast between the kind of sediment, fine brown clay with abundant shells of planktonic foraminifera, which occurs in the cores from the mounds, and the almost continuous series of silt layers alternating with gray clay devoid of foraminifera in the cores from the surrounding plain.

We had not lost sight of our original objective, to find an unbroken record of the climatic and biological changes that occurred during the Pleistocene. It had only been temporarily subordinated to the study of the graded layers. When we felt fairly sure that we understood the process by which they are formed and where and how they occur, we were in a better position to avoid being led astray by the depositional confusion created by turbidity currents. At least we knew where not to core if we wanted long, continuous records of past climatic events. To core the bottoms of broad basins was useless; all these basins, at least in the Atlantic, are filled with rapidly deposited graded layers. Accordingly, we concentrated our attention on cores from isolated rises.

When we began to study the cores taken on the rises, however, we encountered another source of confusion. Whereas the cores from deep basins contained "noisy layers" deposited by turbidity currents, the cores from rises were incomplete, as if one group of cores had lost what the others had gained. Many cores from rises had somehow lost sections of sediment representing tens of thousands or even many millions of years of accumulation of sediment.

We now realize that these losses are due to slumping of sediment. Masses of water-saturated sediment on slopes are necessarily somewhat unstable. As the rain of fine particles from above slowly adds layer upon layer of sediment, the instability becomes critical. Any disturbance, such as a minor earth tremor, suffices to trigger a debacle. The initial result is what on land we would call a landslide. On the sea floor, however, the sliding mass of sediment gathers speed, tumbles over itself, and in the churning process becomes thoroughly mixed with water until at last it assumes the nature of a great "storm" of mud, sand, gravel, and water. Moving with the energy of a hurricane, it cascades down undersea slopes like an unseen Niagara. The effect on all life along the course of the storm must be catastrophic. Upon reaching gentler slopes, the mass of turbid water loses velocity and the coarser fraction of sediment settles out of suspension. Slumping constitutes another mode of origin of turbidity currents, an origin independent of the lower stands of sea level of the ice ages. Turbidity currents generated in this way are very probably responsible for the relatively rare graded layers that occur in the upper parts of cores, which have certainly been deposited since the end of the last ice age.

The local occurrence of discontinuities in cores due to loss of some part of the section by slumping complicated our search for a complete record of the climatic events of the Pleistocene. In order to avoid being misled by these hiatuses in the record, we needed to study many more cores from widely separated areas. This unforeseen contingency left us no alternative but to put to sea once again.

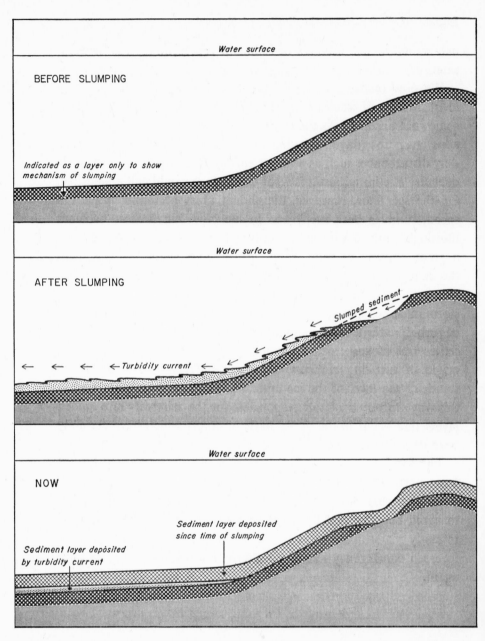

FIGURE 4 *Mechanism of slumping and generation of a turbidity current. The turbidity current created by slumping erodes sediment as it flows down the steep part of the slope, thus removing part of the sediment record. On reaching the nearly level part of the floor of the ocean, however, the mass of turbid water loses velocity and the sediment settles to the bottom.*

4

MOVING AHEAD TOWARD

THE COMPLETE RECORD

OF THE ICE AGES

EACH expedition has its highlights. We remember most vividly some rough and windy January days in 1951 when we were coring in the Caribbean.

The first days of the cruise in the Caribbean were severe. We ran into a gale which swept over the sea like a broom run wild. The *Atlantis* was hove to under a storm trysail, with the engine at rest. The single sail was too small to drive the *Atlantis* ahead; all it could do was reduce her roll, and it kept her headed more or less in the same direction with respect to the wind. It was useless to think of working on deck. Only the echo sounder kept up its endless routine.

In the early days of oceanography, oceanic depths could be measured only by lowering a weight on the end of a hemp line. In shallow water this was good enough; in really deep water the combined effect of the ship's drift and deep currents was to put great S-shaped curves into the line, with the result that depths as recorded were always greater, sometimes by a large amount, than the real depths. By the time the *Challenger* put to sea in 1872, piano wire had been substituted for the hemp line. This was an improvement. The wire offered less resistance to the moving water, but there were serious disadvantages still. Erratic soundings by the *Challenger* in regions of strong currents, such as the Gulf Stream, show that the wire could also go astray, and it took hours to make a single sounding. In such weather as we were experiencing, soundings by the old methods would have been impossible. And yet, all through the gale, while the *Atlantis* was rolling her lee rail under, the faithful echo sounder was sending down a "ping" every few seconds.

Off watch, one went below and listened to a monotonous symphony, mostly in tympany, and almost as formless as a composition by John Cage. There was the sound of the unknown heavy object which constantly rolled a short distance on the steel deck and fetched up with a hollow wooden thud; there was the clinking in unison of dozens of sample bottles, reinforced by a chorus of ticks, chirps, and squeaks of mysterious origin, perhaps emanating from the fabric of the straining ship. Through this chaos of sound came a single note of order, the perfectly timed, high-pitched, fluty "pings" of the echo sounder. Behind a window on the instrument, a stylus on a rotating arm swept across a slowly moving strip of calibrated paper. At each arrival of an echo, a spark passed between the stylus and the specially coated paper, leaving a black mark to indicate the depth. As the closely spaced echoes came in, the black marks coalesced to form a continuous line rising and falling as the *Atlantis* passed over hills and valleys far below the keel. It seemed as if we were flying over an unknown planet hidden from view but outlined on a radar screen.

On deck we forgot about unknown planets. Monstrous hissing waves surged up and poured over the deck, adding their voices to that of the wind. When she was on the crest of a wave, the entire ship would vibrate with the force of the gale, and then do a sickening plunge into the trough, only to be wrenched up again like a lift and be assaulted by the following mountain of water.

During normal weather, while we were busy testing, measuring, and studying particular aspects of the sea, we tended to lose sight of the whole. But during the gale the sea as an entity forced itself upon us, and the enforced leisure that it brought gave us a chance to see the beauty we normally missed. We could enjoy the dolphins sparkling in the waves, their long dorsal fins and backs a brilliant blue shading to silvery white below, with purple and gold reflections. On their heads and backs they had a series of bright blue spots; the fins and tails were a dazzling yellow.

Now and then we saw flying fish as they glided alongside the ship. Breaking the surface of the water, they spread their wings, the greatly enlarged pectoral fins, and taxied ahead until they had speed enough for the glide. With their wings motionless while in the air, they looked like small model Spitfires.

Oddly enough, we found the closest intimacy with the life of the sea in our cabin, which was on the lee side and had a single large porthole. At one moment, as the ship rose on a wave, we could look out over the foam-crested waves; at the next, the ship would sink into a trough and roll to leeward. Then, as the porthole plunged under, we looked deep into blue-green water. Looking into and not upon the surface of the water gave us a truly fish-eye view of the sea. It was fascinating to watch the bouquets and long garlands of drifting seaweed go by. When the ship surged ahead, these things passed in a blur, but when she was met by a particularly powerful wave, she would come to a standstill, and then we would find ourselves face to face with some big-eyed fish peering out from a bushy frond of weed, or it might be a weird shrimp-like creature with eyes on long stalks. Once the many tentacles of a Portuguese man-of-war came into sight. Looking up, we saw the underside of the translucent gas-filled float, glowing pinkish-blue in the light from above. We imagined how it would feel to be a little fish caught in the stinging tentacles.

Also across the porthole flowed an endless stream of plankton— the collective name for all those organisms, mostly small, which cannot swim at all or else swim so feebly as to be entirely at the mercy of winds and currents. In shape and color these particles of

life were infinitely varied; many were blue, blue-green, or yellowish
green; others were silvery, deep crimson, or purple. Shapes varied
from the umbrella-like jellyfish to the translucent Bathothauma
with bodies like floppy bags; then there was the streamlined Cal-
liteuthis, to say nothing of the bizarre-shaped larvae of all sorts of
crustacea.

But it was particularly at night that the planktonic creatures
appeared in full glory. What fireworks they displayed then as they
glowed, pulsated, and flashed with yellow, red, blue, and white
light. In some the light was diffused; in others, it was emitted by
lantern-like organs with lens and reflector, which threw powerful
and directed beams. A few of the larger forms could eject clouds
of luminous substance to confuse their enemies. Others used their
lights to aid them in catching food; not by lighting it up to see it,
but by setting themselves aglow and acting as a lure. Possibly some
were females, merely showing off their splendor to entice an unwary
male. The ability to emit light, known as bioluminescence, is shared
by members of most of the major animal groups that live in the
oceans, from microscopic single-celled forms to the highly developed vertebrates. Many marine bacteria are also luminescent.

Although the ability to emit light is commonly called phospho-
rescence, the chemical element phosphorus has nothing to do with
it. The luminescence is brought about by the oxidation of a substance called luciferin. Actually, the process is a little more complicated. Before light can be produced by union with oxygen, an
enzyme, luciferase, must be present as a catalyst to accelerate the
oxidation. The nervous control over light emission possessed by
some organisms results from their ability to bring the two substances
together when stimulated by some outside influence.

Bioluminescence is not confined to organisms near the surface
of the sea. About half of the fish in the dark ocean depths have
light-emitting organs. This is probably why fish collected from the
greatest depths have well-developed eyes and coloration, quite unlike the blind and colorless species that have evolved in caves.

After the storm had calmed down, we ranged over many square
miles of sea and watched the wire meter on the winch tick off thou-

sands of meters of wire. Sometimes hours of hard work would go for naught when a bent and twisted coring tube containing no core was hauled up, or when we stowed below samples of sediment of no more than average interest.

Once more we prepared the coring instrument for lowering and sent it down to the bottom of the sea. When it came back to the surface, we discovered that the tube was broken off about ten feet from the top. However, the part that had been broken off was not lost; it was hanging on the wire attached to the piston, which, fortunately, had caught in the upper part of the broken section where the wall of the tube had been squeezed together a little bit before breaking. It looked as though the piston would slide through at any moment. This was alarming; we didn't want to lose the thirty-foot-long core the broken section probably contained.

We reached down to haul it up, but the coating of mud outside the tube made it impossible to lift. Captain Lane came over to help, but even the three of us could not lift it near enough to the railing.

"Get us a line!" Captain Lane called.

The great weight of the tube told us that it must be full of sediment. This made us double our effort to hold it. Yet it slid slowly through our hands and into the water. One of the seamen came running with a line. The captain reached far over the railing and took a hitch around the coring tube. We all grabbed the line and heaved away on it, but the line came off the slippery tube and we all went sprawling on deck.

"We'll have to get a longer line and make it fast below the coupling," said the skipper.

The coupling was about ten feet below the break. When Captain Lane tried to fasten the line below the coupling, he found that it was beyond his reach. In the meantime, we held on to the end of the tube as best we could.

"Grab my legs and I'll hang over the side. I think I can reach it then," the skipper ordered.

A couple of seamen took hold of his legs while he tried to reach below the coupling. Still it was beyond his reach.

Again we tried to get it up by brute force, but no matter how we knotted the line or how tightly we gripped the tube, it evaded us like an eel.

"Hold my feet," called the captain. So down he went, until only his feet were above the gunwale. After several dousings, he succeeded in making the line fast below the coupling.

At last the tube lay safely on deck, and we extruded the core. This we did by means of a tube of small diameter that fitted inside the coring tube. On one end of this "extruding rod" was a piston, which we placed against the sediment. The other end was butted against the break in the poop deck, the step-like rise separating the after part of the deck. Then a line was hitched around the pipe and taken to a winch, which pulled the coring tube against the stationary piston and rod. Thus the tube was pulled back while the core remained stationary. A tray lined with impervious paper placed beneath the coring tube received the core as the tube was pulled back. After we had made a preliminary examination of the core, we wrapped the paper around the core and stapled the edges. We then put the wrapped sections of the core into ten-foot lengths of galvanized gutter pipe, the ends of which we closed with tin caps held in place and sealed with friction tape. In this way the core could be kept on board ship without serious loss of water.

A preliminary examination of the core gave us the impression that, for our purposes, it was the best we had yet obtained. It had been taken on the gently sloping flank of a ridge. Since we had not had success in obtaining cores with long and continuous sedimentary records of climatic changes from the flat floors of basins or the tops of isolated rises, we had turned our attention to gentle slopes.

Examinations of cores on shipboard are never really satisfactory. Freshly extruded cores are always coated on the outside by smeared sediment, which completely hides the nature of the real core. One can scrape off the smear to some extent, but it is not possible to do so thoroughly enough to reveal all the important details. The only way to do this is to slice the core longitudinally through the center. And this is never done on shipboard. It is just about impossible to bring the halves back into their original relationship, and to wrap and store the halves separately is to risk serious damage and contamination to the sediment. However, judging from what we could see of this core, it was free of any evidence of deposition by turbidity currents or disturbance by slumping. It was just over nine meters long and consisted throughout of nearly uniform clay or lutite, with an abundance of shells of foraminifera. The only variation from level to level that we could see consisted of changes between darker and lighter brown. But how long a time the sediment in the core represented or how many faunal zones recording climatic changes it included we had no way of knowing until we could give it a thorough investigation in the laboratory.

At last the day came when with intense interest we took the sections of this core out of the gutter pipes, unwrapped it, and sliced it lengthwise at the laboratory. Three longitudinal quarters of the core were stored in galvanized trays 245 centimeters long and a little wider than the core diameter, 63 millimeters. The fourth longitudinal quarter was preserved in sections of pyrex tubing, 120 centimeters long, the ends of which were closed with rubber stoppers. In this way, the original water content could be retained indefinitely without refrigeration, shrinkage was eliminated, and color change could be reduced to a minimum. Growth of molds and bacteria was inhibited by the addition of a few milliliters of formaldehyde neutralized with some sodium bicarbonate, which we poured into the tube under the strip of celluloid that supported the core. The core section so preserved would be of importance for reference during the microscopic and chemical study of samples taken from the other three quarters, which had been put into the metal trays and would in time become completely dry. We knew that the pyrex would remain clear and permit visual examination of the sediment, even with a low-power hand lens, without removal of the core section from the tube.

Immediately after slicing the core, we photographed it and wrote a description of its various sedimentary zones. Next we took samples from one longitudinal quarter, for study of the microfossils. Each was one centimeter thick, and they were taken at intervals of ten centimeters. We concentrated the microfossils by washing the samples on a sieve with openings 74 microns[1] in diameter. After the coarse fractions of the samples had been dried, they were ready for study of the microfossils under a binocular microscope.

For many persons, the words *fossil* and *paleontology* evoke pictures of dinosaur bones or other good-sized pieces of vertebrate skeletons. In the micropaleontological study of ocean sediments, one deals with fossils of an entirely different magnitude. These are the shells, or more accurately, the tests—that is, skeletons—of minute aquatic organisms. All of these are too small to be studied without the help of a strong magnifying glass or microscope. Because of their minuteness, they are especially useful in geological research. They can be brought up unbroken and in enormous numbers by the narrow coring tube, and in small samples of sediment and rock from oil wells.

To meet the needs of the micropaleontologist, an organism must have characteristics other than small size. The organism must build a skeleton, shell, or some kind of hard part durable enough to survive attack by bacteria and the wear and tear of normal conditions of sedimentation. Moreover, the form of the hard part should be sufficiently distinctive to permit it to be identified at least as to genus, and preferably as to species. This implies some complexity of organization. In general, the species which have evolved most rapidly and have, therefore, flourished during the shortest periods of time and which have, on the other hand, extended their geographical ranges over the widest areas are the most useful geological indicators. They make it possible to differentiate sharply between layers of sedimentary rock of different ages and to match strata in widely separated parts of the earth.

In order to obtain evidence of past climates and other environmental conditions, the scientist must think of fossils as organisms that were once alive and had specialized adaptations to their particular surroundings. He then tries to reconstruct those surroundings by analogy with the ecological requirements of still-living near-

---

[1] A micron is one thousandth of a millimeter. The openings of the sieve are, therefore, 0.074 millimeter in diameter.

relatives of the ancient organisms. As can be expected, the method becomes more difficult as the evolutionary distance between the fossils and the living organisms increases. A paleontologist who would be a paleoecologist must first learn to be a good detective and find meaning in all sorts of seemingly trivial and irrelevant observations.

Curiosity, pure and simple, must have motivated the early students of microfossils. To their contemporaries, their peerings through microscopes at little dead things must have seemed an almost sinful waste of time. And doubtless they would be astonished if they could know how much wealth their "hobby" has helped to produce.

Among the various kinds of microfossils, the foraminifera have been by far the most thoroughly studied. Over the years a wealth of information on all aspects of foraminifera has accumulated. Most of this information is readily available. For example, all older descriptions of genera and species have been brought together in an enormous catalogue by Brooks F. Ellis and Angelina R. Messina of the American Museum of Natural History. Since the catalogue was first published by the museum in 1940, it has expanded until now it comprises sixty-nine volumes. And it is constantly growing, as descriptions of new species are added. The catalogue gives the place where the type specimen was collected, and if it was a fossil, as most species described are, the geological age of the rock in which it was found is also given.

The foraminifera are single-celled animals, or protozoa, almost exclusively marine, which construct tests or shells of various materials. Depending on the material of the shells the foraminifera are divided into two groups. The first includes the species that secrete shells of calcium carbonate precipitated directly from the calcium carbonate in solution in sea water; these are known as the calcareous species. The other group includes all species that make their shells out of sand grains, flakes of mica, sponge spicules, or even the small discarded calcareous shells of other species, which they fasten together with iron oxide or a calcareous cement; these are the arenaceous species. As a rule, the arenaceous species are rather particular about their building blocks; a species that customarily builds with sponge spicules will have nothing to do with mica flakes, and vice versa. Others, which use sand grains, show a preference for the so-called "heavy minerals," such as garnet, magnetite, and other iron-bearing minerals. In this case the discrimination cannot be based on the shape of the particles because on the average the heavy mineral particles are quite similar in their geometry to the quartz particles. Is it possible that the foraminifera actually "hefts" each mineral particle before incorporating it into its shell? Whatever the method, this degree of discrimination on the part of a single-celled organism is rather amazing.

The sizes of the shells vary greatly from species to species. Some extinct species constructed pancake-shaped shells which reached diameters of as much as fifteen centimeters, but few species living today have diameters of more than a few millimeters, and the great majority of the forms which occur in deep-sea sediments are less than one millimeter in diameter.

The architectural unit of the shell is the chamber. In the simplest forms the shell includes a single chamber, but most species construct shells with from two to several hundred chambers. Normally there is an aperture, or "doorway," opening into the last-formed chamber; in some species there are several apertures leading into the earlier chambers as well. In addition, fine pores pass through the walls of the shells of many species. In the course of evolution the foraminifera have improvised endlessly on these basic principles of structure. To duplicate all the strangely shaped chambers devised by the foraminifera, and the intricate arrangements thereof, would tax the ingenuity of a topologist. Of course, it is precisely this versatility in geometry which has made it possible for micropaleontologists to distinguish the thousands of species that have come and gone during the past 500 million years since the foraminifera first appeared in the Ordovician period. In spite of the great diversity of form from species to species, the individual variation within most species is small; as a rule, it is not much greater than that found within species of much more highly developed creatures such as clams and snails.

The vast majority of species are benthic in habit; that is, they live on the ocean floor. Some of these attach themselves to stones or even to seaweeds, but most species drag or push themselves about by means of long, branching, net-like pseudopodia, or strands of protoplasm which they send out through the aperture, or pores, of their shells. The more swift species can cover the ground at the rate of several centimeters an hour, but most potter along at a few millimeters an hour. The pseudopodia also serve to seize food and carry it to the animal by a streaming motion of the protoplasm. Microscopic algae, known as diatoms, are a favorite source of nourishment, and foraminifera cultivated in the laboratory have been seen to capture and digest small crustacea. Many species that live at fairly shallow depths and within reach of sunlight have entered into partnership with single-celled algae known as zooxanthellae. These tiny algae live within the protoplasm of their hosts. As algae they are capable of photosynthesis, the direct conversion of carbon dioxide and water into carbohydrates by means of light energy. Presumably they produce a surplus of these substances, which is utilized by the host foraminifer, and thus pay for the protection they receive inside the shell of the foraminifer. Many species, however, live far below the greatest depth reached by sunlight, where zooxanthellae would be useless and there are no living diatoms. Probably these dwellers of the deep—and some have been found at the greatest oceanic depths—feed on bacteria and the dead organic matter that rains down from the upper layer of water within which photosynthesis takes place.

At the beginning of Upper Cretaceous time, a mutation appeared among some foraminifera which enabled the mutant strain to leave the floor of the sea and float near the surface as a member of the group of organisms known collectively as plankton—that is, organisms without the ability to swim, which are therefore dependent on ocean currents for their distribution. Only about one percent of the known species of foraminifera are planktonic, but the enormous volume of living space open to those few species has permitted a correspondingly great proliferation of individuals. In the geological past, slow accumulation of the calcareous shells of planktonic foraminifera on the sea floor has resulted in thick deposits of chalk. The Upper Cretaceous is particularly known for its deposits of chalk—*creta,* in Latin. The white cliffs of Dover and Normandy are such deposits, now uplifted and partly worn away by erosion. Today large areas of the bottoms of the world's oceans are receiving a slow but constant rain of discarded shells of planktonic foraminifera.

The architecture of the shells of the important planktonic species living today is fairly simple. The dominant plan is a series of chambers arranged in a plane spiral or in a conical spiral much like a snail shell. The chambers gradually increase in size as they are added during the growth of the animal. When the spiral is conical, as is the case with most species, the geometry of the shell is basically similar to that of a snail shell. As with snails, the shells coil either to the right or to the left, the two kinds being mirror images of each other. Populations of planktonic foraminifera are strongly biased toward coiling in one direction or the other; mixed populations are rare. Why this should be so is somewhat of a mystery at present. Shells of species belonging to the genus *Globigerina* are covered with long, slender, fragile spines during the youthful stages of their development. At maturity the spines are shed or resorbed. The purpose of the spines is not clear. It is hardly likely that they are useful in flotation; the tests of the other highly successful genus of planktonic foraminifera, *Globorotalia,* are without spines.

Reproduction among the foraminifera is complicated by the necessity of producing many individuals on the one hand and of maintaining a flow of genetical material within the population on the other.[2] These needs are taken care of by a process called alternation of generations. Production of a sufficient number of individuals to keep the species going is fulfilled by simple fission. When an individual has reached the adult stage, the nucleus divides into a large number of smaller nuclei. Each of these then surrounds itself

[2] According to *Principles of Genetics,* by Edmund W. Sinnott, L. C. Dunn, and Theodosius Dobzhansky (New York: McGraw-Hill Book Company, Inc.; Fifth Edition, 1958, p. 254), "the success of this type of reproduction (that is, sexual reproduction) is probably due to the fact that it results in gene recombination, and gene recombination furnishes the raw materials among which natural selection picks out the adaptively most suitable genotypes."

with a small spherical mass of protoplasm, leaves the shell by way of the aperture, and proceeds to develop the first chamber of an embryonic shell. However, when the members of this asexual generation reach maturity, the process of simple fission is not necessarily repeated. Instead, fission of the nucleus may give rise to a great number of tiny objects called zoospores, provided with flagella, by means of which they can swim about—though their swimming range must be severely limited by their very small size. The important point is that a single zoospore cannot develop into an embryo; an embryo can arise only when two zoospores from two different foraminifera meet and conjugate. In most populations of planktonic foraminifera, such chance encounters between zoospores of the same species must be rather rare. Were propagation of the species to depend solely upon such meetings, it is probable that most species would become extinct. Nevertheless, it is reasonable to suppose that encounters do take place from time to time, and when this happens, recombinations of genetical materials arise. Apparently, such crossings between different strains of the same species are essential to the genetical health of a population; at any rate, some provision for their taking place is well nigh universal, if not in fact quite universal, within the organic world.

The successful adaptation of an organism to an environment is normally due to a complex of mutually reinforcing traits resulting from the accretion of many favorable genes which have arisen through chance mutations in earlier generations. This probably accounts for the prevalence of sex, or something very like it. In a population that reproduces sexually, there is a reasonable probability that favorable mutations that occur at about the same time in different individuals may be brought together without much delay, through gene flow, in some of the individuals of later generations. Thus, at least some of the individuals of future generations of such species stand to benefit from *all* earlier favorable mutations within the species. And the accretion of favorable genes is accelerated.

Among organisms that reproduce by fission, combinations of mutually reinforcing genes in an individual can come about only through successive favorable mutations within the individual's *single* line of ancestors. Beneficial genes acquired as a result of mutations within other strains of earlier generations of the species are unavailable to it and its descendants. This prolongs the process of accretion of beneficial genes and may lead to fatal delay in the adaptation of a species to a changing environment.

Because of the rapid succession of distinctive, easily recognizable species during geological time, the foraminifera are ideally suited to the needs of the practical geologist, who must deal with thick sections of many different kinds of sediments, sometimes strongly folded and faulted. If one were asked to invent a class of ideal fossils for the purpose, it is doubtful if the foraminifera could be much improved on. It view of this, it is small wonder that among the hundreds of paleontologists working for oil companies, the majority devote their full time to the study of foraminifera.

But the foraminifera are a good deal more than mere tags of identification for particular layers of sedimentary rocks. To scientists in pure geology, and particularly to those in the hybrid branch known as marine geology, they furnish invaluable clues to conditions in the remote past.

In deciphering the deep-sea record of climatic changes by studying the foraminifera in sediment cores, we follow the principle that the present is the key to the past. Our first question, then, concerns the present. How are the common planktonic species distributed in the oceans today? Living foraminifera have been collected in various parts of the oceans, and we have a fairly good general picture of the geographical distribution of most of the species. We know from these data that no species of planktonic foraminifera is completely cosmopolitan and that some species are rather severely limited in distribution. In general, the boundaries of the geographical ranges of the species trend east and west, which suggests that temperature is the most important factor limiting their ranges.

Since 1872, when H. M. S. *Challenger* set out on the first great oceanographic expedition, many samples of sediment have been raised from the floors of the oceans, particularly from the North Atlantic. For the most part, these samples have been taken close to the surface of the sediment, or at most only a few centimeters below the surface. Various investigators have studied the planktonic foraminifera in the samples, and from their data have emerged patterns of the areal distribution of the eighteen most common species now living in the Atlantic. Strictly speaking, the patterns give the distribution of the empty shells on the sea floor. Transportation of the shells over appreciable distances is unlikely on theoretical grounds, however. Furthermore, the records of living foraminifera caught in plankton nets support the view that the distribution of the shells on the sea floor closely reflects the distribution of the living species in the layers of water above. From the charts of areal distribution, one can divide the planktonic species into three groups: those confined to low latitudes—i.e., near the Equator; those abundant in middle latitudes; and those which live most abundantly in high latitudes. One species, *Globigerina pachyderma,* ranges up to the North Pole. The fact that the distribution with respect to latitude is the same both in the northern and in the southern hemispheres lends further weight to the conclusion that climate is the controlling factor in the geographical distribution of the species. This is of primary importance in our attempt to decipher the record of past climatic changes. Evidently some species of planktonic foraminifera are sensitive to temperature, and their geographical distributions are limited accordingly.

Studies by W. Schott, J. A. Cushman and L. G. Henbest, F. B Phleger, C. D. Ovey, F. L. Parker, J. D. H. Wiseman, and others, of the planktonic foraminifera in sediment cores have shown that there is a variation, from level to level, in the relative abundance of the species that are sensitive to temperature. It is agreed by these investigators that the variations record shifts in the geographical ranges of the species and that these shifts were a consequence of the climatic changes of the late Pleistocene.

Dating by radioactive carbon has proved that the most recent faunal change did in fact coincide in time with the rise in temperature at the end of the last ice age. This justifies the conclusion that similar faunal changes lower in the sedimentary section record earlier climatic changes of comparable importance. But have we justification for applying this method of interpreting the climatic record to the earliest phases of the Pleistocene? We believe that we have. For one thing, the species we and others have used as climatic indicators for the late Pleistocene are the same throughout the Pleistocene section; nowhere do we need to resort to evidence from extinct species. Moreover, the earliest faunal changes in the Pleistocene record are as well defined as the later ones. To attribute them to a cause other than climatic changes of about the same degree as those of the late Pleistocene would be gratuitous and would violate the spirit of the principle of uniformity, according to which the present is the key to the past. If we are sure of the meaning of the later faunal changes in terms of climate, we have no justification for seeing a different meaning in the earlier ones.

In the core that we raised from a gentle slope at a depth of about 4,250 meters in the Caribbean on that memorable day in January 1951, we found more faunal zones defined by variations in abundance of temperature-sensitive foraminifera than we had ever found before. The core passed through a zone of cold-water species corresponding to the last ice age, the so-called Wisconsin Ice Age, and into a zone containing a warm-water assemblage dominated by the species *Globorotalia menardii*. The general aspect of this assemblage was very similar to that of the present-day assemblage in the Caribbean. We correlated this zone with the Sangamon Interglacial Age.[3] We could make this correlation with confidence because the zone of warm-water foraminifera was directly below the zone that we knew to be equivalent to the Wisconsin Ice Age; and the Sangamon Interglacial directly preceded the Wisconsin Ice Age.

Better yet, the core was long enough to pass completely through the Sangamon zone and into a lower zone dominated again by cold-water species. Because of the thickness of this zone, comparable with that of the Wisconsin zone, we felt sure that it represented a major division of the Pleistocene. And because of its position beneath the Sangamon zone, we reasoned that it must represent the Illinoian Ice Age, the last but one. This was the first core in which we had found evidence of the Illinoian.

[3] See list of climatic events of the Pleistocene on page 76.

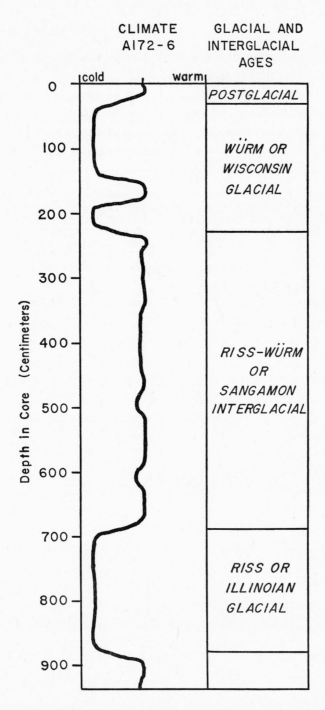

FIGURE 5 *Curve of climatic changes based on the study of samples of planktonic foraminifera taken at intervals of ten centimeters in a deep-sea core. The climatic changes are correlated with glacial and interglacial ages of the Pleistocene. It is estimated that the record spans the last 400,000 years.*

Since the texture of the core was uniform from top to bottom, we were sure that the sediment had accumulated at a uniform rate. From the chronology of the upper part of the core, as determined by radiocarbon dating, we could extrapolate downward and estimate a time scale for an important part of the Pleistocene.[4] This estimate indicated that we now had in our hands a record of climatic events spanning the last 300,000 years.[5]

[4] Estimating time intervals on the basis of thicknesses of deep-sea sediments is much like measuring time with an hourglass: the more sand collects in the lower half of the glass, the longer the time interval. But since rates of accumulation of sediment vary from place to place, it is necessary to take into account the relationship between rates of accumulation and texture, or percentage of particles of diameters greater than 74 microns. In general, the coarser the sediment, the slower the rate of accumulation. The truth of this relationship and its corollary, that uniformity of texture in a core means uniformity of rate of accumulation of sediment, is supported by a large number of determinations, by radiocarbon dating, of rates of accumulation of sediments of different textures.

[5] Further investigations have proved that the time spanned by this core is about 400,000 years.

5

THE COILING OF SHELLS

SHOWS THE WAY

FROM the evidence of Pleistocene glaciations on the continents, we knew that before we could hope to discover a complete record of the Pleistocene Epoch in ocean sediments we would have to obtain cores that went back farther in time than 300,000 years and recorded more than two ice ages.

The evidence relied upon by geologists for the former existence of great ice sheets that once covered the northern regions of America and Europe is mainly of two kinds: (1) the peculiar erosion of bedrock surfaces by the under surface of the moving mass of ice, and (2) the nature and disposition of material transported by the ice.

Erosion by continental glaciers gave smooth, rounded outlines to rock exposures, in marked contrast to the pinnacled, irregular surfaces produced by ordinary weathering and stream erosion. The rounding of rock exposures was accompanied by grooving and striation of the surfaces of the rock by the many angular rock fragments embedded in the overriding ice. Without these "tools," the ice would have had little grinding power in spite of its great pressure. Such glacial scratches, or striae, are of great interest to students of former glaciers, as they indicate the last direction in which the vanished ice sheet moved. In general, sculpturing by moving ice may take any number of forms, from minor scratches to valleys excavated or wide surfaces laid bare. Erosion by glaciers necessarily created a great amount of rock detritus, which was carried along by the glacier. Much of this was deposited along the margins of the ice sheet. These deposits may be divided into two groups: those composed of material transported and deposited directly by the moving ice; and those carried by water that flowed under, upon, or from the ice sheet and deposited in streams and lakes more or less modified or created by the mass of melting ice.

A particularly characteristic deposit unmistakably due to glaciation is known as boulder clay or glacial till. Piles of this material form topographical features called terminal or marginal moraines. As the names imply, these deposits accumulated at the terminal ends of mountain glaciers and along the margins of continental glaciers. Similar material, but spread in broad sheets with little topographical relief, sometimes accumulated beneath the ice; these are ground moraines. Boulder clays, or glacial tills, are characteristically composed of rock detritus which is quite unsorted as to size of constituent particles. This is implied by the term *boulder clay*—that is, a deposit composed of material of all sizes, from clay to boulders. However, the term *boulder clay* is rather unfortunate. Deposits laid down directly by the ice do not always contain boulders, and some do not contain clay. But they always contain particles in a large range of sizes, which sets them apart from sediments deposited by water.

The nature of the detritus in glacial deposits is especially distinctive; the fine fraction called clay consists of particles of clay size but not necessarily of clay minerals. Much of it is "rock flour" composed of the various minerals that make up hard igneous and metamorphic rocks, which have been reduced to fine powder by the powerful grinding action of the moving mass of ice and the "millstones" embedded in its base. The coarser rock fragments in tills are distinctive both in shape and in composition; they are mostly angular and are often faceted or soled, which means that they have acquired, through grinding, one or more plane or slightly curved surfaces. These are frequently polished and may also have more or less parallel striations. In composition the rock fragments are characteristically heterogeneous. This is understandable when one considers the vast area from which a continental glacier gathers its burden of detritus; a rock fragment in a till on Long Island may have originated hundreds of miles away in eastern Canada, or anywhere in between.

When we turn to the fluvioglacial deposits that were laid down by streams of melt water flowing from the glacier, we find a bewildering variety of stratified and partially bedded deposits of gravel, sand, and clay which occur separately and in every conceivable condition of association. Widespread deposits of sediment laid down beyond the glaciers by streams of melt water that originated within or on the ice are known as outwash deposits. Extensive sheets of freshly deposited outwash were, in turn, the source of another kind of Pleistocene sediment, called loess. This sediment is composed chiefly of silt-size particles—that is, of sizes between sand and clay. Normally, loess is unconsolidated and without bedding. The problem of the origin of loess has generated much controversy and resulted in a great deal of literature. Present-day opinion favors the theory that loess deposits originated through the action of high winds which picked up the finer material from actively growing outwash deposits and transported it sometimes to great distances from the source. In the western states, Iowa and Nebraska particularly, and in Europe, notably European Russia, continuous sheets of loess, ten to fifteen meters thick, cover areas of many thousands of square kilometers.

Most loess accumulated during the ice ages rather than the interglacials. This is shown by the fact that some layers of loess are known to split at the outer limit of a till sheet so that some of the loess lies below and some above the till, a clear indication that accumulation of loess was going on during the advance as well as the retreat of the ice. Furthermore, when loess overlies sediment deposited during an interglacial, the sediment is commonly weathered, whereas till overlain by loess ordinarily shows little or no weathering of pre-loess age. The great volume of loess (in Kansas alone it has been estimated as 50,000 cubic miles, or 200,000 cubic kilometers) and its occurrence in widespread areas leave one with the impression that high winds must have been particularly prevalent during the ice ages. However, R. F. Flint, who has given the question a good deal of attention, doubts that the ice ages were any more windy that the present time; the critical condition for abundant deposition of loess, in his opinion, was an ample source of fine sediment—that is, broad exposures of outwash sediment.

If deposits in glaciated regions consisted only of the kinds mentioned above, it would be simple enough to interpret the climatic events of the Pleistocene. But the picture is greatly complicated by zones of weathering, stratified sediments containing fresh-water or marine shells, and layers of peat separating sheets of till. Study of the shells and plant remains, particularly the kinds of pollen grains, in these deposits indicates that climate during the time they were accumulating was as mild as it is at present; in some instances the evidence points to even milder climate.

This evidence of a series of glaciations separated by intervals of mild climate was uncovered more than a hundred years ago, before the glacial theory had become widely accepted. Since then, geologists working in Europe and North America have more or less agreed on the following sequence of events:

GENERAL SEQUENCE	NORTH AMERICA	EUROPE
Postglacial or Recent time	Recent	Recent
Fourth Ice Age	Main Wisconsin Ice Age	Main Würm Ice Age
	Minor Interglacial or Interstadial	Minor Interglacial or Interstadial
	Early Wisconsin Ice Age	Early Würm Ice Age
Third Interglacial	Sangamon Interglacial	Riss-Würm Interglacial
Third Ice Age	Illinoian Ice Age	Riss Ice Age
Second Interglacial	Yarmouth Interglacial	Mindel-Riss Interglacial
Second Ice Age	Kansan Ice Age	Mindel Ice Age
First Interglacial	Aftonian Interglacial	Günz-Mindel Interglacial
First Ice Age	Nebraskan Ice Age	Günz Ice Age

The evidence on land, however, in favor of these subdivisions both in America and Europe is fragmentary. At no single locality on the continents has anyone ever found a complete sequence of Pleistocene deposits. The record as given has had to be pieced together from the study of ragged remanents of deposits at many scattered localities. It would be surprising if this were not so; the destructive effect of each succeeding glaciation tended to obliterate the traces of earlier glaciations. In many places, the evidence of recession of the ice sheet during an interglacial does not consist of actual deposits; instead, the record amounts to nothing more than an altered zone in the till laid down during the preceding glaciation. And altered or weathered zones can be easily destroyed or, for that matter, overlooked. In view of all this, it is remarkable that it has been possible to reach any agreement regarding the number of ice ages and interglacials. As can be expected, a minority of geologists do not accept the classic sequence. Some insist that the Pleistocene included six glaciations separated by five intervals of mild climate, and others accept only three ice ages and two interglacials. A few refuse to admit that there was more than one interglacial.

The problem is important and has many ramifications which reach far beyond the bounds of stratigraphical geology. To us, the most important fact is that our physical and cultural evolution took place during the Pleistocene, and almost certainly this was not by mere coincidence. As Harlow Shapley has put it: "Climatic and continental changes usefully force us inhabitants of this sun-controlled planet to evolve in adaptability. If the warm spell and vegetable lushness of the mid-Mesozoic era, which prevailed for a hundred million years, had persisted to the present, we almost certainly would not be here to write essays on climate." Archaeologists and students of fossil men, in collaboration with Pleistocene geologists, have been successful in correlating the main stages of the physical and cultural evolution of man with the various subdivisions of the Pleistocene. Thus, we have a fairly good idea of the sequence of intermeshing events. But what of the timing?

Many ingenious attempts have been made to measure the time intervals of the Pleistocene. One method of measurement that strongly influenced subsequent thinking about the chronology of the Pleistocene was devised more than fifty years ago by Walter Penck, who applied it to glacial deposits in the Alps. It makes use of the thickness of weathered zones developed during interglacials on the surface of glacial tills. Because of the oxidation of iron-bearing minerals, the weathered upper layer of a till is of a different color from the fresh material below. From measurements of these zones, Penck concluded that the third interglacial had lasted three times, and the second interglacial twelve times, as long as the time elapsed since the end of the last ice age. To convert these relative durations into years, Penck needed some way of estimating postglacial time. Accordingly, he went to a delta in Lake Lucerne; and on the basis of the amount of sediment being added to the delta each year, the size of the delta, and the assumption that growth of the delta must have begun after the end of the last ice age, he estimated the duration of postglacial time as about 20,000 years. He then calculated that the third interglacial had lasted 60,000 years and the second interglacial 240,000 years. Later an American geologist, G. F. Kay, applied the same method to leached zones in Iowa and on the basis of his findings estimated the durations of these interglacials as 120,000 years and 300,000 years.

Evidently the method was far from exact. One source of error was Penck's estimate of postglacial time; recent measurements show that the final retreat of the continental glaciers began about 11,000 years ago. Accordingly, these early estimates of the durations of the interglacials ought to be halved. Another probable source of error was the assumption that the rate of weathering was constant. One would expect the rate of weathering to vary from time to time, depending on climatic variations within the interglacials and on local conditions such as density of vegetation. Moreover, it is reasonably certain that the depth of weathering would not be proportional to its duration; as the oxidized zone became thicker, it would increasingly protect the underlying till and thus greatly reduce the rate of oxidation. Actually, then, the duration of the interglacials was greater, by some unknown amount, than estimated. Although Penck's method could apply only to the interglacials, he concluded from his estimates that the total duration of the Pleistocene must have been several hundred thousand years. Subsequent rounding off of Penck's estimate has led to the widespread surmise that the Pleistocene lasted about one million years.

Today we have more sophisticated ways of measuring geological time by means of radioactive isotopes, and it is fashionable to scoff a little at the weathering method as naïve and almost uselessly inexact. But at the time this method, and others like it, served a useful purpose by showing convincingly that the earlier interglacial ages were of longer duration than postglacial time, and that the Pleistocene Epoch as a whole had been vast in comparison with the time encompassed by recorded history. In 1908, when Penck's estimates were made, the study of radioactivity was in its infancy and the awe-inspiring span of geological time was not generally appreciated.

Two other methods of measuring time are in theory very exact; however, they are applicable to short time intervals only. The tree-ring analysis was first used more than a hundred and fifty years ago by De Witt Clinton, who counted the growth rings of trees on the earthworks near Canandaigua, New York. From this count he estimated that the earthworks were a thousand years old and therefore were not built by Europeans or present-day Indians but rather by some prehistoric people.

In the hands of A. E. Douglas, Ernst Antevs, and others, tree-ring analysis in the past fifty years has become a branch of science known as dendrochronology. It is based on the fact that a tree growing in a region of regular seasonal changes of climate adds a new growth ring each year. Anyone who has seen the section of a giant sequoia in the American Museum of Natural History will probably have noticed that the rings are not all of the same thickness. As a tree grows older, the rings become narrower, but superimposed on this normal trend are irregular variations caused by changes in climate from time to time. Trees from any one locality all exhibit similar variations in their ring records. This has enabled dendrochronologists to correlate the inner rings of young trees with the outer rings of older trees. In the southwestern states they have carried the chronology back about two thousand years. To do this it was necessary to go beyond the oldest living trees and apply the method to tree trunks that had been used as beams in long-abandoned Indian pueblos. In California the tree-ring chronology goes back a little over three thousand years because of the amazingly long lives of the giant sequoias.

In spite of the fact that this chronology does not reach even the end of the last ice age, it provides information that is eagerly seized upon by students of past climates. It is more than a chronology; it is also a climatic record, and a very well dated one at that. For example, the ring record of the Colorado River basin shows that the thirteenth century was exceedingly dry, and that it was followed, in the fourteenth century, by persistent storminess. Furthermore, the sequence of rings records a little more than purely terrestrial events; it has a particularly evident cycle with an average length of a little more than eleven years. This almost certainly reflects the sunspot cycle, that is, the cyclical occurrence of dark spots on the sun—an indication that even minor fluctuations of solar radiation have left traces on the earth. This suggests the possibility that the wider and longer climatic fluctuations of the Pleistocene may also have been due to variations in quantity and perhaps nature of radiant energy from the sun.

Another method of measuring time in years depends on annual layers of sediment found in the beds of former proglacial lakes, that is, lakes once near or even in contact with the margin of the ice sheet, and fed by melt water. In summer, when melting is intense, the lake receives a large supply of melt water laden with a fine suspension of sand and clay derived from the detritus carried in and under the glacier. The suspension spreads over the whole lake and the mineral particles gradually settle. The coarse particles settle first; the finer material may remain in suspension until winter comes and the lake freezes over, but it settles before spring. Each annual cycle, then, consists of two layers: a lower, silty layer of light color and an upper, clayey layer of dark color. The thicknesses of the cycles vary from a few millimeters to several centimeters. Gerard de Geer, who first studied these layers, called them "varves" —from the Swedish word *varv*, meaning a periodic repetition. Most proglacial lakes were short-lived. However, the thicknesses of varves, like tree rings, are influenced by variations in climate, and consequently one can identify sequences of varves and cross-correlate them from one deposit to another. In this way de Geer was able to trace the retreat of the last continental ice sheet northward from southern Sweden for a distance of nearly a thousand kilometers and extending back in time from 1900 A.D. to 15,100 B.C.

The varve chronology is necessarily limited to the time of retreat of the last continental glaciers. Without doubt, proglacial lakes existed during the retreats of the earlier ice sheets; in fact, varved deposits, probably of middle Pleistocene age, are known in Silesia and at Ipswich in England. But the destructive effect of subsequent glaciations has orphaned these deposits and they cannot be fitted into a continuous chronology. Once more we find ourselves in a blind alley in our search for a method of measuring the major time intervals of the Pleistocene, that tantalizing epoch of repeated discontinuities.

Most theories that attempt to explain the climatic changes of the Pleistocene do not entail any particular chronology of events. An exception is the theory based on the geometrical variations in the elements of the earth's orbit. Astronomers have determined the periods of these variations with a good deal of accuracy. They are as follows: the precession of the equinoxes, 21,000 years; variation in the eccentricity of the earth's orbit, 91,800 years; and variation in the angle between the earth's axis and the plane of the earth's orbit, about 40,000 years. As a result of these variations in the attitude of the earth with respect to the sun, the amount of heat received at a given latitude varies, although the total amount of heat received by earth remains the same. From the periods one can calculate the variations in amount of heat received at, let us say, sixty-five degrees north latitude during the past hundreds of thousands of years, or as far back as one has the patience to calculate. On the basis of these variations, Milutin Milankovitch, a Serbian mathematician, elaborated a chronology of Pleistocene climatic events and concluded that the four principal ice ages must have occurred within the past 600,000 years.

On the face of it, this theory and the conclusions derived from it seem to answer all our questions. But can we accept the astronomical theory as a satisfactory explanation of the ice ages? Unfortunately, there are a number of serious, if not fatal, objections. Some of the opponents of the theory contend that the calculated temperature variations are too small to account for the large climatic changes in the Pleistocene. Furthermore, the geometrical properties of the motion of the earth around the sun must have been established long before the Pleistocene, but apparently they brought about no ice ages during the earlier epochs of the Cenozoic Period. On this evidence alone, we can be sure that astronomical variations cannot have been the sole cause of the ice ages, though they may have been a contributing factor and may have determined the timing of the ice ages in conjunction with some other effect, such as the uplift of mountain ranges. This would account for their occurrence during the Pleistocene rather than earlier in the Cenozoic.

The validity of the astronomical theory could be tested by comparing the chronology derived from it with a reliable chronology derived independently of it. The weathering method used by Penck yielded estimates of the durations of the interglacials which were in startlingly close agreement with those calculated by Milankovitch. Both had led to the conclusion that the Pleistocene had lasted 600,000 years. Yet we know that the weathering method could not possibly have been so accurate; at best it could only provide an order of magnitude, not an estimate accurate to the nearest hundred thousand years. For the time being, therefore, it is best to ascribe the agreement between these chronologies to one of those coincidences that now and again turn up in science—a coincidental agreement that seems to prove so much and really proves nothing at all.

For almost fifty years the decay of radioactive elements has been used to measure the ages of rocks. In theory the method is fairly simple: knowing the rate of disintegration of an element, one can calculate the time elapsed since the formation of a rock by measuring the quantity of the element left or the products of its disintegration. Until fairly recently, however, these methods were hardly applicable to deposits of Pleistocene age. The elements or isotopes known decayed at such unconscionably slow rates that they were quite use-less in the measurement of time intervals as minuscule as the 600,000 or one million years of the Pleistocene; the errors inherent in the method were greater than the time intervals.

Then, less than twenty years ago, came the discovery of radio-carbon, a radioactive isotope of the element carbon. In its chemical behavior it is indistinguishable from ordinary carbon, from which it differs only in its atomic weight—which is fourteen instead of twelve, the atomic weight of the most common isotope of carbon—and in being radioactive. It has a half life of about 5,730 years, which means that the ratio of radiocarbon to total carbon in a clam shell, for example, which is 5,730 years old will be one half of what the ratio was when the clam died. With such a short half life, radiocarbon would have disappeared from the world long ago, ex-cept for the fact that it is constantly being generated in the upper atmosphere through the neutron bombardment of nitrogen atoms. Because of the constant rate of production of radiocarbon, the con-stant reservoir of ordinary carbon, and a constant rate of decay, living plants and animals, as well as the water on the surface of the ocean, contain a constant concentration of radiocarbon. When, however, a plant or animal dies, its supply of radiocarbon is no longer replenished. From that time on, the ratio of radiocarbon to ordinary carbon decreases at a known rate. In theory the method is applicable to just about anything that contains carbon and has been secreted by an organism. This makes radiocarbon dating eminently suitable to Pleistocene deposits that contain wood, peat, bones, or shells.

Can we now proceed to determine a complete chronology of the Pleistocene? Alas, no, at least not by direct radiocarbon dating of Pleistocene objects. Once again we are held back by the limited range of the method, about 35,000 years. This is a marked improve-ment over varve counting, however; it permits us to date the end of the last ice age and minor events during the latter part of the last ice age, but it is not good enough to span the last ice age completely. We did hope that it might enable us to determine the rate of some process that had been continuous throughout the Pleistocene. It was unlikely that an unbroken record of any such continuous process would be found on the continents, but cores of sediment from the ocean depths might provide what we needed. The cores contained abundant calcareous shells of planktonic foraminifera, which could be dated by radiocarbon; and according to classical theory, the sediment had accumulated slowly, at a constant rate, and presumably continuously throughout the Pleistocene.

However, the classical theory had greatly oversimplified matters. It had not taken into account the disturbing effect of turbidity currents and the confusion they introduce into the core records. To avoid this confusion, we concentrated on cores taken on rises that were high enough to be above the influence of turbidity currents, which, like streams on land, seek depressions as they flow over the floor of the ocean. Cores from such topographical highs seemed to be just what we needed; the uniformity of texture from top to bottom gave us reason to hope that the sediment had accumulated slowly and at a uniform rate. When we looked at samples taken at intervals of ten centimeters, we found that they contained clearly defined zones, identified by the shells of various species of planktonic foraminifera. Presumably, these zones corresponded to those found by Schott in the cores collected in the equatorial Atlantic during the oceanographic cruise of the *Meteor*. As a practical way of keeping track of the progress of our study of the foraminifera in the cores, we plotted the sequence of foraminiferal zones in each core on strips of paper.

On the assumption that the zones represented the world-wide climatic phases of the Pleistocene, we expected to find the same sequence of zones in all the cores. But when we compared the strips of paper, or "logs" of the cores, we found bewildering discrepancies that amounted to chaos in the lower parts of the sedimentary section, just where our interest was greatest. Once again, the beautifully simple classical conception of the accumulation of sediment in the deep ocean basins proved to be unrealistic.

As we pressed ahead with our rapid examination of all cores as they reached the laboratory, we sometimes found unmistakable evidence that, here and there on the ocean floor, thicknesses of sediment amounting to at least tens of meters had been lost from the local sedimentary section. There were obvious hiatuses in the sedimentary record which involved millions of years in the accumulation of sediment.

As we have explained, the many extinct species of foraminifera have been catalogued and their time ranges in the geological record have been determined. When one finds certain extinct species in a sediment, one can assign the sediment to its proper place in the composite sequence of sediments which is recognized all over the world.

In a certain core, for example, white chalky sediment containing species of foraminifera that lived only during the Oligocene Epoch, that is, between 26 million and 34 million years ago, was directly overlain by brown sediment of late Pleistocene age, with a sharply defined and conspicuous break between the two kinds of sediment. Evidently at some time during the late Pleistocene a critical degree of instability had been reached by the plastic, water-saturated sediment deposited on that particular part of the ocean floor during the interval between the Oligocene and the late Pleistocene. Finally, perhaps disturbed by a seismic shock, this sediment slid downslope, leaving the Oligocene sediment uncovered. Immediately afterwards fresh sediment began to accumulate on the newly uncovered surface. Plainly this could happen only on rises where the sea floor sloped slightly; it was on just such rises that the Pleistocene cores that did not correlate had been taken. If large thicknesses of older sediment could be lost by slumping, why not parts of the Pleistocene section? Obviously these could also be lost by slumping. Furthermore, because of the vertical uniformity of the Pleistocene sediment in color, texture, and degree of compaction, it would be impossible to detect the resulting hiatuses in the record by merely looking at the cores. We had been trying to correlate foraminiferal zones in incomplete Pleistocene sections; naturally, they did not match very well. There were altogether improbable discrepancies in the thicknesses of the zones as they appeared in the various cores.

At that earlier stage in our work we were unable to distinguish, by the foraminifera alone, a zone representing an early interglacial from one representing a late interglacial. The same was true of the zones corresponding to ice ages. This suggested to us the possibility of unwittingly making false correlations; it could easily happen when two zones, both containing cold-water foraminifera, but of different ages, happened to be of about the same thickness. A confusion at some stage of a scientific investigation is unfortunate, but sometimes unavoidable; when the data begin to make "sense," however, and one is thereby misled into drawing false conclusions with complete confidence, the situation becomes tragic. We were in no mood to abandon the job; something had to be done, but what? We knew that no way existed to distinguish, on the basis of chemical, physical, or mineral differences, among the various zones representing ice ages and interglacials.

Then we made a seemingly irrevelant observation. The direction of coiling of the shells of some species of planktonic foraminifera seemed to follow a certain pattern. Most species of planktonic foraminifera build their shells in the form of a conical spiral; All shells belonging to these species can therefore be distinguished as coiling to the right or to the left. In other words, the shells are either dextral or sinistral, as is the case with snail shells. This property, known among topologists as chirality, had already attracted the attention of H. Bolli, a micropaleontologist in Trinidad. Bolli found that some species of planktonic foraminifera in the Cretaceous sediments of Trinidad had no coiling preference the first time they appeared in the section. Right- and left-coiling shells were about equally abundant. But higher in the section the same species developed a strong preference for either right or left coiling, depending on the particular species. This was very interesting from the evolutionary point of view, but it was not particularly helpful in making stratigraphical correlations.

As we studied the foraminifera in the uppermost centimeter of sediment in cores from the North Atlantic, we noticed that in some samples almost all the shells of a certain species, *Globorotalia truncatulinoides,* coiled to the right, whereas in other samples almost all coiled to the left. Since these top samples represented the same time interval—the last few hundred years up to the present time—it was evident that the dominant direction of coiling must change from place to place in the North Atlantic. To find out more about this unexpected behavior of the species, we made a census of the shells in the tops of all cores from the North Atlantic. When we plotted the percentages of right- and left-coiling shells on a chart of the North Atlantic, a consistent pattern of distribution emerged. Right coiling was dominant south of a boundary line extending roughly from the Cape Verde Islands off Africa to the Bahamas. Everywhere north of this line, left coiling dominated, except for a northeastern province of right coiling bounded by a line running west from the Straits of Gibraltar to the Azores Islands and thence northward toward Greenland.

At this time we also counted the right- and left-coiling shells of the same species in samples taken at intervals of ten centimeters in various cores, and found that the dominant direction of coiling changed abruptly, and in some cores fairly frequently, at various levels in the core sections. These observations gave us some insight into what had been going on in the past. Evidently the boundary lines between coiling provinces had shifted about during the Pleistocene; each time a boundary line had passed over a point on the ocean floor where a core was later taken, the passage had been registered by a change in coiling direction in the layer of sediment deposited at the time. As we studied the coiling in more cores, we found evidence that the boundaries between the coiling provinces had remained stationary during the last eleven thousand years, or since the end of the last ice age. This cast an interesting sidelight on the biological difference between the animals that built these shells. Geologically speaking, eleven thousand years is a trivial time interval. But it is not trivial in the lives of protozoa or in terms of oceanic circulation, which in a much shorter time than eleven thousand years ought to have brought about complete mixing of the animals that coiled to the right and those that coiled to the left. There was only one possible conclusion; some chemical or physical property of the waters kept the animals from mixing. The best guess we can make at present is that the controlling condition of the water

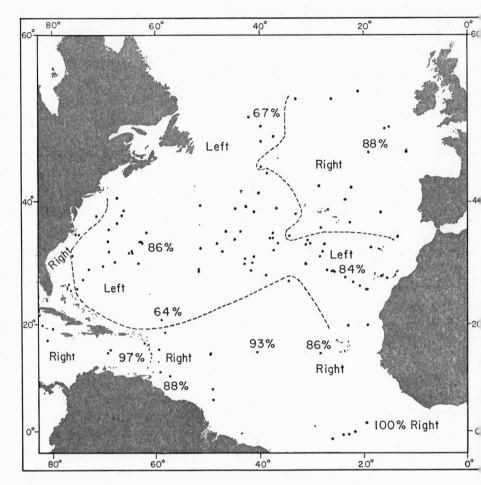

FIGURE 6 *The three provinces of the Atlantic defined by the coiling direction of
living races of* Globorotalia truncatulinoides, *a species of planktonic foraminifera.
Dashed lines mark the boundaries; dots indicate points at which cores were taken.*

is temperature. This is suggested by the shifting positions of the
boundaries below the level in the cores that represents eleven thousand years, or during the earlier climatic changes of the Pleistocene.
But this is only a suggestion. The evidence is not as clear as we wish
it were, nor as clear as it is in the case of another species, *Globigerina pachyderma.*

   Globigerina pachyderma is a nondescript little species which has
the distinction of being the only species of planktonic foraminifera

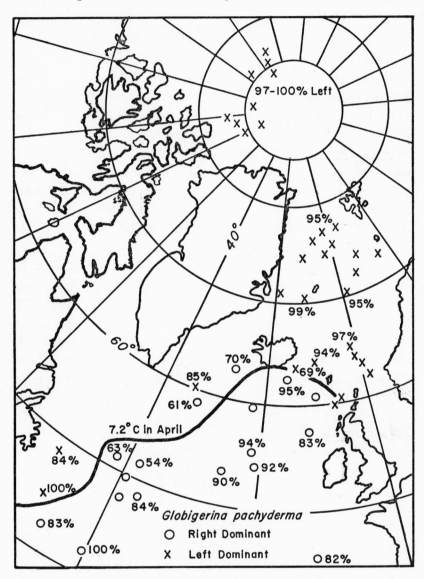

FIGURE 7 *Water temperature and coiling direction of* Globigerina pachyderma. *Coiling to the right dominates in relatively low latitudes; coiling to the left, in high latitudes and in polar waters. The dividing line coincides approximately with the boundary between water temperatures above and below 7.2° Celcius in April.*

hardy enough to live, and even thrive, in the Arctic Ocean. The populations of the polar and subarctic regions all coil to the left. Farther south, however, as in the area south of Iceland and west of the British Isles, the species is very abundant and coils to the right. We had plotted the percentages of right- and left-coiling shells in the top centimeter of sediment in cores from the North Atlantic and had found that the boundary between the right and left coilers coincided fairly closely with the position in April of the 7.2 degrees Celsius isothermal line—the line that marks the division between water colder than 7.2 degrees to the north and water warmer than 7.2 degrees to the south. In April the isotherm extends from the northern tip of Scotland to the south coast of Iceland and southwest to the Grand Banks off Newfoundland.

Our findings in this instance have interesting implications. In order to learn more about the position of the boundary line during the late Pleistocene, we looked at samples from lower levels in the cores. In all cores from points north of the present position of the boundary, left coiling was strongly dominant from top to bottom, clear evidence that since the last ice age the position of the 7.2 degree isothermal line has not been much farther north than it is now. On the other hand, we found an abrupt swing to left coiling between ten and twenty centimeters below the tops of cores from points south of the present boundary. This we regard as unmistakable evidence of the refrigeration of the North Atlantic during the last ice age. If we had longer cores from this critical region, we could almost certainly detect all the climatic changes of the Pleistocene merely by counting the right- and left-coiling shells of *Globigerina pachyderma*. In fact, alas, all cores from this region end in sediment deposited during the last ice age. Longer cores are available from farther south, but on these the method is inapplicable; the species is too rare at most levels to yield meaningful counts.

Although the interrelationship between climate and changes in coiling of *Globorotalia truncatulinoides* is less clear, we have been able to use past shifts in the coiling of this species to great advantage. These shifts precisely define stratigraphical levels that can be traced from core to core in suites of cores from widely scattered points.

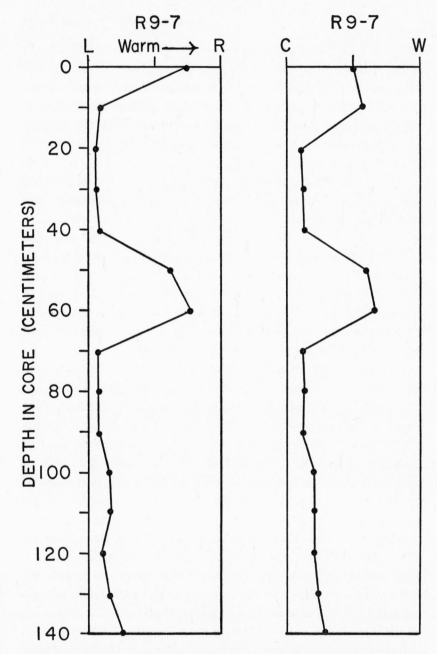

FIGURE 8 *Correlation of climate curves based on changes in percentage of left-coiling and right-coiling shells of* Globigerina pachyderma *(curve on the left) and on relative numbers of cold-water and warm-water species of planktonic foraminifera other than* Globigerina pachyderma *(curve on right), in samples taken at ten-centimeter intervals in a deep-sea core. The scale of coiling is from a hundred percent left at the left margin of the column to a hundred percent right at the right margin. C indicates cold climate and W warm climate.*

These well-defined levels, together with rates of accumulation of sediment determined by radiocarbon dating, have helped us to a better understanding of the influence of deep circulation and bottom topography on the texture of sediments and, most important, on rates of accumulation. Only in this way have we been able to convert the sequence of climatic changes as recorded in the cores into a chronology of the Pleistocene.

The first fact that emerged from the precise correlation of many cores was that the rate of accumulation varied considerably from place to place, and that, as a rule, accumulation was slower on topographical rises and faster in depressions. If the depth exceeded five thousand meters, however, solution of calcium carbonate reduced the rate of accumulation and destroyed the climatic record. The relationship between depth and rate of accumulation was not so consistent that we could estimate rates from depths, but another interrelation, that between texture, or coarseness of sediment, and rate of accumulation proved to be very consistent.

The classic conception of conditions at depth in the oceans assumed that deep circulation was so extremely slow that it could not have any appreciable influence on sedimentation. This led to the theory of the universal veil of sediment, according to which all parts of the floor of the ocean were covered by a continuous layer of sediment of uniform thickness. But evidence from the cores of sediment has changed all that. We now realize that deep, continuous currents in the Atlantic are capable of sweeping fine particles—that is, particles of silt and clay size—from the upper parts of rises and concentrating them in depressions. The coarser particles, mostly the shells of foraminifera, and some finer material that lodges between them, are left to accumulate on the rises. Since by this process the depressions gain what the rises lose, rates of accumulation of sediment and textures of sediments vary from place to place, depending on the direction of currents and on local features of topography.

For our purpose the important relationship is that between texture and rate of accumulation; we have confirmed this relationship by radiocarbon dating of late Pleistocene sections and by precise correlation of earlier sections. For example, when radiocarbon dates

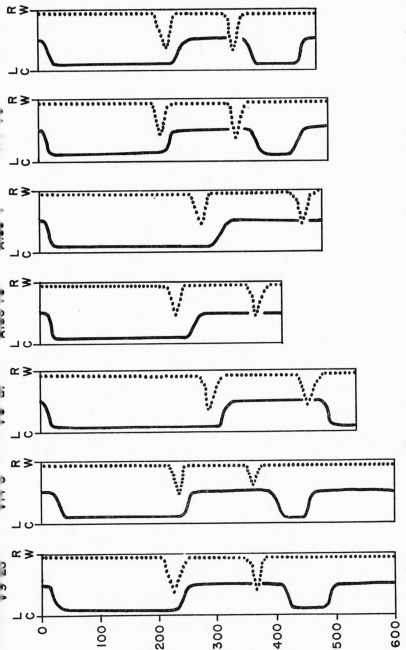

FIGURE 9 Changes in the coiling direction (dotted lines) of Globorotalia truncatulinoides along the length of the cores make it possible to correlate precisely defined levels in cores from different locations. The scale of coiling is a hundred percent left at the left margin of each column to a hundred percent right at the right margin. The solid lines are climate curves based on relative numbers of (C) cold-water and warm-water (W) species of planktonic foraminifera in samples taken at ten-centimeter intervals in the cores. Climate as of the present time is plotted on the midpoint between C and W at the top of each column; the solid lines to the left indicate cooler climate, and the solid lines to the right indicate warmer climate. The distance between core V9-28 and core A180-72 is about 1,300 kilometers, or 700 nautical miles.

show that the rate of accumulation of the upper part of one core has been twice as fast as that of the upper part of some other core, cross correlation shows that corresponding layers in the lower part of the one core are consistently twice as thick as those in the other core. In other words, the ratio of two to one between the rates of accumulation, as determined by radiocarbon dating of the upper parts, is also true of the lower parts, which are beyond the range of the radiocarbon method. But, and this is a most important "but," we find such consistent relationships only in cores that differ from each other in texture but are individually uniform in texture from top to bottom. When cores contain variations in texture from layer to layer, and the variations are not due to deposition by turbidity currents, cross correlation with other cores that have vertical uniformity of texture shows that the coarse layers have accumulated more slowly than the finer layers.

The validity of the relationship between vertical uniformity of texture and constant rate of accumulation with time is so well supported by numerous instances and by sound theory that we feel no misgivings about using it as the basis of our chronology of the Pleistocene.

6

CORRELATION OF THE

PLEISTOCENE RECORD

IT has been more than ten years since we discovered the importance of the coiling direction of shells for the study of cores of deep-sea sediment. The "coiling-direction method" we devised is used today in almost all laboratories where deep-sea cores are studied. As we look back now, this discovery stands out as one of the most exciting events in our search for the complete Pleistocene record. But, of course, to us almost everything connected with the Pleistocene is exciting. Of all the periods of geological history, the Pleistocene is the most dramatic and fascinating. For one thing, it is close to us; the traces of its events, particularly those of the last great glaciation, are fresh before our eyes. The landscape of a third of the earth's surface is still essentially as it was when the last ice sheets melted—hardly, if at all, modified by subsequent geological processes. So close in time was the last refrigeration that the frozen carcasses of of extinct animals can still be found in a few places. Among these are the woolly mammoths found in the frozen tundra of Siberia and the baby mammoth uncovered in the course of mining a gold-bearing gravel in Alaska. The latter is now safely sheltered in the American Museum of Natural History.

Our ancestors, people physically quite like ourselves, saw the last ice sheet and hunted the large mammals that had survived the earlier climatic changes of the Pleistocene. In certain places in Europe we can see some of this giant game through Stone Age eyes: woolly mammoths and deer with enormous antlers engraved on bits of ivory, and best of all, bison, deer, boars, and horses painted in color on the walls and ceilings of caves.

We have said that the Pleistocene is near to us; correctly speaking, we are living in a continuation of the Pleistocene. Since the recession of the last continental glaciers, nothing of a geological or climatic nature has occurred by which we can logically set the present time apart from the Pleistocene as a whole. For convenience, we may speak of the present as postglacial time. Even that may be a trifle euphemistic; after all, about one tenth of our total land surface is still covered by ice, in comparison with thirty percent during the height of the last ice age. In any case, we have no reason to refer to the present as post-Pleistocene time. Of course, it is possible that there will be no more ice ages, at least not for many millions of years, but we have no evidence that this will be so. Disappearance of the ice sheets of North America and Europe proves nothing; at least three times during the earlier Pleistocene the continental glaciers melted.

This Pleistocene world of ours is an exciting place, exciting in contrast with the relatively featureless world of most of geological time. According to the record of the rocks, the continents normally have been areas of little topographical relief, largely flooded by shallow seas. Only during short and widely spaced intervals in the record is there evidence of high continents, deep oceans, and continental glaciers. Geologists refer to the earlier paroxysms of mountain building as geological revolutions; on all the evidence, the Pleistocene should be regarded as a time of revolution fully as much as any of the former. Our Andes, Alps, and Everests bear witness to the fact; and probably no less do the still greater undersea mountain ranges, the mid-ocean ridges.

No wonder that the phenomena of the Pleistocene have evoked widely divergent views among geologists, and many non-geologists, for that matter. The Pleistocene has inspired a flood of conjecture and literature. James Geikie, in writing the first edition of his book *The Great Ice Age,* around 1870, had to abandon his plan of preparing a complete bibliography because it would have required a volume in itself. Today, after a lapse of almost a hundred years during which the output of literature on the Pleistocene has accelerated vastly, such a task would be almost impossible.

The Pleistocene and its phenomena pose many fundamental questions. In spite of much field work, discussion, and writing on the subject by able scientists, many of these questions remain largely unanswered. We still have much to learn about the mechanism of ice flow, glacial erosion, the mode of deposition of till, and how glaciers constructed drumlins—streamlined masses of till presumably molded under the ice. More general problems are the extent of variations in sea level during the ice ages, the cause and mechanism of uplift of once heavily glaciated regions such as the Scandinavian Peninsula and a large part of eastern Canada and New England, the number and durations of the glacial and interglacial ages and their relationship to the pluvial and interpluvial ages, to name only a few examples. Above all, we would like to know how these events influenced the evolution of man and his cultures throughout the world.

As we have pointed out, no complete succession of Pleistocene deposits has been found in any one place on the continents. To piece together a complete sequence, one must somehow establish connections between isolated deposits or traces of climatic change such as weathered zones and erosion surfaces. This is far from easy. In addition to the gaps in the record introduced by the destructive nature of glaciation, the very nearness in time of the events adds to the difficulty. Our focus on the problems is almost too close; we see a vast amount of confusing detail which tends to obscure the overall problem and adds to the complexity of our task of disentangling the sequence of events. In the relatively short time interval of the Pleistocene Epoch, drastic changes in conditions followed each other in rapid alternation. The course of events during most of the history of

the earth proceeded at a more leisurely pace. For example, the Pliocene Epoch, which immediately preceded the Pleistocene, is known
from radioactive dating to have lasted twelve million years, in
contrast with the estimated 300,000 to one and a half million years
of the Pleistocene. Yet the Pliocene was relatively uneventful; the
climate gradually became cooler, but there is no evidence of climatic
changes of such a dramatic nature, yet such short duration as those
which occurred during the Pleistocene. When one traces the course
of events during the Pliocene Epoch, a discrepancy in time of a hundred thousand years is negligible; an error of that order in correlating deposits of Pleistocene age can lead to complete confusion.

The five chief means by which Pleistocene deposits may be correlated are: fossils; cultures of early men; climatic evidence; lithology, or physical and chemical characteristics of deposits; and
absolute dating. In practice, these ways and means overlap to a
considerable extent; fossils, for example, often supply good evidence
of former climate, from which in turn the significance of the lithology
of the deposit containing the fossils may be inferred.

For Pleistocene, as well as for older strata, fossils constitute the
best means of correlation. In the case of older sediments, fossils
were, until the discovery of radioactive dating, the only means of establishing the approximate synchronism of widely separated deposits. The principle is simple: the central theme of the history of
life has been irreversible change. We call this evolution. The high
degree of variability among living things which evolution implies
is possible because of the extraordinary chemical behavior of carbon
atoms; their versatility in combining with atoms of other elements
and themselves is seemingly endless. This versatility plays its most
critical role in the permutations of the complex molecules that constitute the genetical material of all living cells. These are the main-
springs of variation among organisms, the raw material upon which
natural selection works. Nothing of comparable complexity exists
in the inorganic world. It is safe to say that not a single innovation in
inorganic chemical reactions or substances has appeared since the
beginning of the Cambrian Period 600 million years ago. A quartz
crystal in a granite of that time is indistinguishable from a quartz

crystal in a recent lava. The only continuous and irreversible change in the inorganic world is radioactive decay, but this is not analogous to organic evolution. Radioactive disintegration leads to a state of greater entropy or disorder; organic evolution leads to what is at least a local decrease in disorder.

Because of this unique property of living things—irreversible variation with time—fossilized remains of organisms are of great practical value to geologists in determining the chronological sequence of the sedimentary rocks. Each major interval of geological time is marked by a group of characteristic fossils. In addition to being useful as an index to the book of earth history, fossils often provide information by which specialists can reconstruct conditions in the past. In scientific efforts to trace changes of climate during the late Pleistocene, pollen has been particularly helpful. Pollen grains are durable, are shed in great quantities, are dispersed widely by wind, and many kinds can be identified as to genus and even species. Since many of the species found in late Pleistocene deposits are still living somewhere in the world, their environmental needs are well known. For example, at Meinendorf near Hamburg, Germany, an ancient settlement of reindeer hunters was discovered under several meters of peat. These people had camped on the shore of a glacial lake probably no more than a couple of hundred years after the region had been uncovered by the melting of the margin of the continental glacier. The pollen tells that at that time the surrounding country was dominated by tundra, without forests; the few trees were subarctic dwarf species of birch and willow. Then, as the climate became milder, birch forests encroached; and still higher up in the peat section the pollen shows that pines entered the region and became dominant over the birch. As the birch gradually disappeared, more warmth-loving trees such as hazel, oak, elm, and lime appeared. The record at Meinendorf ends with the dominance of a mixed oak forest. Elsewhere, early man's first attempts at agriculture are recorded by abrupt changes in pollen.

Fossil mammals and plants can also provide useful hints regarding geographical changes, such as the former presence of land bridges or waterways or topographical barriers to migration in the form of mountain ranges.

Unfortunately, the application of these paleontological methods to Pleistocene deposits encounters peculiar difficulties; most deposits of detritus transported and laid down directly by ice are devoid of fossils. Outside of the glaciated regions, fossils are rarely abundant; the continental environment of deposition is anything but favorable to the preservation of organic remains. In consequence, fossils in Pleistocene deposits occur only in isolated and discontinuous patches.

Because of the much more rapid evolution of certain primates, the bones of our early ancestors could be very useful in correlating Pleistocene deposits, were it not for their extreme rarity. However, their tools of enduring flint are in some places fairly common. Because many of the primitive peoples adhered to certain fashions and customs in making tools and other objects, successions of cultures, or complexes of types of tools, can be correlated from place to place. In Europe, central and southern Africa, and elsewhere, attempts have been made to use the known succession of cultures established in Central Europe to correlate the climatic events of the Pleistocene. Prehistorians have debated the reliability of this method. Recent thinking inclines to the opinion that cultural stages are steeply "time transgressive," which is one way of saying that fashions in chipping flint probably spread from tribe to tribe at an extremely slow rate. In this connection it is well to remember that Fuegians were still chipping flints while Europeans were making microscopes. What was true so recently must have been equally true during earlier stages of development, when contact between tribes was infrequent, though no doubt the contrasts between cultures in those earlier days were less glaring. What we really need is some quite independent way of correlating the cultural levels of widely separated sites. This could provide valuable evidence of differential rates of cultural evolution—information which would be of great interest to anthropologists.

Some approach to this end may be possible when we know more about the timing of the climatic changes of the Pleistocene. The growing evidence that the ice ages were synchronous throughout the world is a step in that direction.

But what about regions which were beyond the direct influence of the ice sheets? It would be strange if the unglaciated regions had not been subject to vicissitudes of climate during times of glaciation elsewhere. In fact, students of past climates have found abundant evidence of what they call pluvials, or times of heavy rainfall, and interpluvials, or times of dry climate much as at present. Spectacular evidence of the most recent pluvial consists of ancient beaches, strandlines defined by deposits of tufa, or porous lime, and other kinds of lake deposits in the many closed basins of the southwestern states. These basins now are either dry or contain small lakes—which are hardly more than puddles in comparison with their predecessors. The Great Salt Lake of Utah is such a remnant of a lake which once had an area of more than twenty thousand square miles and an extreme depth of at least a thousand feet, or three hundred meters. Radiocarbon ages of calcareous deposits left by this lake and some others of the 119 former lakes identified in the United States show that water level had begun to fall a little more than 11,500 years ago, or at about the same time that rapid recession of the continental glaciers set in. Similar traces of large pluvial lakes in basins which are now dry or contain only small lakes have been found in Mexico, South America, Asia, Africa, and Australia. Although deposits from these lakes have not been dated by radiocarbon, the inference that they were contemporaneous with the American lakes, and therefore with the last ice age, is surely reasonable.

The earlier histories of these basins are less easy to reconstruct, but borings into the deposits on the floor of the basins of the largest American lakes have discovered layers of salt separated by layers of clay. The salt deposits must record times of reduced rainfall when former lakes were drying up. On this evidence, it is probable that these basins were filled during each ice age or pluvial of the earlier Pleistocene, while during the interglacials or interpluvials they became empty or nearly so. Until some way of directly dating deposits older than the range of the radiocarbon method can be devised, however, this cannot be regarded as proved.

Even the Sahara region was somewhat less dry at a not very remote time, judging from the abundance in the central Sahara of
Neolithic stone tools, rock drawings, and remains of elephants, hip-
popotamuses, horses, gazelles, and cattle.

Evidence of alternating wet and dry climate has also been found
in cave deposits containing the tools and bones of early men together
with the bones of the animals on which they feasted. The Grotte
de l'Observatoire at Monaco is a classic example. In excavating the
floor, archaeologists found four layers of calcium carbonate deposited by lime-laden water which must have dripped from the
ceiling. Between these layers were loose deposits of cave earth.
Since no calcium carbonate, or stalagmite, is accumulating in the
cave under present climatic conditions, it appears probable that the
stalagmitic deposits represent four periods in which the climate was
more humid. Do they represent the four ice ages of the Pleistocene?
No, in Pleistocene geology nothing is ever so simple as that. A succession of stone tools was found in the intervening layers of cave
earth. On the evidence of the cultural levels which these represent,
the whole section cannot be older than the late Pleistocene. Probably
the upper two layers of stalagmite were deposited during the first
and second phases of the last ice age. The lower two would then
correspond to the two phases of the preceding glaciation, or the Riss
Ice Age. Here the archaeological evidence must be accepted; the
sequence of cultures and their interrelation with the climatic events
was established in Western Europe. No appreciable time lag in cultural evolution is at all likely in this case.

Within the past ten years the remarkable Shanidar Cave in
northern Iraq has been excavated. Here again a layer of stalagmitic
lime gives evidence of a former time of more abundant rainfall.
Flint tools typical of the Neanderthal culture occur in the section
that contains the stalagmite layer. Three Neanderthal skeletons, one
that of a child, confirm the identification of the culture. Evidence of
almost continuous fires during the Neanderthal tenancy suggests cold
as well as wet weather; the time was probably that of the last ice age.

In correlating the sediments of earlier periods of earth history,
distinctive lithological units can be quite useful. This is particularly

true of the sediments laid down in the shallow seas which flooded enormous areas of the continents. Conditions in these ancient seas must have been quite uniform over wide regions; beds of limestone, shale, and sandstone only a few meters thick can be traced for long distances. In sections penetrated by oil wells, successions of lithological types can often serve to establish correlations without the use of fossils. In Pleistocene deposits, however, lithological characteristics are not very helpful, though they are not entirely useless; in some cases, till sheets can be distinguished by differences in the kind of rock detritus they contain. Fragments of a particular kind of limestone may provide a clear distinction between two superposed tills. When the source of the limestone is known, it can also indicate a difference in direction of movement of the glaciers that deposited the two different tills.

We have mentioned the wind-transported deposits of silt, called loess, which cover enormous areas of Europe and North America. Most geologists now believe that loess deposition took place during phases of the ice ages. Then, during the intervening interglacials and mild interstadials, deposition was interrupted and weathering ensued. Weathered soils enable us to recognize successions of loess layers and corresponding climatic changes. In Central and Western Europe six layers of loess can be distinguished. Apparently the loess terrain provided ample food for grazing mammals. These attracted early men, and the remains of their hunting sites preserved in the loess now attract archaeologists. The uppermost three layers of loess in Western Europe, like the stalagmite layers of caves, have been correlated with three cold phases of the last ice age. This correlation is confirmed by the fact that the local layers of loess lie on river terraces that can be traced upstream into districts which were invaded by glaciers. A thick soil that indicates a long period of weathering during the last interglacial separates the upper three layers of loess from the lower series. Presumably the lower layers represent earlier glacial phases, but just which has not yet been decided. Absence of a lower, very thick weathered zone corresponding to the Mindel-Riss Interglacial Age is surprising. Apparently the lower part of the section is incomplete.

River terraces afford important evidence by which sequences of climatic changes can be reconstructed in regions not reached by glaciers. Much fruitful work on terraces has been done in Central Europe in the unglaciated region that separated the Scandinavian and Alpine ice sheets. During temperate phases of climate, as today, the valleys contained sufficient water to carry a load of sediment and to erode their beds at the same time. During ice ages, however, scanty vegetation within the areas of drainage, and freezing and thawing along the banks, brought great quantities of rock waste into these valleys; yet during most seasons the supply of water was limited. As a result, the rivers filled the valleys with gravel sheets, over which they meandered. During the following temperate phase, erosion was resumed; as the rivers cut down into the gravel sheets, they left terraces of the gravel along their courses. Repetition of this cycle has resulted in a sequence of terraces, each representing a time of glaciation. The usefulness of climatic terraces is enhanced by the fact that some can be traced into the glaciated region of the Alps and can be connected with tills and other glacial deposits that are part of the classical sequence. Thus these European terraces serve as invaluable links between deposits directly due to glaciation and loess layers and archaeological sites, which could not otherwise be fitted into the main sequence of events.

There is still a good deal of ice on our planet; in fact, one continent and the largest island in the world are just about covered with ice. If our climate should turn warmer and these ice caps and the many mountain glaciers throughout the world should melt, sea level would rise; estimates of the amount vary between twenty and fifty meters, or between sixty-five and a hundred sixty-five feet. A rise of this kind in sea level, due to change in the total amount of water in the oceans, is called eustatic. Naturally, eustatic changes in sea level are the same all over the world, in contrast with changes of sea level due to local uplift or subsidence of coastlines. The northerly ranges of species of plants and animals adapted to warmth which occur as fossils in interglacial deposits indicate that the climates of the interglacials were, at least at times, warmer than our present climate. At such times it is probable that Greenland was free of ice and the Antarctic ice cap was much restricted, though for reasons which we will discuss in Chapter 9, it is unlikely that Antarctica was wholly free of ice at any time during the Pleistocene.

Ancient beaches well above present sea level have been recorded along the coasts of lands which have never been glaciated and which therefore have not experienced the removal of the great weight of a former ice sheet and a consequent rise. These beaches seem to provide confirmation of higher eustatic stands of sea level that would result from a decrease in ice on the continents during former interglacials. Such evidence comes from the Atlantic coast of the southern United States, where two wave-cut scarps have been traced for many hundreds of miles. The altitudes of the scarps are nine meters and thirty-two meters above sea level. Richard F. Flint has attributed the higher scarp to the Yarmouth Interglacial and the lower one to the Sangamon Interglacial. The altitude of the higher scarp is about what would be expected in an ice-free world. A succession of ancient strandlines along the coast of the Mediterranean has been known for almost fifty years. Most of these beaches have been correlated with some warm oscillation of the Pleistocene and named accordingly. However, there are several rather odd things about the succession. In consequence, the validity of these strandlines as indicators of former sea levels is not accepted by some geologists; other geologists find a good deal of significance in them.

The highest of these beaches, which may antedate the Pleistocene, is about a hundred meters above sea level. The next two are at elevations of eighty and sixty meters. But, as we have said, fifty meters is the most generous estimate of rise in sea level due to the melting of all the ice in the world. In addition, there are three lower beaches. The highest is at thirty meters and poses no problem. One way to account for the anomalous height of the high beaches is to appeal to local uplift of the Mediterranean basin. There would be nothing extraordinary about such uplift; the geological record is full of similar examples. If this is the correct explanation, the higher strandlines are truly "raised" beaches and have no significance as indicators of former sea level. Other scientists, however, insist that strandlines at about the same elevations can be identified elsewhere, as on the coasts of northern France and North America and on the shores of the Pacific. If we grant the validity of these widely scattered strandlines, we are forced to admit that a good deal of water has gone somewhere since the time represented by the three highest beaches. A hypothetical lowering of some part of the floor of the Pacific during the earlier half of the Pleistocene is one possible explanation. This would give climatic significance once more to the high Mediterranean beaches, which would record relatively short intervals of high eustatic sea level superimposed on a more or less continuous fall in sea level.

At the beginning of the 1950's the boundary between the present phase of mild climate and the preceding ice age was considered to be as poorly defined as the boundary between the Pleistocene and the Pliocene was then thought to be. At that time the prevalent conception was of a gradual shading of one climatic phase into the next. Attempts had been made to define and date the boundary, but without much success. Postglacial time was generally believed to have begun about twenty thousand years ago, but this was based on the insecure evidence of an estimate of the time needed to build a delta in Lake Lucerne.

We have explained in Chapter 5 how the shells of certain species of planktonic foraminifera, by their alternating presence and absence in the succession of layers of sediment of the deep ocean basins, record the climatic changes of the Pleistocene. A change of this kind had been found by Schott at a depth of only fifteen to twenty centimeters below the surface of sediment in a suite of cores from the equatorial Atlantic. By the beginning of the 1950's we had also found this change, which indicated a marked rise in temperature, in hundreds of cores from widely scattered points in the Atlantic and adjacent seas. The position of these layers near the tops of the cores showed that they recorded the last major climatic event of the Pleistocene, which could scarcely have been anything but the worldwide rise in temperature at the end of the last ice age.

In order to correlate this evidence of a rise in temperature with the continental record of events which had occurred at the end of the last ice age, radiocarbon dating was applied to samples from six sediment cores from different localities which represented different types of sediment and different rates of accumulation of sediment. These studies were made by W. S. Broecker and J. L. Kulp of the geochemistry laboratory of the Lamont Geological Observatory.

We had carefully selected these cores on the basis of micropaleontological, lithological, and calcium-carbonate analyses. Some other considerations determined our choice of the particular cores. Wide separation in latitude and longitude was desirable in order to make clear that the faunal variations from which the climatic changes had been inferred were not due to local but to ocean-wide changes in conditions, and in order to detect any possible variations with latitude. The east-to-west distance between the most widely spaced coring stations was more than 4,000 miles; the north-to-south range was about 3,000 miles. We selected cores from areas of varied topography; we had found that the configuration of the ocean floor strongly influences sedimentary processes, particularly the rate of accumulation of sediment. The topographical settings included a submarine canyon, a basin, the crest of a ridge, and gentle slopes.

The radiocarbon assays of the cores indicated that the last ice age had ended about 11,500 years ago. They also showed that the change from glacial to postglacial climate had occurred just about simultaneously throughout the North Atlantic and adjacent seas. The dates corroborated what we had inferred from our curves of climatic change—that the climatic change had been rather sudden, geologically speaking, that is, within an interval of no more than a thousand years, as opposed to the commonly held view that the change had taken place gradually.

Although the date we assigned to the end of the last ice age— 11,000 years before the present—was quite different from the generally accepted date of 20,000 or even 25,000 years before the present, it agreed with some radiocarbon dates of continental deposits that record events which occurred at or near the end of the last ice age. It slightly postdated the last advance of the ice on land at Two Creeks, Wisconsin, where trees, drowned by the rise of a proglacial lake, had been pushed down and overridden by the advancing ice. Wood from these trees proved to be 11,850 years old when it was subjected to radiocarbon dating by Broecker and Farrand. Other datings showed that short advances of glaciers in Puget Sound and southern British Columbia had taken place between 11,000 and 12,000 years ago, after which rapid retreat had occurred. At about this time further agreement was found in the radiocarbon dates of a change in sedimentation from sand to silt in the Mississippi Delta region and of the rapid drying up of pluvial Lake Lahontan, events which were considered to have taken place at the end of the last ice age. The radiocarbon process showed that both had occurred just about 11,000 years ago.

This considerable shortening of postglacial time led many geologists to conclude that the estimate of the total duration of the Pleistocene ought to be shortened proportionately. Whereas it had been customary to think of the duration of the Pleistocene in terms of something like a million years, it soon became the vogue to speak of the first ice age as having begun about 300,000 years ago.

At about the same time that the radiocarbon datings were being made on the cores of deep-sea sediment, determinations of paleotemperature were being made by the oxygen-isotope method on samples from some of the cores, including one which contained the longest continuous climatic record we had found up to that time. This method was developed by H. C. Urey at the University of Chicago in 1947. It is based on the fact that atoms of oxygen are not all alike; most have an atomic weight of 16, but one in five hundred has a weight of 18. Although these two kinds of oxygen— or isotopes, as they are called—form the same combinations with other chemical elements, they tend to concentrate to different extents in different combinations. Since the tendency of oxygen-18 to concentrate in calcium carbonate decreases with rise of temperature, all else being equal, the smaller the ratio of oxygen-18 to oxygen-16 in a fossil shell, the higher the temperature of the water in which the shell was secreted. Unfortunately, all else is never equal—this was particularly so during the ice ages. The isotopic composition of the water also influences the ratio of isotopes in the final composition of the shell, and the composition of the water is influenced by evaporation from the surface of the sea and by rainfall. An attempt to correct for variation in isotopic composition has led to a reduction in the extreme temperature fluctuations from 9 degrees Celsius as given by the ratio of isotopes, to 6 degrees, which is supposed to be the "true" difference in temperature between interglacials and ice ages. It has been claimed that the correction of three degrees has been "calculated." But the truth of the matter is that no one knows nearly enough about the balance between evaporation and precipitation, or other pertinent conditions, in the Caribbean during the ice ages to be able to calculate the isotopic composition of the water. The correction is a guess, pure and simple. However, the fact that a certain ratio has been measured with a high degree of precision by a very expensive mass spectrometer has created an illusion of infallibility and objectivity. Actually, the temperatures as corrected by guesswork are neither "true temperatures" nor "absolute temperatures," though both euphemisms have been applied to them.

The paleotemperature measurements on the samples from the six especially selected cores were made by Cesare Emiliani. Comparison between the curves of isotopic temperature variation and the climatic curves that we had derived from analyses of the assemblages of planktonic foraminifera showed good agreement within the sections of the cores which included an earlier zone of mild climate, the latter part of the last ice age, and the final change to the mild climate of the present. But there were serious discrepancies in the curves representing the earlier parts of the records.

On the evidence of his paleotemperatures and radiocarbon dating by H. E. Suess, Emiliani concluded that the core with the longest continuous record included zones representing four ice ages and three interglacials. This led Emiliani to announce that the first ice age must have begun a little less than 300,000 years ago.

We do not agree with this. We believe that the core includes a record of no more than two ice ages and the last interglacial This implies that there is some flaw in the oxygen-isotope method as applied to samples from cores of deep-sea sediment.

Emiliani used only the shells of certain species of planktonic foraminifera and went on to assume that all the carbonate of the shells had been secreted in the photic zone—the sunlit, upper hundred meters of the ocean. This is a crucial assumption in the theory of the method. We question its validity. To interpret correctly the ratios of the isotopes, the depth at which the shells were secreted must be known. Deep waters at all latitudes are quite cold.

Ever since the expedition of the *Challenger,* it has been known that various species of foraminifera can be caught by towing a net of fine gauze in the photic zone. This led to the universal belief that most, if not all, species of planktonic foraminifera pass their entire lives in the photic zone. Evidently, some critical stage in the life cycles of most foraminifera must take place in the photic zone; if this were not so, the geographical ranges of the various species would not be limited by latitude to the extent that we know they are, for it is only in the photic zone that the temperature of the water varies significantly with latitude.

But the naturalists of the *Challenger,* and others after them, noticed that the shells of the foraminifera caught in the photic zone had thin, transparent walls, whereas the shells of the same species in samples taken from the bottom were for the most part heavily encrusted with calcium carbonate or calcite. Until recently it has been held that the encrusting calcite was a purely chemical precipitate deposited on the shells after they had come to rest on the floor of the ocean. This was really a most improbable theory; it is surprising that it should ever have gained currency. For one thing, oceanographers all agree that the chemical environment at depths below several thousand meters causes the solution of calcium carbonate. Evidence of partial solution of the shells of foraminifera is evident in most samples from depths greater than 4,500 meters. However, our observation that the calcite layer is always thickest on the chamber of the shell that was formed earliest and is always either lacking or very thin on the final chamber settled the question of the origin of the calcite crust once and for all; only the living organism could precipitate the calcite in this selective pattern. But if so, why is it that the shells of living specimens caught in the photic zone never have a calcite crust? The answer is that the creatures in the photic zone are immature; as the animals approach maturity, they sink below the photic zone and there precipitate the heavy outer layer of calcite.

As final proof that we were correct in our deduction from the pattern of distribution of the calcite layer, Allan Bé of the Lamont Geological Observatory towed plankton nets which could be opened and closed at depths of between five hundred and a thousand meters. At such depths, as we had predicted, he caught living specimens with heavily encrusted shells. A further deduction from our observations is that the species of foraminifera with encrusted shells must reproduce at some depth below five hundred meters, after which the embryos must rise into the photic zone to fatten on diatoms and other photosynthesizing organisms. This discovery that the life cycles of many, if not all, planktonic foraminifera include a vertical migration through a considerable depth of water does not conflict with the theory that temperature variations in the upper layers of water determine the geographical distributions of certain species; evidently temperature in the photic zone is a critical condition during the early stage of growth.

However, this insight into the lives of planktonic foraminifera has a critical bearing on the theory of paleotemperatures as determined by the oxygen-isotope method. These temperatures are supposed to represent temperatures of surface or near-surface waters, but if most species secrete not less than three quarters of the calcium carbonate of their shells at depths below five hundred meters, the ratio of oxygen isotopes in the shells is no longer representative of conditions in the water near the surface. Water below five hundred meters differs not only in temperature but also in isotopic composition. Here, it seems, is another basic assumption of the oxygen-isotope method of determining paleotemperatures which needs reconsideration.

7

DEEP-SEA SEDIMENTATION

IN COMPARISON with other scientists working on the problem of Pleistocene climates and sedimentary processes as recorded in deep-sea cores, we have been in a uniquely favorable position because at the Lamont Geological Observatory we have had at our disposal far more long cores than exist at any other laboratory. This is the result of Ewing's early realization that the deep oceanic environment had many facets and that to understand them it would be essential to have many cores from as many widely scattered points on the ocean floor as possible.

Since the beginning of the 1950's about two hundred new cores have been added each year to the collection at Lamont, in recent years more than three hundred cores a year have been taken. This has led to days and nights of intense activity in the building where the cores are unwrapped, split, and described. Many a time we have kept the lights burning well past midnight when a series of important cores had been opened during the day and it was necessary to describe them without delay so that the tables could be cleared for the opening of a new batch on the following day.

In describing the cores, we had constantly to remind ourselves that our purpose was not to accumulate many highly detailed descriptions of cores, but rather to gain an understanding of present and past conditions in the oceans in order the better to interpret the climatic record of the Pleistocene. There is always a temptation to become lost in the study of puzzling peculiarities of individual cores and to lose sight of important features common to suites of cores, the very features which have ocean-wide significance.

For example, a core from a point southeast of Bermuda contained throughout its length a series of thin layers full of the minute pillbox-like siliceous shells of the planktonic algae called diatoms. The obvious explanation, as it seemed to us at the time, was that each layer must record an enormous bloom of diatoms in the surface waters of the region, something which might have a useful bearing on climate. But when we looked for similar layering in other cores from the general vicinity we were surprised to find that they contained few diatoms and no distinct layers. It was highly improbable that dense blooms of diatoms could have occurred repeatedly during many thousands of years within a relatively small area of the open ocean without ever spreading into the adjacent areas where the other cores had been taken. Living conditions in the surface water could not have remained so rigidly localized over so long a period of time in a region of deep water where the local topography of the bottom could not have had any influence on the surface layer of water in which the diatoms bloomed. And yet the topography of the bottom was somehow involved; it was the only condition of the general environment which could be depended upon to have remained constant within the time interval represented by the cores. This hint led to a working hypothesis: the concentrations of diatoms in the single core were not due to blooms in the surface water, but instead to mechanical concentration of the shells on the bottom. The relief of the sea floor in the region southeast of Bermuda is what one might call hilly, not at all spectacular, but with some pronounced rises and depressions. We made the guess that the core with the many diatom layers had been raised from a depression in the sea floor which acted as a sediment trap into which the finest fraction of sediment particles had been wafted and concentrated from the surrounding rises by gentle current scour. The tiny, extremely thin and light disc-shaped shells, or frustules, of the diatoms would be particularly susceptible to this kind of transportation. As for the diatom blooms, presumably they had taken place much as one would expect, that is, sporadically throughout the region.

At this point another feature of the core with the diatoms took on meaning; its fine bedding was quite undisturbed by burrowing, unlike the nearby cores, which were strongly mottled by burrows. Obviously the deep current that had swept together the diatom frustules must also have moved clay particles and concentrated them in the same sediment trap. This implied a rate of sediment accumulation considerably faster in the depression than on the nearby rises, a condition which would discourage life on the bottom. Unfortunately the echo-sounding records made in this region were rather sketchy. This was tantalizing; we felt that with more information about the topography of the bottom around the diatom core we might have been able to infer the direction of flow of the deep current that had wafted together the diatoms. To measure bottom currents at depths of 4,500 meters is costly and time-consuming. A method of determining the direction of currents on the bottom by means of cores could be useful; better still, the method might provide us with information unobtainable with a current meter. It might give us indications of changes in the direction of currents during earlier subdivisions of the Pleistocene Epoch, which could be helpful in devising a hypothesis to explain the climatic fluctuations of the ice ages.

But it was already past midnight. If more cores were to be opened on the following day, we would have to finish our descriptions and clear the tables before morning.

To meet the situation, we have been compelled to streamline our methods of describing the cores. This has led to careful examination of our objectives. Why do we describe cores? Not primarily to fit them into a classification. Nor are the descriptions themselves an objective. The cores are of interest to us only to the extent that we can use them to learn about present and past conditions in the oceans, about the processes that have played a part in shaping the floor of the ocean, about the timing and intensities of the climatic changes of the Pleistocene Epoch, and about other dynamic aspects of the oceanic environment. To make the cores yield their information, we had to describe objectively and not merely name—or what is much the same thing, classify—the sediments therein. Early in our investigation we gave up the use of the terms *globigerina ooze, diatome ooze, red clay,* and *blue clay.* These terms have been in use by oceanographers for more than a hundred years and have been hallowed by usage in the great report on the samples of deep-sea sediment collected by the *Challenger.* They are excellent terms, but they do not serve our purpose.

For example, the sediment classified as "red clay" is never red and is only partly composed of clay minerals. No description of such a sediment is worth the paper it is written on unless it includes some definition of the color. But if we describe a certain sample as dark brown, what but confusion results from calling it a red clay? Instead of clay we prefer the term *lutite,* which by general agreement among students of sediments designates a sediment composed dominantly of mineral particles of clay size, or smaller than 0.004 millimeter, but not necessarily composed of clay minerals.

For a long time the term *globigerina ooze* was used very loosely. To correct this, it was redefined to include only sediments containing a certain minimum percentage of the shells of planktonic foraminifera. Not infrequently, the percentage of foraminifera falls somewhere near the border line, and with a hand lens it is impossible to tell whether the particular sediment is properly a globigerina ooze or not. Then again, many sediments obviously do not contain enough foraminifera to be classed as globigerina oozes, although they equally obviously contain far too many to be called red clays. What were we to do with them?

At that point we cut the Gordian knot. We would forget about classification and classic terms. We would, instead, describe the sediments in simple, objective terms, and then, if from our descriptions the basis for a natural classification emerged, well and good. In fact, that is just about what has happened. We can now distinguish two great groups of deep-sea sediments which differ in their mode of origin. One group includes those sediments laid down by the extremely slow but continuous settling of mineral particles and the hard parts of planktonic organisms; the other includes sediments deposited almost instantaneously by turbidity currents—gravity-induced bottom currents of water made dense by mineral matter in suspension.

In order to hew to our line and avoid becoming bogged down in masses of detail of doubtful value, we imposed some rules on ourselves. In describing the cores we would limit ourselves to the use of a hand lens, some hydrochloric acid, and a color dictionary. The color dictionary is a book whose pages are covered with squares of gradational hues and shades, coded with letters and numbers. Its use is necessary when one wants to record a color with some degree of precision. But matching the sediments against the colored squares is time-consuming, and as yet the refined distinctions of color possible through its use have not proved helpful in attaining our objective, an understanding of sedimentary processes.

Color is a significant property of sediments, but in our experience the vital color differences can be recorded sufficiently well for all practical purposes by means of the common color names in various combinations.

In cores from deep stations where "red clay"—brown lutite— normally occurs, we sometimes find one or more layers of gray clay interbedded with the normal brown lutite. These anomalous layers containing a relatively large amount of calcium carbonate are meaningful for the marine geologist. They owe their existence to a process of transportation and emplacement entirely different from that responsible for the accumulation of brown lutite. They belong to the class of turbidites, or sediments deposited almost instantaneously by turbidity currents. Rapid deposition has prevented the cold, solvent bottom water of the deep basins in which these sediments occur from dissolving the finely divided calcium carbonate that they commonly contain. In describing these layers, it is important to distinguish the color contrast between them and the interbedded brown lutites, but this can be done quite well with the simple words *gray* and *brown*.

A finer distinction is helpful when reddish-brown lutite occurs in cores from deep stations, where "red clay" would be the normal sediment. The reddish-brown layers are in every way similar to the gray layers except in color. All evidence shows that they too have been deposited by turbidity currents. They differ only in the source of the material, which in their case is exposures of old and thoroughly oxidized sediments on the continent.

A layer of this kind occurs in cores from the abyssal plain of the Sigsbee Deep in the Gulf of Mexico. Masquerading as a "red clay," this layer has led to some rather farfetched speculations regarding former conditions in the Sigsbee Deep, which at a depth of about 3,600 meters is too shallow for the accumulation of abyssal brown lutite. The answer is that the reddish-brown layer is not a brown lutite at all. It is composed of old sediment reworked from outcrops north of the Gulf, sediments which in suspension give the Red River its name. If earlier students had used the word *red* less loosely, the true nature of this bed might have been recognized sooner. When the reddish-brown sediment and a sample of abyssal brown lutite are compared side by side, the color difference is easy to see. Actually, the two kinds of sediment differ in other ways. The reddish-brown sediment is graded; that is, the basal part of the layer, which is about thirty centimeters thick, is silty whereas the upper part is mostly clay. The lower part is thinly laminated and without trace of burrow mottling, whereas brown lutites show little vertical variation in texture and are consistently burrow-mottled throughout.

Another coloration of importance in the interpretation of the cores is due to a mineral called hydrotroilite, an amorphous monosulfide of iron. Sediments containing hydrotroilite look as if they had been splashed with ink. In contact with air, this colloidal sulfide rapidly decomposes; in a few hours the inky stains change to rusty brown through oxidation of the iron.

Various kinds of bacteria produce hydrogen sulfide by working on substances containing sulfur, such as proteins and calcium sulfate.

Some of the hydrogen sulfide then reacts with iron salts to form hydrotroilite. But these bacteria are active only in the absence of free oxygen. Thus, the presence of hydrotroilite in a sediment is a sure sign of the absence of free oxygen. Since we have never found hydrotroilite in the top centimeter of any core from the Atlantic, we are sure that the water at the bottom of the deepest basins under present conditions contains free oxygen. On the other hand, hydrotroilite is sometimes abundant a few tens of centimeters below the tops of cores. At first glance, this might be construed as evidence of stagnation of the bottom water of the Atlantic during the last ice age. The presence, at all levels in these cores, of burrow mottling and the shells of foraminifera that dwell at the bottom prove, however, that this cannot have been the case. The explanation of this seeming paradox is that another kind of bacteria which use free oxygen in their metabolism gradually use up the oxygen in the interstitial water of the sediment. Eventually, when all the free oxygen has been exhausted, the sulfur bacteria take over and production of hydrogen sulfide commences, which in turn gives rise to hydrotroilite.

Hydrotroilite is particularly prevalent in the clayey upper parts of thick graded layers deposited by turbidity currents. Probably this is because such layers contain much organic matter; in fact, much plant detritus is sometimes plainly recognizable. Because of the almost instantaneous deposition of considerable thicknesses of this kind of sediment, much of the organic matter is buried too deeply to be reached by the ordinary scavengers. But bacteria are always there.

Most of the cores of foraminiferal lutite which contain well-defined faunal zones corresponding to the climatic changes of the Pleistocene are various shades of tan or khaki. The exceptions are four cores from the equatorial Atlantic and two from off the coast of Africa. In the equatorial suite, the layers containing foraminifera indicative of mild climate are tan, whereas those containing evidence of cool climate are various shades of gray. Particularly remarkable is the subdivision in these cores of the upper gray zone corresponding to the last ice age into nine cyclical layers, each of which starts out with an abrupt change to dark gray, shows a gradual change upward to light gray, followed by an abrupt change to dark gray, and so on.

Since the gray layers, on the evidence of the foraminifera, correspond to ice ages, they must also correspond to what were pluvials in Africa—that is, times of moist climate. Most students of the Pleistocene agree that the great dry regions of Africa supported abundant vegetation during the last ice age. Probably during that time the rivers of northern Africa, larger than they are now, were pouring quantities of plant detritus into the Atlantic. If the system of currents in the Atlantic was then about what it is now, much of this material must have been swept southwestward and across the Atlantic somewhere near the Equator. We think it probable, therefore, that the gray color is due partly to carbonaceous pigment and partly to the chemical effect of the organic matter which would, perhaps with the help of bacteria, tend to reduce iron in the sediment from brown ferric oxide to colorless ferrous salts. But why the cyclical changes of shade within the upper gray layer? The thicknesses of the gray cycles range from fifteen to about thirty centimeters which would correspond to time intervals varying from 4,000 to 8,000 years. To our knowledge, no evidence of a climatic cycle of about this period has been found anywhere else than in these cores.

Similar cyclical color changes occur in two cores from points northwest of Cape Verde, French West Africa. As can be expected at stations that are relatively near the shore, the cyclical layers are thicker because of more rapid accumulation of sediment. They vary from a half meter to a little more than one meter. Unfortunately, neither core includes a lower layer that can be identified with certainty as having been deposited during the preceding time of mild climate, the time of dry climate in Africa. Consequently, we cannot be sure that there is a layer-by-layer correlation between these cores and the equatorial suite.

One of the important features of the sediments which should always be noted in logging or describing the cores is the presence or absence of burrow mottling. We have already mentioned how burrow mottling provides evidence that the deep water at the bottom of the Atlantic has contained some oxygen throughout the Pleistocene Epoch. We find this kind of evidence wherever sedimentation has been slow and continuous. On the other hand, the sudden flooding of a region by a torrent of turbid water must play havoc with the smaller forms of life that dwell at the bottom. When the mineral matter has settled out of suspension, the newly created surface must be very nearly a desert. In time, a new population colonizes the disaster area, but the mud-feeding members of the colonists confine their burrowing to the upper ten centimeters of the newly deposited sediment. This provides us with a good way of distinguishing between sediment of slow accumulation, in which burrows are evenly distributed, and layers deposited by turbidity currents, the lower parts of which are quite free of burrowing and sometimes have beautiful, paper-thin bedding. Another characteristic of layers created by deposition by catastrophic turbidity currents is a sharply defined base beneath which there is normal, greatly burrowed sediment.

Presumably, isolated layers only two or three centimeters thick deposited by turbidity currents may be completely obliterated by the churning effect of mud-feeders. But when flooding by turbid water is fairly frequent, recolonization is impossible and the region becomes a permanent desert. Under such conditions, even very thin layers deposited by turbidity currents are well preserved. These were the conditions over the large area of the flat bottom of the Sigsbee Deep in the Gulf of Mexico during the last ice age. Great quantities of sediment were pouring into the Gulf of Mexico by way of the Mississippi River during that time. At the same time, sea level was lower, by a hundred meters or more, than it had been during the previous interglacial age. This was due to withdrawal of water from the oceans to form the continental ice sheets. In consequence, masses of unconsolidated sediment must have been exposed to wave erosion in the region of the Mississippi Delta. Long cores from the abyssal plain of the Sigsbee Deep contain an almost unbroken series of finely bedded gray lutites and thin silt layers. Except for one short period about 20,000 years ago, during which a few centimeters of burrow-mottled tan lutite accumulated on the plain, the nearly level floor of the deep must have been almost completely devoid of life.

Near the center of the Sigsbee abyssal plain are three low hills known as the Sigsbee Knolls, which rise to a height of about 125 meters above the surrounding plain. When the plain was flooded, these knolls stood above the surrounding sea of turbid water like islands. Like islands, they were peopled by isolated populations of animals. We know this because three cores taken on or near the tops of the knolls contain only tan lutite with abundant burrow-mottling from top to bottom.

Some years ago, when the exploration of the floor of the Gulf of Mexico was in an early stage, certain geologists advanced the hypothesis that the gray lutites and silts of the Sigsbee abyssal plain had been deposited in shallow water and that subsequently, near the end of the last ice age, the bottom had subsided to its present depth of 3,600 meters. As evidence in favor of this idea, the geologists cited the fact that the gray clays and silts of the abyssal plain were not graded, as should be the case if they had been deposited by turbidity currents. Now, a graded layer is one in which the size of the particles gradually decreases from the bottom to the top. When a graded layer is composed of sand and silt particles, the vertical change in the size of particles can usually be seen easily, but the gray layers of the Sigsbee Deep were largely composed of clay. We were thoroughly convinced that they had been deposited by turbidity currents, but we had to admit that even with a hand lens one could not see any vertical change in texture. In such a case, one would normally take samples from several levels in a single layer and determine the average size of particles in each by mechanical analysis. But mechanical analyses are time-consuming and tedious; the fine sediment must be put into suspension in distilled water, which necessitates the removal of every trace of salt. Then the sizes of the particles are determined by letting the sediment settle in a glass cylinder, but it may take days for the finer fractions to settle. Mechanical analyses are depressing affairs; one puts so much time and effort into them and learns so little.

When we went to the cores to sample them, we saw the answer to the problem. By that time the cores were dry. In drying, a mass of quartz or calcite particles behaves very differently from a mass of clay particles; the quartz does not shrink at all, the clay may shrink to about half its wet volume. Dry, each section of the cores which included a graded layer now tapered upward from the basal silt layer, which had not shrunk at all, to the top, where the diameter had decreased by about a third. Here was clear visual proof of the gradual and smooth decrease upward of the ratio of relatively coarse quartz particles to fine clay particles. The alleged absence of grading was a myth; we were able to prove it by means of a photograph.

However, this was not the only evidence against recent subsidence of the bottom of the Gulf of Mexico. Many other bits of irresistible evidence soon relegated this hypothesis to the limbo of spectacular theories which cannot stand close scrutiny.

Since then, we have used shrinkage as a quick and sure way of detecting changes in texture in thick sections of sediment of slow and continuous accumulation. For this purpose, we measure shrinkage in the vertical dimension. With no apparatus other than a meter stick, we can learn as much or more about vertical changes in texture as we could in weeks of laborious mechanical analysis. The gradual changes of texture in cores of abyssal brown lutite revealed by differential shrinkage extend through time intervals of the order of tens and hundreds of thousands of years. It is tempting to speculate that the variations in texture may be connected with the climatic changes of the Pleistocene.

In Chapter 5 we mentioned the widespread occurrence on the continents of a particular sediment called loess. Pleistocene geologists believe that loess accumulated during the ice ages as wind-blown dust. The enormous areas of North America, Europe, and Asia covered by loess suggest that at least some of the finest of this wind-blown material must have found its way out over the oceans. Since the rate of accumulation of abyssal brown lutite is extremely slow, any additional element, far too small to make itself felt in other depositional environments, could easily have an appreciable effect upon the physical character of brown lutite. It is quite possible, therefore, that the zones of least shrinkage in the brown lutite cores correspond to times of loess deposition on the continents. As yet, lack of time has prevented us from exploring the possibility of elaborating a sequence of Pleistocene climatic events by measuring the shrinkage of brown lutite cores.

In describing the cores, we find a few which give promise of containing long continuous records of the climatic changes of the Pleistocene. These are not cores that would be impressive to the layman; they contain no abrupt changes or bright colors. The cores we choose consist of monotonous, tan, burrow-mottled foraminiferal lutite. We sample these at intervals of ten centimeters. After drying, the samples are weighed and washed on a sieve that retains particles larger than 74 microns. These coarse fractions, which consist mostly of the shells of planktonic foraminifera, are dried and weighed. From the final weighings we calculate the percentage of coarse fractions in each of the original samples of sediment. Other cores that appear to have less interest as climatic records are sampled at intervals of fifty centimeters, but all samples go through the same process of weighing and washing. These percentages of coarse fractions are not quite comparable to complete mechanical analyses, but they provide us with much valuable information about environments and processes of deposition and involve little expenditure of time and effort. For example, cores from the Atlantic off the coast of Africa contain sediment of rapid accumulation; there is an abundant supply of fine mineral matter from the nearby continent. The coarse fractions in these sediments rarely exceed two percent. As we go farther from the continent, the percentage of coarse fractions rapidly increases. We are entering a region of high productivity of planktonic foraminifera and have passed beyond the range of abundant fine material from the continent. In this region the coarse fraction varies from ten percent to sixty percent, or even more, depending upon a variety of factors.

Still farther out in the Atlantic, and at depths greater than five thousand meters, we find the classic "red clay" or abyssal brown lutite, which contains less than one percent of coarse material. Though small in amount, the coarse fractions of brown lutites are distinctive. They include almost always a few shells of foraminifera that dwell on the bottom, minute teeth of fishes, and often mineral particles known as chondrules and tiny spheres of magnetic iron oxide and sometimes of metallic iron. These little spheres and the chondrules are believed to fall from outer space. At any rate, nothing quite like the chondrules is known to occur anywhere else on earth except in stony meteorites. Percentages of coarse fractions are also useful as numerical measures of grading in sand layers deposited by turbidity currents.

Early explorers of the ocean basins on very rare occasions found fairly coarse, well-sorted sands far out in the oceans and at great depths. The then known processes of transportation and deposition were inadequate to explain the origin of these strange sands. Various hypotheses were conceived in attempts to explain their origin. Among these were transportation by violent winds, transportation by drifting ice during an excessively cold ice age, and deposition at some early epoch of earth history when the configuration of the ocean basins was very different. Subsequently the sands would have been forced up through the overlying sediment by a kind of "sedimentary vulcanism," the mechanics of which are not very clear. According to the most popular hypothesis, these sands had been deposited at a relatively recent time of greatly lowered sea level. However, as these sands were very rarely found, they were not given very serious attention.

We now know that sands and accompanying finer sediments occur widely in the ocean basins and are, in fact, the dominant type of sediment in the broad deep basins of the Atlantic. How did it happen that sediments of such broad distribution were largely overlooked by earlier explorers? This was partly due to the fact that deposition of most of the sands took place during the last ice age. In consequence, most are covered by from ten to twenty centimeters of normal deep-sea sediment, but the sampling devices in common use could penetrate only the uppermost layer of sediment. During the voyage of the *Challenger,* a coring tube about sixty centimeters long was frequently used. It was long enough to reach sand, but clean sand is notoriously difficult to retain; except where the tube penetrated a layer of sand and entered clay underneath, the sand would run out of the tube like water. It was when long coring tubes came into use that marine geologists began to be aware of the broad areal distribution of these sediments.

As a result of our study of about three thousand cores of sediment from the Atlantic, the Caribbean, the Gulf of Mexico, the Mediterranean, and subarctic seas, we have come to the firm conviction that deep-sea sands and associated graded sediments were deposited by turbidity currents. This theory of origin has met every test. Nothing confirms the validity of a theory so well as the verification of predictions based upon it. Here the theory of turbidity currents has come off with flying colors. If turbidity currents owe their velocity to the pull of gravity, their courses along the bottom should be guided by the topography of the bottom over which they flow. With this in mind, one can chart the areas in which deposits by turbidity currents ought to occur, as well as areas where they should not occur. All predictions of this kind when tested have been verified; and many have been tested, as witness the thousands of cores in the collection at Lamont. The Puerto Rico Trench is a good example. We knew that graded layers ought to occur on the floor of the trench. By splicing together cables from two research vessels, Maurice Ewing, on board the *Atlantis,* succeeded in reaching bottom twice with a coring tube. As predicted, both cores contained ideal examples of graded beds. Like many other similar sediments from great depths, these contained the remains of organisms that live only in shallow water. Among the coarse particles near the sharply defined bases of the graded layers, we found fragments of Halimeda, a lime-secreting marine plant which cannnot grow without sunlight. Many cores have been taken on the sloping sides of the Puerto Rico Trench, but none has contained graded layers.

If we really needed to classify deep-sea sediments, we would draw a line between those which accumulate slowly and continuously and the sharply differentiated sediments that are laid down almost instantaneously by intermittent turbidity currents.

Graded layers seem to be less widespread in the Pacific. This may be due in part to the deep trenches that parallel the continental slopes of North and South America. These act as traps and catch and retain floods of turbid water generated by slumping of masses of sediment on the continental slope, and thereby prevent them from spreading graded layers over the floor of the Pacific. Where the

trenches have been sampled, graded layers have been found. However, the continental slopes are not the only sources of turbidity
currents. Slumping may occur on the flanks of any rise. We prophesy,
therefore, that as more cores are taken in the Pacific, more evidence
of the activity of turbidity currents will be found. In the Atlantic,
the Mid-Atlantic Ridge must have been a prolific source of turbidity
currents. The common occurrence of lacunae in the sedimentary
sections of cores from the flanks of the ridge is evidence of the
prevalence of slumping along this seismically active feature of the
face of the earth.

Evidently this process—the loss of material from rises by slumping, followed by a flow of sediment in the form of turbidity currents
to the bottoms of the deep basins—must have a leveling effect. The
extraordinary smoothness of the almost level floors of these basins
has been a cause of amazement ever since the first ships equipped
with echo sounders crossed them.

One hypothesis to explain the smoothness appealed to vast outpourings of very fluid lava. Supposedly, at some time in the past
lava erupted through the ocean floor and flowed out on the bottom,
drowning all topographical irregularities and thus giving rise to a
smooth surface on which sediment has subsequently accumulated.
But very recently the seismic profiler has rendered this hypothesis
untenable. The profiler in principle is very similar to the echo
sounder. As the ship proceeds, half-pound charges of dynamite are
thrown overboard at intervals of three minutes. These explode at
a depth of a few meters. The sound waves reflected back from the
floor of the ocean and from layers beneath the floor are picked up
by the profiler, which draws an almost continuous profile of the
bottom and the structure beneath. In the language of seismologists,
the sediment in the deep basins is very "transparent"—it is fairly
homogeneous and freely transmits sound energy. When the sound
wave encounters hard, dense rock such as frozen lava, a large part
of the energy is reflected and registers on the profiler as a strongly
defined boundary which cannot be confused with less well defined
discontinuities within the sediment.

Doubtless, the most surprising thing the profiler records have shown is the highly uneven surface of the basement rocks beneath the smooth abyssal plains of the North and South Atlantic. If the basement is composed of extrusive volcanic rock, and it is difficult to see how it can be anything else, the outpouring of lava on the ocean floor has had anything but a smoothing effect. Actually, this newly found evidence of a rugged surface beneath the abyssal plains underscores the effectiveness of turbidity currents as modifiers of topography on the bottom of the ocean. As the problem stands now, repeated flooding by turbidity currents provides the only plausible explanation for the filling of the depressions and the smoothing over of the many irregularities of the surface of the basement.

The discovery of the smoothing effect of turbidity currents was an unforseen byproduct of the theory of turbidity currents, which, as we have said, was first put to use by Daly to explain the erosion of submarine canyons. In this way, the overall theory of turbidity currents gains powerful support. When a hypothesis originally intended to explain a single phenomenon later serves to explain a series of previously unknown phenomena, it is well on the way to final proof. We must remember that when Daly attributed the erosion of submarine canyons to turbidity currents, he knew nothing about the prevalence of deep-sea sands or the rough surface of the basement beneath the floors of the deep ocean basins.

But if this process of filling is so effective, why are the floors of the oceans not vast, featureless plains? How can trenches like the Puerto Rico Trench and those off the west coasts of North and South America persist? As we see it, there is only one possible answer; the trenches are youthful features of the earth's surface. They have come into existence so recently that turbidity currents have not had enough time to fill them with sediment.

8

REACHING THE YARMOUTH

INTERGLACIAL

LONG ago we attended some lectures by an eminent and venerable geologist; he had been born before the publication of *The Origin of Species*. The subject of his lectures was the sculpturing of the surfaces of the continents by erosion, the slow but relentless work of frost, wind, rain, and streams, which tends to reduce the continental surfaces to monotonous plains, and would eventually do so if forces within the earth did not now and again renew the topographical relief of the continents. To emphasize the ceaseless change of the continental environment, he drew us a contrasting picture of the ocean floor. There, he told us, as the millions of years rolled by, nothing happened; nothing except the occasional slow settling of a microscopic shell or particle of clay, to be added to the all-enveloping layer of sediment.

We sometimes think of this peaceful vision and wish that it were real; it would have made the task of translating layers of deep-sea sediment into the chronology of the Pleistocene so simple. In reality, the bottom of the ocean is swept by various kinds of currents, and occasional slumping of the upper layer of sediment here and there gives rise to elisions in the sedimentary record, as we have explained earlier. Yet, in spite of all this, exceptional areas of the ocean floor exist where Neptune's sandglass has been running uninterruptedly for long intervals of time, at least long enough to record events in the Pleistocene and in the evolution of man. The problem is to recognize such areas.

Then there is the additional problem of determining the rate at which the sandglass runs. The geologist R. Schwinner attempted to calculate rates of accumulation of sediment from the number of particles believed to be of extraterrestrial origin in samples of ocean sediment. Since the days of the *Challenger* expedition, it has been known that deep-sea sediments contain magnetic spherules of metallic iron and iron oxide, most of which are less than a millimeter in diameter. Other equally small particles known as chondrules are identical with certain crystal aggregates found in stony meteorites; nothing quite like them has ever been found in a rock of terrestrial origin. Schwinner estimated that the yearly fall of this kind of dust from outer space was five hundred tons and concluded that it took a thousand years for four centimeters of globigerina ooze, or clay containing many shells of foraminifera, to accumulate.

Later, K. E. Lohman used the rate of productivity of the Coccolithophoridae, tiny organisms which secrete minute plates of calcium carbonate—called coccoliths—about which we have written in Chapter 2. He estimated that a sample of sediment in which from fifty to seventy percent of the particles were coccoliths had accumulated at the rate of 0.1 centimeter in a thousand years. But sediment containing such a large proportion of coccoliths is abnormal, and like the layers of diatoms in the core from the region southeast of Bermuda, which we described in Chapter 7, probably accumulated in a depression where fine material was concentrated as it was swept from a nearby rise by deep current scour. If so, the rate of accumulation in the depression was largely independent of the productivity of the Coccolithophoridae. We judge that such sediments which contain an excess of fine material accumulate abnormally fast. When Lohman applied his method to a normal globigerina ooze, he found the rate of accumulation to be between one and two centimeters in a thousand years.

Both Schwinner's and Lohman's methods are unsatisfactory in that they merely shift the problem from one unknown, the rate of accumulation of sediment, to an almost equally uncertain rate, the fall of meteoritic dust or the productivity of the Coccolithophoridae. Even today, there is little agreement among students of meteorites regarding the total amount of dust which reaches the surface of the earth from outer space, and the conditions that govern the productivity of the Coccolithophoridae are still little understood.

In Chapter 6 we told how W. Schott used the shells of foraminifera to identify the level in a suite of cores which corresponded to the end of the last ice age. On the basis of this, Schott attempted to calculate the rate of accumulation of sediment. However, in 1935, when Schott published his study, the commonly accepted figure for the duration of postglacial time was 20,000 years. This was little better than a reasonable guess and turned out later to be nearly double the real duration.

In spite of the inaccuracies of these methods, they were useful in that they showed that accumulation of sediment is very slow. It might be possible, therefore, to find a complete record of the Pleistocene if longer cores could be obtained. Schott's discovery was particularly important because it suggested the possibility of deriving a chronology of the Pleistocene from dated levels in long sediment cores. Radiochemistry showed promise of providing the answer.

Shortly after Schott had published his conclusions, C. S. Piggot and W. M. D. Urry developed a method of determining rates of accumulation which depends on initial disequilibrium between uranium and unsupported thorium[230] or ionium. They found that the decrease in radioactivity of samples from successively deeper levels in sediment cores was due to the decay of excess ionium and radium precipitated on the sea floor and unsupported by the decay of uranium. Disintegration of these excess amounts gradually reduces the radioactivity of the sediment until their rate of decay and their rate of production by the disintegration of uranium atoms are in balance. Now, the half life—the period in which any given quantity of a radioactive element is reduced by spontaneous disintegration to one half of the original amount—is 82,000 years for ionium and 1,700 years for radium. On the basis of these rates of decay, mathematical analysis of the curve of decrease in radioactivity with depth in the sediment yields the time elapsed since each layer was deposited on the floor of the sea. Theoretically, the method is applicable to sediments deposited within the past 300,000 years.

By this method, Piggot and Urry found that the rate of accumulation alongside the Mid-Atlantic Rise was eleven centimeters in a thousand years. In the center of the western basin of the North Atlantic, the rate for an impure globigerina ooze was four centimeters in a thousand years. A core of globigerina ooze from the Caribbean gave a slower rate, namely 0.6 centimeter in a thousand years, and a core of "red clay" from the Pacific, five hundred kilometers from the coast of California, yielded a rate of 0.5 centimeter in a thousand years. The physical properties and biostratigraphy of some of the cores dated by Piggot and Urry were studied in detail by M. N. Bramlette, W. H. Bradley, J. A. Cushman, and L. G. Henbest.

Some of the assumptions on which the method is based are difficult to accept. One of these, that the radioactive elements were deposited in the same ratio to each other during the time interval to be measured, is particularly so in the light of what we have learned from the Lamont cores about the diversity of depositional processes prevalent on the ocean floor. For this reason many investigators believe that reliable determinations of age by this method are possible only on relatively rare samples deposited under ideal conditions.

In 1941 J. A. Cushman, a well-known micropaleontologist, published a study of the foraminifera in a short core taken in the Caribbean with the Piggot corer, which we describe in Chapter 1. From Cushman's report on the foraminifera, it was clear that the core included the same climatic zones of the late Pleistocene that we had found. It also appeared that the sediment in this core had accumulated under the ideal conditions necessary for the success of

Urry's method of dating. When we compared the chronology of our zones, as estimated from rates of accumulation based on radiocarbon dating, with Urry's chronology, we found amazing agreement between the two. According to the combined chronologies and our interpretation of the zones, the last glaciation was bracketed between 11,000 and 115,000 years ago, which would indicate that the Sangamon Interglacial came to an end about 115,000 years ago. During the ten years since we made the comparison, all new findings have tended to confirm this chronology.

Recently, these dates have received further support from age measurements by J. N. Rosholt, C. Emiliani, J. Geiss, F. F. Koczy, and P. J. Wangersky, who used a method that depends on change in the ratio of protactinium to ionium—or, in chemical symbols, Pa^{231}/Th^{230}. Urry's method based on ionium disequilibrium requires, among other conditions, that the supply of uranium-supported ionium in sea water and the rate of non-carbonate sedimentation remain essentially constant during the time interval to be measured. But this requirement need not be met if the ratio Pa^{231}/Th^{230} is used. Since protactinium and ionium are daughter elements of the same element, uranium, and since they decay at different rates, the relative amounts of each which are present at any level in a sediment are a measure of the time elapsed since burial of the particles of sediment.

However, for our purpose both methods have an unsatisfactory feature. While information regarding the history of the Pleistocene has been obtained almost exclusively by micropaleontological and isotopic analyses of the carbonate component of the cores, dating on the basis both of ionium disequilibrium and of the ratio of protactinium to ionium depends on the concentration of the radioactive substances on clay particles. But the carbonate component and the clay component have different sources and their distributions over the ocean floor are controlled largely by different depositional processes. The carbonate particles are precipitated by organisms living in the layers of water near the surface of the ocean, whereas the clay particles derive from the weathering and erosion of ancient rocks on the continents and come to rest on the floor of the ocean only after relatively long travel in suspension in ocean water. It is during this sojourn in suspension that the clay particles adsorb radioactive substances from the sea water. If a particular clay particle, once having reached the bottom, remains there undisturbed until it is brought up in a coring tube, all is well; in a geochemical laboratory, the radioactive substances it adsorbed will give a correct measure of the time since it came to rest.

But the world of the ocean floor is a dynamic one; continuous accumulation over long periods of time is exceptional. Slumping uncovers old sediments from which clay particles may be swept into nearby depressions, to accumulate with the recently secreted shells of foraminifera. The new place of deposition is not likely to be far from the old, however, and the time during which the particle is again in contact with sea water will be short, too short for renewal of the radioactive substances it has adsorbed. If enough of these radioactively old particles have been redeposited out of context in a certain faunal zone of a core, the "age" of the zone as determined by either of the methods will have no relevancy to the age of the associated foraminifera. The same process of erosion and redeposition can affect the carbonate fraction as well, but much less frequently, simply because the shells of foraminifera are much larger and heavier than clay particles. Because of this difference, erosion by deep current scour normally leads to separation between the shells of foraminifera and clay particles. Probably the best way to avoid the influence of reworked clay is to select for dating by the protactinium method only cores from somewhat elevated features of the sea floor and concentrate on sediments that have only small amounts of clay.

Within its time range, about 35,000 years,[1] the radiocarbon method of determining the ages of faunal zones in deep-sea sedi-

---

[1] Ages of samples of peat and wood as great as 60,000 years determined by the radiocarbon method were published some years ago. Former champions of these datings now admit to skepticism regarding their validity; we have always been skeptical. The "age" is irreconcilable with the level in the Pleistocene sequence from which the samples came. The fault seems to have been in the samples rather than in the procedure; some contamination of ancient peat and wood by new radiocarbon appears to be very common. Within the range of 35,000 years the effect of a little contamination is negligible, but it can be quite misleading when the material is much older.

ments is by far the most reliable. Here, in contrast to the ionium and the protactinium-thorium methods, passage of time is measured by the disintegration of the radiocarbon locked in the shells of the foraminifera, which in turn determine the stratigraphical positions of the dated layers. Thus, the dates are as reliable as the stratigraphical sequence itself, which can be confirmed by cross-correlation.

By application of the radiocarbon method of dating to the shells of foraminifera in sediments, we have found that rates of accumulation of foraminiferal lutite vary considerably from place to place. In Chapter 5 we discuss this variation and our reason for believing that it is due to the interaction between continuous deep currents, quite unrelated to turbidity currents, and irregularities of topography on the bottom. Furthermore, as we point out in Chapter 5, variations in the rate of accumulation of sediment are accompanied by variations in the texture of the sediment from place to place, the coarser-grained sediments having accumulated more slowly than the finer-grained sediments. From this we have reasoned that uniformity of texture from top to bottom in a core is an indication that the rate of accumulation at the point on the ocean floor where the core was taken has remained constant with time.

Finally, we have the supporting evidence of the dates and chronologies provided by the two different radiochemical methods of Urry and Rosholt, metioned earlier in this chapter. From all this the following principles stand forth: when the texture of a core is uniform from top to bottom, the rate of accumulation of the sediment has remained constant with time; and among several cores, those with similar textures have accumulated at similar rates. These principles, supported by evidence from hundreds of cores, have enabled us to translate thicknesses of faunal zones into intervals of time to an extent far beyond the range of any method of dating now available for application to deep-sea sediments.

Our first time scale determined in this way extended from the present back to about 250,000 years ago. According to this chronology, Recent, or postglacial time, began 11,000 years ago; the late phase of the last glaciation occurred between 11,000 and 60,000 years ago; an interstadial of warm climate came between 60,000 and 95,000 years ago; the early phase of the last glaciation took place between 95,000 and 115,000 years ago; and the last interglacial, the Sangamon, occurred between 115,000 and 235,000 years ago. Thus, the penultimate ice age, the Illinoian, came to an end about 235,000 years ago.

The cores by which we determined this 250,000-year chronology contained six faunal zones, whose ocean-wide validity had been established by cross-correlation of hundreds of cores from stations scattered through the region extending from the Canary Islands, southwestward across the equatorial Atlantic, through the Caribbean and the Gulf of Mexico, and back into the western Atlantic to about the latitude of the Azores Islands. The persistence of these zones throughout so broad a region amounted to proof that the faunal changes marking them must reflect changes in conditions in the past on a global scale. In order to emphasize the objective existence of the zones in contrast to the necessarily subjective interpretation of them in terms of Pleistocene climatic events, we have designated them for convenience of discussion by the following letters of the alphabet: *z, y, x, w, v,* and *u.*

One faunal change that defines the boundary between two zones can be fitted into the known sequence of climatic events with certainty, as a result of the radiocarbon method of dating. This is the faunal change that marks the boundary between zones *z* and *y;* it took place about 11,000 years ago. There is no doubt, then, that it coincided with the climatic change that led to the recession of the continental glaciers at the close of the last ice age. Because this climatic change was the most recent important event of the Pleistocene, the evidence of it on the continents is still fresh and undisturbed by subsequent glaciations. Moreover, it occurred so recently that it can be easily and accurately dated by radiocarbon. All dates of continental deposits indicate that rapid retreat of the continental glaciers set in about 11,000 years ago. In 1935 W. Schott concluded that the appearance of the planktonic foraminifer *Globorotalia menardii* in abundance in the uppermost layer of sediment in cores from the equatorial Atlantic recorded the commencement of postglacial time, and that the underlying layer without *Globorotalia menardii* represented deposition during the last ice age. Radiocarbon dating has fully confirmed Schott's surmise. In turn, this has provided us with a good indication of the kind of faunal changes to look for as evidence of earlier climatic changes of similar degree.

Many students of past climates have assumed that the course of temperature change during the Pleistocene followed a smooth curve, that temperature gradually rose to a peak in each interglacial, then turned down and gradually descended till it reached a minimum in the following interval of cold climate. However, the evidence from the cores opposes this view; it seems rather that the climatic phases were bounded by abrupt changes. Undoubtedly, minor fluctuations in temperature occurred within the ice ages and the interglacials, but on the whole, the Pleistocene climate seems to have been very definitely one or the other. Long intermediate intervals of slowly rising or falling temperature do not seem to have occurred. This is indicated by the abruptness of the faunal changes at the boundaries between the clearly defined faunal zones.

Very probably, the climatic changes themselves were more abrupt than the faunal changes as preserved in the cores; mud-eating burrowers have mixed the sediment at the boundaries. However, we can get an indication of the abruptness of change from some cores which were taken in a trench along the north coast of Venezuela. The bottom water of this trench at a depth of 1,300 meters is devoid of oxygen and therefore of bottom dwellers. In consequence, the sediment has been laid down without trace of disturbance in well-defined annual layers, much like the varves or rhythmites of glacial lakes. Counts of these layers show that the trench has been stagnant for 10,750 years, the approximate duration of postglacial time. But during the preceding ice age the bottom water must not have been stagnant; the cores show every evidence of abundant life on the bottom. Since the bottom dwellers vacated the trench at the time of the climatic change, the boundary in these cores is defined with particular sharpness. On the evidence of the thickness of the transition zone, the change from aerated bottom water to stagnant bottom water as the surface became warmer took less than two hundred years.

There is complete agreement among Pleistocene scientists regarding the identification of the final faunal change in the cores; all agree that it records the end of the last ice age. This unanimity does not extend to the earlier faunal changes, however. Part of the difficulty arises from uncertainties and disagreements among Pleistocene geologists regarding the interpretation of the record of Pleistocene events as found on the continents. This is not surprising; as we have pointed out, the record on the continents is in confusion, and the confusion increases the farther back in time we go. Each succeeding glaciation has tended to obliterate or seriously disarrange the deposits and traces of all earlier glaciations. This is precisely why study of the marine record is so important.

That there should be disagreement regarding the interpretation of the marine record is less understandable. To some extent the disagreement probably arises from the fact that two quite different methods of determining paleoclimates have been applied to the cores.

A widely accepted chronology of the Pleistocene has been published by C. Emiliani. It is based on series of paleotemperatures estimated by Emiliani from oxygen-isotope ratios in the calcium carbonate of the shells of certain species of planktonic foraminifera. As first published, his isotopic data were derived from samples from two cores in the Lamont collection, cores which we had studied and which we had selected for his work. Subsequently, he has applied the oxygen-isotope method to several other cores taken by other oceanographic institutions. In general, the sequence of climatic zones and the chronology set up by Emiliani agree well with ours, down to and including the top of the v zone. We disagree with Emiliani, however, in our correlation of these zones with the generally accepted sequence of climatic events as deduced from the glacial deposits on the continents. According to Emiliani, our zone x corresponds to the Sangamon, or last, Interglacial, and our zone w to the Illinoian, or penultimate, Ice Age. From here on down, our climatic curve, based on relative numbers of warm-water and cool-water species, parts company with Emiliani's curve. Within our zone v, Emiliani finds evidence of the first ice age, the Nebraskan, as well as the second ice age, the Kansan. Admittedly, the v zone includes several fluctuations in abundance of species of foraminifera. We agree that most probably these record variations in

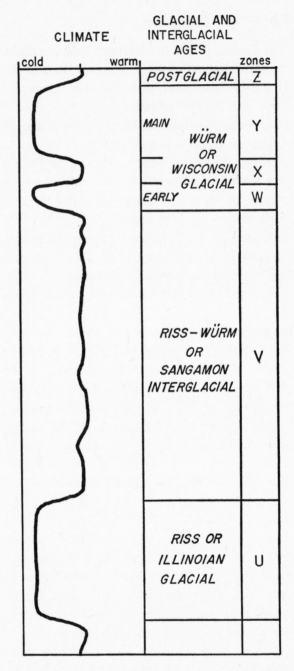

FIGURE 10 *Climate curve based on the study of planktonic foraminifera in deep-sea cores. The climatic zones, designated by letters from U to Z in the right-hand column, are correlated with the glacial and interglacial ages of the late Pleistocene.*

climate, but in these fluctuations we cannot find evidence of climatic changes of the same order of magnitude as those indicated by zones w and y. In short, on the evidence of the foraminifera, climate during the time interval represented by zone v was at no time as cool as it was directly before and after the time interval represented by zone x.

In view of this, to us unsatisfactory, aspect of Emiliani's interpretation of the climatic record, we have proposed two alternative interpretations. As a first surmise, we have suggested that zone x corresponds to the warm interstadial of the last ice age. Zone w then becomes equivalent to the early phase of the last ice age; zone v to the last interglacial, the Sangamon; and zone u should represent the penultimate ice age, the Illinoian.

As a second working hypothesis, we have considered the possibility that zone x represents the Sangamon Interglacial. This would make zone w equivalent to the Illinoian Ice Age; and since we could find no evidence of ice ages within zone v, we had to attribute zone u to the Kansan Ice Age. But it seemed to us that there were several objections to this interpretation. For one thing, where was there any evidence of the warm interstadial of the last ice age? We have diligently sought for some trace of a warm interval within the y zone, but without success. It is difficult to believe that this time of warm climate, which seems to have left such a well-defined record in the continental deposits, should have made no impression whatever upon the planktonic foraminifera. Moreover, this interpretation of the record leads to an excessive disproportion between the durations of the Sangamon and the Yarmouth interglacials. Geologists who have studied the depth of weathering of glacial deposits as a clue to the relative durations of the interglacials believe that the Yarmouth was the longest of the three interglacials, but we know of no evidence that the difference in durations was so great as this interpretation of the core sections implies. For these reasons we favor our first interpretation, which makes zone x equivalent to the warm interstadial of the last ice age and zone v equivalent to the Sangamon Interglacial; this gives a time scale such as we have presented earlier.

In the meantime, opinion regarding the chronology of the Pleistocene had crystallized. On the one hand there were Emiliani and most other Pleistocene scientists who were convinced that his cores included all four ages and the three interglacials. For them, the problem of Pleistocene chronology had been solved; the total duration was 290,000 years. To obtain a measure of how long the subdivisions had lasted, one had only to scale off the thicknesses of the zones and apply the average rate of accumulation to convert thickness into millennia.

We were not so sure that the problem had been settled. We believed that the longest cores had penetrated only to the final part of the Illinoian Ice Age and that they represented perhaps somewhat less than one quarter of the whole Pleistocene. On one thing we all agreed—the total time in years represented by the core sections. As we have explained, this had been determined by rates of accumulation measured by many radiocarbon dates, a straightforward operation that leaves little room for disagreement.

Although we, the dissenters, were of the opinion that the problem of Pleistocene chronology had not been solved, we were equally confident that we could eventually find the answer by studying more and longer cores of deep-sea sediment.

Many cores must be studied and little time was available; we were compelled to search for short cuts. In studying the faunal changes in cores, earlier workers had been in the habit of counting every shell of every planktonic species in the samples. This is, of course, an exact treatment of the samples, but it consumes much time. Furthermore, it is wasteful of time. Much of the effort goes into counting the usually very abundant shells of temperature-tolerant species which have no climatic significance except as a background against which the counts of the temperature-sensitive species may be assessed. It was out of the question to use this laborious method to analyze in detail the many new cores that were constantly coming to the laboratory. We knew from experience that the main faunal zones were well defined and could be recognized without careful counts. Since our first concern was to cross-correlate many cores in order to recognize those with long continuous sections, we developed the following rapid method of faunal analysis.

Sediment samples of a dry weight of about five grams are taken at intervals of ten centimeters in the cores. These are dried, weighed, and washed on a sieve which retains particles larger than 74 microns (a thousandth of a centimeter). A quantity of the dried, coarse fraction, which in cores of foraminiferal lutite is composed almost exclusively of the shells of planktonic foraminifera, is spread out so as to cover a microscopic tray with an area of fifty square centimeters. We examine the material on the trays with a binocular microscope and grade the frequencies of the significant species according to the following scale: rare, one to five shells in a tray; frequent, six to ten; common, eleven to twenty-four; abundant, twenty-five to a hundred; and very abundant, more than a hundred shells. The great advantage of the method is that with practice one can estimate the grades without making counts. The method is particularly effective in recognizing the main faunal zones, which are distinguished by variations in key species from rare or absent to very abundant; these variations can be seen at a glance. At the same time it is quite adequate for the recognition of subzones. For example, the *y* zone includes a lower subzone marked by very abundant shells of *Pulleniatina obliquiloculata*, and an upper subzone in which this species is absent. In our faunal analyses we note the following species and subspecies: *Globorotalia menardii menardii, G. menardii tumida, G. menardii flexuosa, G. hirsuta hirsuta, G. hirsuta punctulata, G. truncatulinoides, G. scitula, Globigerina inflata, G. bulloides, G. pachyderma, G. eggeri, Globigerinoides rubra, G. sacculifera, G. conglobata, Globigerinella aequilateralis, Orbulina universa, Pulleniatina obliquiloculata,* and *Sphaeroidinella dehiscens.*

The species of most significance as climatic indicators in equatorial and mid-latitude waters are the races of *Globorotalia menardii,* which are indicative of mild climate, and *Globigerina inflata,* an indicator of cool climate. In more northerly waters, *Globigerina bulloides, G. pachyderma,* and *Globorotalia hirsuta* are useful.

The speed possible with this method has enabled us to identify and correlate faunal zones in hundreds of cores from widely scattered areas in the Atlantic and connected seas. The quantity of

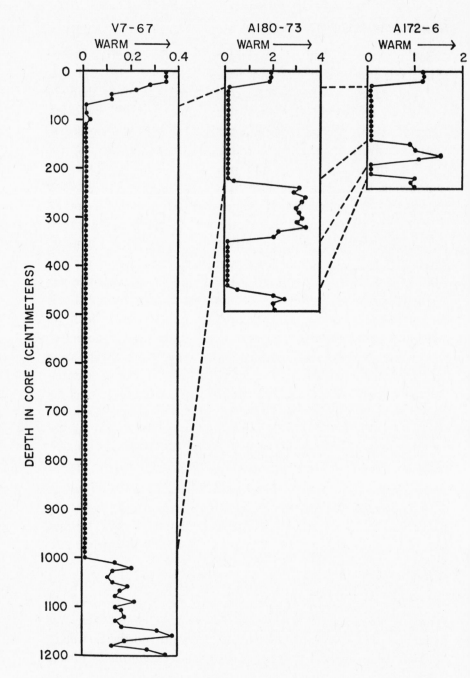

FIGURE 11 *Curves based on frequency of the shells of* Globorotalia menardii *in three deep-sea cores. Each dot represents a sample in which the species was counted. The dashed lines connect faunal changes believed to have occurred at the same time at the various locations. Obviously, rates of sedimentation have differed widely. The different rates of accumulation can easily be detected by differences in the texture of the cores and the abundance of planktonic foraminifera.*

consistent data so obtained has eliminated any possibility that the faunal zones are merely chance concentrations of shells brought about by local conditions of accumulation. Most important, the method has permitted us to select from among more than three thousand cores those which were most likely to contain reliable records of Pleistocene climates and which were best suited for more detailed study.

The most serious shortcoming of the method is lack of sensitivity. It lumps together samples containing twenty-six shells of a certain species with others containing ninety-five shells; similarly, a sample containing a hundred shells is given the same rating as one containing a thousand shells. It was clear that we needed a more sensitive method for the analysis of the cream of the cores, but since the cream included many long cores, we would have to develop a more rapid method than that used by other laboratories.

At this point it occurred to us that we might substitute the weight of the total number of shells for the total count. This was quite feasible. As we have said, the coarse fraction of foraminiferal lutites is composed almost exclusively of the shells of planktonic foraminifera. In actual practice, we take a representative part of the coarse fraction, weigh it to the nearest milligram on chemical balances, count the shells of the one or more species whose variations in time we want to trace, and divide these counts by the weight of the sample in milligrams. The ratio, which we call the "frequency" of the species, is an index of the productivity of the species as compared with the productivity of the total population. The number of specimens counted varies from zero to about two thousand. This method has several major advantages, the most important of which is economy of time. The weighing and preparation of the samples can be done by a technician. After that, the micropaleontologist can concentrate on the few temperature-sensitive species whose variations have real meaning and disregard the rest. This makes it possible for a few people to analyze larger samples and many more of them, thereby increasing the statistical validity of the data.

By means of this method, we have found in the frequency curves of *Globorotalia menardii* and *G. truncatulinoides* well-defined zones that lend themselves to correlation. In general, these curves agree with the climatic curves based on the relative numbers of warm-water and cold-water species.

Thanks to these advances, our investigation leaped ahead, and at last, as we had hoped, we found a core which contained a much longer unbroken record of Pleistocene climates than any we had seen before. This core had been raised from a point in the equatorial Atlantic 3° 13' south and 32° 12' west, in a depth of water of 4,120 meters. It was 1,207 centimeters long, and consisted of a calcareous foraminiferal lutite in various shades of tan and grayish tan. Distinct burrow-mottling throughout its length was assurance that turbidity currents had had no part in the deposition of the sediment.

According to our interpretation of the faunal sequence, the last glaciation, the Sangamon Interglacial, the Illinoian Glaciation, and a part of the Yarmouth Interglacial were represented in this core. We estimated that the sediment at the bottom of the core had been deposited about 600,000 years ago. Since we had found no other core which passed through the Illinoian Ice Age and into a zone deposited during the Yarmouth Interglacial, we could not test the lower part, which amounted to five meters, for continuity by cross-correlation. To confirm our interpretation of the faunal zones, we needed to find more cores with the same long unbroken record of Pleistocene events.

Thus encouraged, we concentrated our efforts and found six more cores which reached below the Illinoian Ice Age. Among these we were able to establish correlations of the lower zones by various methods. We could now feel certain of the continuity of these long sections.

According to our interpretation of Pleistocene events and chronology, however, we were still far from our goal, the discovery of a complete record of the Pleistocene. We needed to find cores in which the complete Yarmouth Interglacial, the Kansan Glaciation, the Aftonian Interglacial, and the Nebraskan Glaciation were represented, and most important we needed to find the boundary between the Pleistocene and the Pliocene.

Coring apparatus about to be lowered.

Coring apparatus lying on brackets along ship's rail.

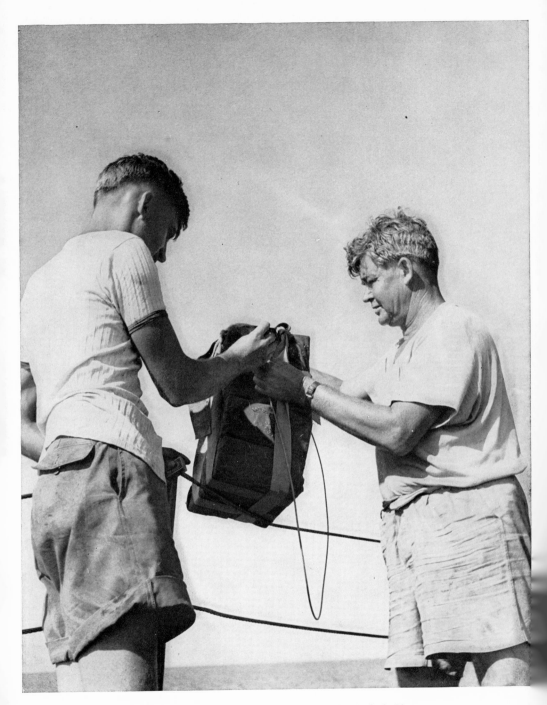

Dr. Maurice Ewing, Director of Lamont Geological Observatory, and an assistant, ready to drop a charge of explosives for seismic measurement.

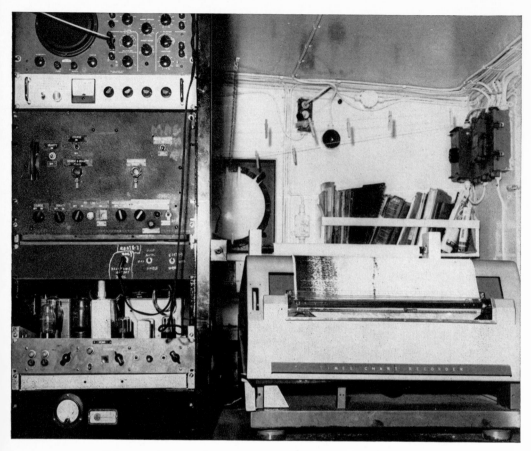

Echo sounder recording topography of the bottom of the ocean.

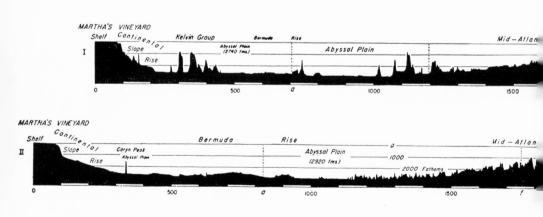

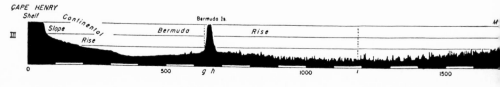

The 202-foot auxiliary schooner *Vema* of the
Lamont Geological Observatory, Columbia
University.

Three profiles of the topography of the bottom of the ocean across the North Atlantic.

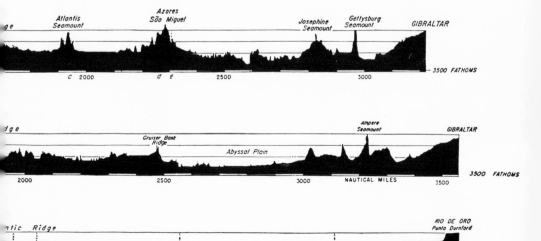

Extruding a core. The coring tube is pulled from the core of
sediment, which lies in the paper-lined tray in the foreground.

Goesta Wollin splitting a core in the laboratory at Lamont Geological Observatory.

A core showing, on the left, typical foraminiferal lutite with burrow mottling. The marbled color pattern of the sections on the right is due to the churning effect of slumping.

UPPER RIGHT: Cores illustrating different characteristics. The section on the left shows black staining by hydrotroilite; the section in the middle consists of foraminiferal lutite with burrow mottling; the one on the right shows thin bedding due to a succession of small turbidity currents.

LOWER RIGHT: Sections of a core containing graded layers of sand deposited by turbidity currents.

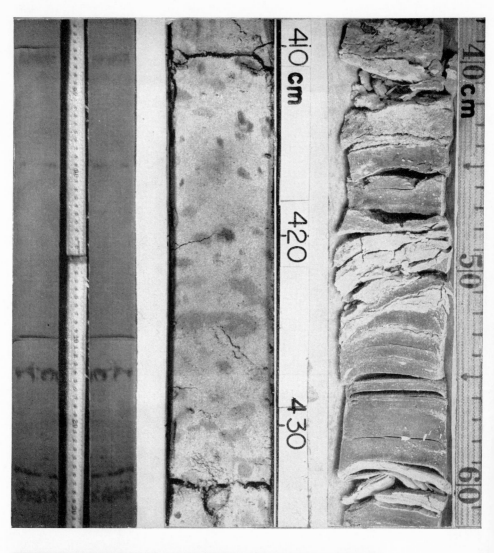

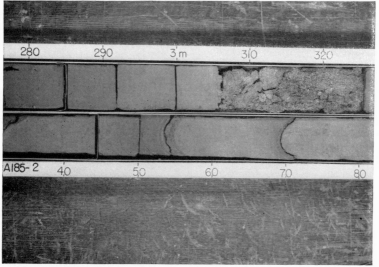

David Ericson studying microfossils from deep-sea cores.

Janet Wollin (Mrs. G.) assisting
in the laboratory investigations.

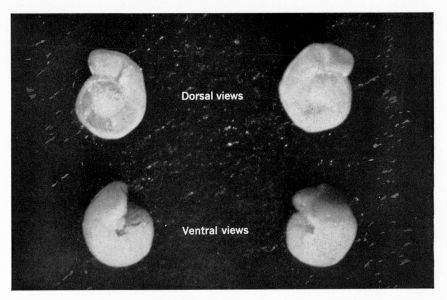

Left-coiling and right-coiling shells of the planktonic species of foraminifera *Globorotalia truncatulinoides*, magnified about 30 diameters.

Globorotalia menardii, an important indicator of past climates. Magnified about 20 diameters.

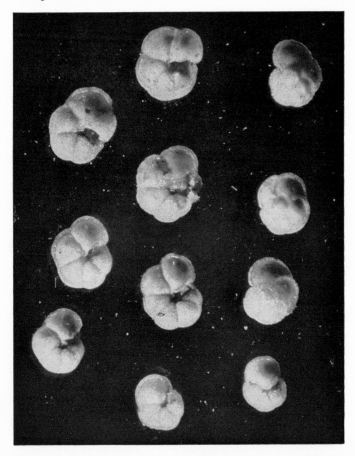

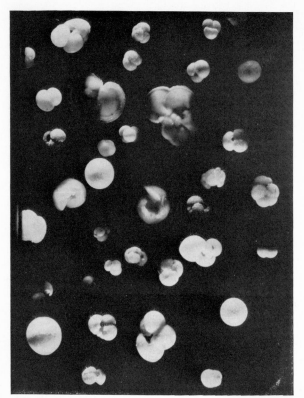

Foraminifera are the most useful microfossils in the study of deep-sea sediments. Various species secreted the shells shown here magnified about 15 diameters.

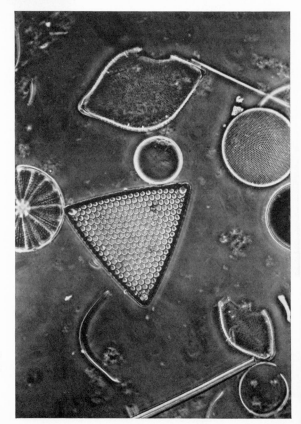

The siliceous skeletons of various kinds of diatoms, magnified about 150 diameters.

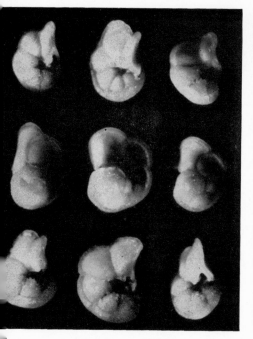

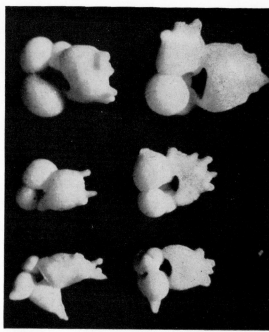

B

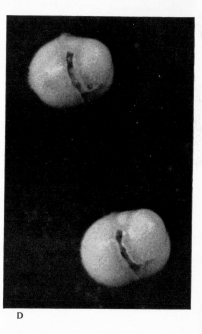

C

D

(A) *Globorotalia menardii flexuosa,* an extinct subspecies of planktonic foraminifera that flourished in the late Pleistocene. Magnified about 20 diameters. (B) *Globigerinoides sacculifera fistulosa,* an indicator of the Pliocene-Pleistocene boundary. Magnified about 20 diameters. (C) *Globorotalia menardii multicamerata,* a subspecies that became extinct at the onset of the first ice age. Magnified about 20 diameters. (D) *Sphaeroidinella dehiscens dehiscens,* a subspecies that is found in Pliocene and Pleistocene sediments. Magnified about 20 diameters.

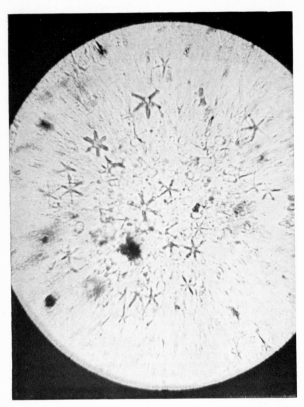

Discoasters, guide fossils that occur directly below the Pliocene-Pleistocene boundary. The organisms that secreted the discoasters became extinct at the onset of the Pleistocene. Magnified about 1,000 diameters.

Discoasters from a lower level in the same core as above. Here *Discoaster challengeri* with its six broad bifurcating rays is abundant. The discovery of discoaster evolution in the Pliocene was a key in identifying the onset of the first ice age. Magnified about 1,000 diameters.

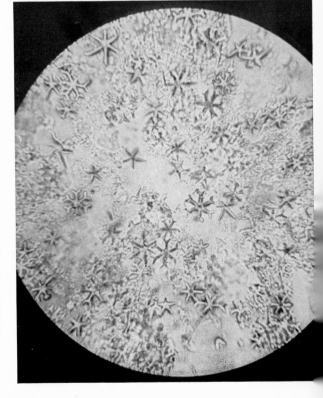

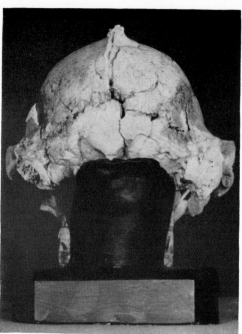

Zinjanthropus skull; three views.

A hand axe from the second interglacial. Height, 14 centimeters.

9

DISCOVERING THE PLIOCENE-
PLEISTOCENE BOUNDARY

IN our search for the complete record of the climatic changes of the Pleistocene Epoch, we focused our attention most closely on the foraminifera, the most useful of microfossils. However, deep-sea sediments contain the remains of other groups of planktonic micro-organisms, which we also studied, particularly in the earlier exploratory stage of our work, when we felt that we needed every clue to past events and every bit of confirmation of our correlations of zones and boundaries as defined by the foraminifera. The groups of microfossils which seemed most likely to be helpful were the ostracodes, diatoms, radiolaria, coccoliths, and discoasters.

Ostracodes, like foraminifera, are convenient fossils because they are large enough to be studied at a low magnification, that is, thirty diameters; distinctions among species of the other groups require magnifications of a hundred to a thousand diameters. The animals themselves, diminutive relatives of crabs and lobsters, flourish wherever there is enough water, whether fresh, brackish, or salty.

Not content with the normal armor of a crustacean, they have developed additional protection in the form of two valves, or shells, which, when tightly shut, completely enclose the animal. The valves look very much like the shells of tiny clams, and like them they have a hinge. Parallel evolution, working through the same need for protection, has given rise to strikingly similar features in these two quite unrelated groups of animals. With the valves open, the ostracode can extend its swimming appendages, paddle about, and grasp particles of food. The valves, which vary from a half millimeter to several millimeters in length, are the parts most frequently preserved in sedimentary rocks. Evidently the seemingly excessive armor of the ostracodes has served them well. The earliest fossil ostracodes occur in sediments which, according to radioactive dating, are 500 million years old; their descendants have survived to abound in every watery habitat of every part of the world. In the course of their long evolutionary history, the shells have varied almost endlessly in shape and ornamentation. Because of rapid evolutionary change, many species have a short range in time, and therefore define with particular precision the stratigraphical positions of the sediments in which they occur. Furthermore, knowledge of the present distributions of living ostracode genera in open salt water, sounds, estuaries, lagoons, or lakes enables the historical geologist to reconstruct past conditions from the distribution of similar genera in ancient sediments.

In spite of many virtues, the ostracodes have not been helpful in our search for a record of Pleistocene climatic changes; there are not enough of them in the open oceanic environment for our purpose. Many samples of washed sediment containing thousands of foraminifera are devoid of ostracodes, and others at best contain no more than five or six valves. Such sparse occurrences are of little help; to be sure of the validity of our data, we need to compare whole populations of organisms.

Among microfossils the diatoms and radiolaria compete for first place in beauty. Both secrete intricate structures made of silica combined with a varying amount of water, a combination which is chemically indistinguishable from the gem mineral opal. In the lacy skeletons of radiolaria the opal looks like colorless spun glass, but in the shells, or frustules, of diatoms it lives up to its jewel-like nature. In reflected light the frustules display a many-colored fire that must be seen to be appreciated. Biologically, the radiolaria and the diatoms are kingdoms apart. The former are protozoa, or single-celled animals, whereas the diatoms are single-celled plants belonging to the great group known as algae, which includes very nearly all the plants that grow in the oceans and seas. In radiolaria the skeleton is in one piece; in diatoms the shells consist of two parts, or valves, which in many marine species fit one over the other, much like an infinitesimal pillbox and its lid. Diatoms, like most plants, nourish themselves by photosynthesis; by means of radiant energy in the form of light, they can directly synthesize carbohydrate food from carbon dioxide and water. Because of this vital dependence on sunlight, they can reproduce in abundance only at shallow depths, that is, within about a hundred meters of the surface. The radiolaria, as animals, feed on organic matter. However, by a curious expedient, they enjoy some advantages of photosynthesis. They accomplish this by means of a partnership with extremely small, plant-like organisms called zooxanthellae, which live within the protoplasm of the radiolaria. In this partnership, or symbiotic relationship, there is a happy dovetailing of interests. The zooxanthellae, in building up sugar molecules by photosynthesis, must have carbon dioxide as a raw material, while they give off oxygen as a by-product, but the radiolaria in the course of their metabolism must have oxygen, which they convert into carbon dioxide. In this way the same materials are used over and over again in a closed cycle of chemical combinations. At times the smug little partnership must operate independently of the rest of the universe, except for the light energy to keep the engine turning over. It would be surprising if such an advantageous arrangement were unique to the radiolaria; in fact, all planktonic foraminifera and all reef-building corals possess zooxanthellae. In the latter, evolution of the inter-relationship has gone so far that the coral polyps cannot live for long without the zooxanthellae, a fact which has geological consequences. When the rate of subsidence of a volcanic island exceeds the rate at which corals can build their limestone platform upward, it is good night for them; once carried down into total darkness, the zooxanthellae die, and with them die the corals. The result is a flat-topped submarine mountain known as a guyot, instead of a coral atoll.

Under favorable conditions, diatoms reproduce, or bloom, in fantastic numbers. Where this has happened in the geological past, as in the shallow seas that once covered parts of California, we find today deposits of diatom frustules that may reach thicknesses of a thousand meters. A necessary condition for the accumulation of such enormous numbers of diatoms is a plentiful supply of silica in the water. It is significant that layers of volcanic ash are interbedded with the great diatom deposits of California. Similar ash beds on the nearby land must have provided a copious and continuous supply of silica carried to the sea in solution in streams. Many other occurrences of abundant diatoms with volcanic ash deposits leave little doubt that the relationship is not due to mere coincidence. Of course, we are now speaking as geologists; our interest is in the diatom frustules which are preserved in the sediments. To the seagoing biologist, the important thing is that diatoms can bloom profusely wherever the water contains an ample supply of fertilizer chemicals, phosphorous, and nitrogen-bearing salts. Were this not so, the oceans and seas would be relatively barren of life, for diatoms are the grass of the oceans. But where the water contains only the normal amount of silica, the thin and fragile frustules dissolve and fail to become part of the sedimentary record. Such has been the case throughout most of the north and equatorial Atlantic during the Pleistocene Epoch. Solution has also taken its toll of the radiolaria; they are too rare in the sediments of the Atlantic to be of use in deciphering the record of Pleistocene climates.

In only one instance have diatoms been useful in defining a correlatable zone. In a suite of four cores from the Mid-Atlantic Rise in the equatorial Atlantic, the frustules of a large species of diatoms are very abundant in a layer hardly more than a couple of centimeters thick. Extension of the layer through four cores and over a distance of more than five hundred kilometers eliminates the possibility that the layer represents a mechanical concentration of frustules due to local current scour. We can only think that it must have resulted from an extraordinary bloom in the surface waters of this region. On the basis of radiocarbon ages of samples from these cores, we estimate that the diatom layer is about 55,000 years old and that the total time interval recorded by the thickness of sediment in the cores is about 125,000 years. What combination of circumstances was responsible for this unique bloom? No other core from the Atlantic or adjoining seas contains a similar layer at this same stratigraphical level; apparently the controlling condition was local in effect. Since there is good evidence that the silica content of the water is the critical factor that determines whether or not the frustules accumulate on the sea floor, we make the guess that the diatom layer records a short period of considerably greater silica content in the equatorial waters as the result of a submarine volcanic eruption somewhere in the vicinity. Whether this was a single eruption or a series during many years, we cannot tell from the thickness of the diatom layer; as usual where sediment accumulation has been slow, the diatoms have been scattered vertically in the sediment by mud-eating burrowers. But whatever the origin of the layer may have been, it marks with unusual precision the same point in time in each core and thereby gives support to our correlation of the faunal zones.

Coccoliths, minute button-shaped plates of calcium carbonate, were found in deep-sea sediments long before the organisms responsible for their secretion were discovered. For a time it was thought that they were a product of inorganic precipitation of calcium carbonate on the ocean floor. When the organisms, the coccolithophores, were found, it was not in a man-made trap but in the food-gathering apparatus of a common marine animal, the salp. It was then clear enough why they had not been caught by plankton nets; they were much too small to be retained by even the finest of gauzes. The coccoliths, which the spherical coccolithophores wear like armor, are even smaller; a cubic centimeter of sediment may contain 800 million of them. Photographs of coccoliths made with the electron microscope show that their structure is remarkably complex and that many different species have come and gone since the group first appeared about 500 million years ago. As is usual with planktonic organisms, the various species of coccolithophores have ocean-wide distributions, an important point in their favor as stratigraphical markers.

The discoasters were discovered almost a hundred years ago, but it has been only within the last few years that anyone has given them much attention. Like coccoliths, they are made of calcium carbonate. They are a trifle larger than coccoliths, and since their features are coarser, one can distinguish the various species fairly easily with a magnification of six hundred diameters. The basic pattern of all discoasters is a star with a variable number of rays. In the older species there is a central boss. The group of organisms, the Discoasteridae, which secreted the little stars, was not long-lived; they made their appearance at the beginning of the Cenozoic Era, about 75 million years ago, and they disappeared with the onset of the first ice age of the Pleistocene Epoch. We have no way of knowing whether they were plants, animals, or members of that ill-defined intermediate kingdom, the Protista. All we can say with assurance is that they lived in the upper layer of water, which is penetrated by light. Only there, within the realm of photosynthesis, could they have found enough nourishment to proliferate on the vast scale indicated by the quantities of discoasters present in many sediments of Cenozoic age. The world-wide distribution of the species indicates that they were planktonic—drifters scattered far and wide by ocean currents. Only rather recently have they been used in stratigraphy, perhaps because of the mistaken notion fostered by textbooks that all of the species have lived continuously from Upper Cretaceous time into the present. In reality, their evolution was fairly rapid and many species had short time ranges, which makes them excellent indicators of the various epochs of the Cenozoic Period.

The evolutionary trend of the discoasters was from complex to simple. Species found in the earliest epoch of the Cenozoic have many rays—some as many as twenty-four—which coalesce to form a disc with a prominent central boss and a deeply scalloped rim. Although these early species have a superficial resemblance to coccoliths, they have one distinguishing feature, the central boss; among coccoliths, the center is open. By Miocene time, that is, about twenty million years ago, the number of rays had decreased to six; these are the "snowflake" discoasters. In the latter part of the Pliocene Epoch, shortly before their extinction, five, four, and even three rays came into fashion. Probably the gradual decrease in complexity was in reaction to the deteriorating environment, particularly to the cooling of the late Cenozoic. Their distribution in the sediments hints that the organisms were more sensitive to temperature than the coccolithophores. This helps to explain their sudden disappearance with the beginning of the first ice age, a trial which the coccolithophores passed with flying colors.

In our effort to solve the problems of the ice ages, the coccoliths and the discoasters, in addition to the planktonic foraminifera, have turned out to be extremely useful. It was because of the discoasters that we finally felt sure that we had discovered the stratigraphical boundary separating the Pliocene and Pleistocene epochs.

The discovery of a well-defined basal boundary of the Pleistocene was both literally and figuratively basic to the problem of the duration of the Pleistocene. Previously, we had had no assurance that a clearly defined boundary existed. As we have explained, the record of climatic events on the continents becomes more and more obscure as one tries to trace it farther back in time. This is a natural consequence of the destructive effect of later glaciations. Before finding the boundary in the cores, we had had no way of knowing that the change from the nonglacial conditions of the Pliocene to the glacial climates of the Pleistocene had not involved a long series of small, almost imperceptible gradations. In fact, the concept of a thoroughly indefinite transition between the epochs was rather popular among students of the Pleistocene. But as it turned out, the clear definition of the boundary brought the problem of the duration of the Pleistocene into sharp focus; we now had an excellent level of reference to define the beginning of the new chronology of the Pleistocene.

In 1951 we found the first evidence of the boundary in a single core from the Blake Plateau, a great platform extending from the Bahama Islands to Cape Hatteras. The evidence was in the form of an abrupt and rather drastic change in the microfossils at a certain level in an otherwise rather uniform core. There were two possibilities. The faunal change might represent a depositional hiatus—the loss of some unknown thickness of sediment by slumping—in which case the faunal change would have little interest for us. Or, on the other hand, if sediment accumulation had been continuous across the faunal change, it must represent an extraordinary change in living conditions, and in that case would be of the greatest stratigraphical, biological, and climatological interest to us.

Admittedly, there was circumstantial evidence for discontinuity because of slumping. The overlying Pleistocene section was far too thin. Some part, probably no less than ten meters of sediment, must have been removed by slumping; otherwise the coring tube could not have reached the older sediment below the faunal change. But if slumping had taken place during the late Pleistocene, why should it not have occurred earlier as well, in short, at the level of the faunal change? After all, we ourselves had published descriptions of many cores from the Atlantic which contained sharply defined discontinuities with Pleistocene sediment resting directly on older sediments.

At the same time, there was something different about this core. In all others there had been a sharply defined change in nature of the sediment at the faunal change, such as a difference in color or in degree of compaction; or the change might be marked by a thin layer of black manganese oxide. Furthermore, in the other cores the faunal changes in themselves were enough to prove depositional discontinuity; from the microfossils below the changes we could tell with certainty that whole epochs of time were missing. In this core from the Blake Plateau, the microfossils below the change indicated a pre-Pleistocene age, but it was also clear that they were of very late pre-Pleistocene age, and possibly belonged in the latest Pliocene.

At that time, however, we were not in the right state of mind

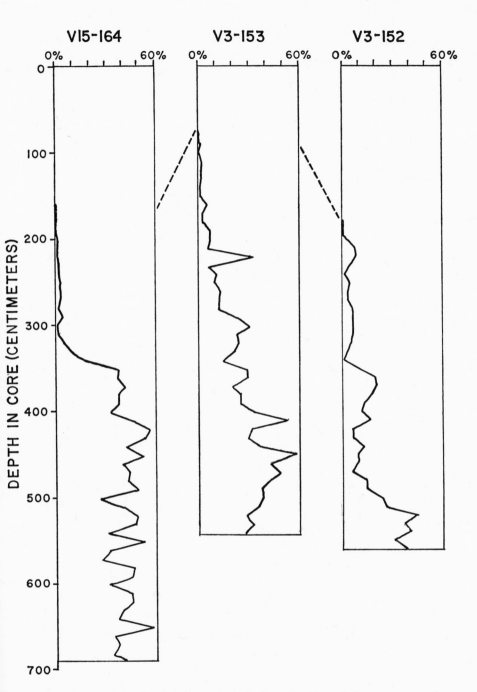

FIGURE 12 *Curves showing decrease upward, or in time, of the percentage of* Discoaster challengeri *in the total population of discoasters in three deep-sea cores sampled at ten-centimeter intervals. The dashed lines connect the Pliocene-Pleistocene boundary in the cores. Discoasters are absent from the Pleistocene sediment above the boundary.*

to accept such suggestive, rather than positive, evidence. For years we had expected to find, as was generally assumed, a gradual and subtle change at the Pliocene–Pleistocene boundary, a change that could be detected only by careful analysis of the microfossils. And so, without feeling really satisfied one way or the other, we left the core and proceeded with the general study of the sediments.

Years went by. Then one night, after everyone else had gone home, we found the crucial evidence. That afternoon a core from the equatorial Atlantic had been opened. In color and texture it was as uniform from top to bottom as Pleistocene cores ever are, and it was mottled throughout its length by the burrows of mud-eating animals, a sure sign, as we explain in Chapter 3, that it contained no layers deposited by turbidity currents. It was the kind of core which might contain a long and continuous record of Pleistocene events. It had not been sampled for foraminifera yet, but we had made a set of slides in order to look at the coccoliths. A convenient thing about coccoliths and about discoasters is that one can examine them without going through the lengthy process of washing them, as is necessary with the foraminifera. All one has to do is to smear an almost invisible film of moist sediment on a glass slide, let it dry, add a drop of immersion oil, and put it under a fairly high-power microscope.

There was nothing remarkable on the first few slides, only a quantity of Pleistocene coccoliths. The fifth slide gave us a surprise; it contained a swarm of discoasters, specifically *Discoaster brouweri*. Our first reaction was disappointment. Evidently the core did not include a long section from the Pleistocene. In fact, it seemed hardly worthwhile to sample it at ten-centimeter intervals for foraminifera. But we still had three more slides; having made them, it seemed a pity not to look at them, although we had no expectation of finding anything but more and more *Discoaster brouweri*. In all our previous experience, the discoasters in pre-Pleistocene cores remained quite uniform from top to bottom. As we expected, *Discoaster brouweri* was very abundant on the next slide, but with a difference. Here almost all had six rays, whereas among those higher up, specimens with five, four, and even three rays had been abundant.

But it was the third slide that gave us a jolt. It was covered with a flood of "snowflakes"—that is, *Discoaster challengeri,* a species with six rays which bifurcate at the ends. In spite of the apparent uniformity of the core, it passed through three distinct zones defined by discoasters, not to mention the upper section, which contained no discoasters. We had found only one other core that was similarly uniform in the nature of its sediment and yet passed from the Pleistocene into older sediment, and that was the core from the Blake Plateau. We got its number from the chart of the Atlantic and looked up the notes on it. Apparently we had looked at only one sample of discoasters; it had been taken directly below the change in the foraminifera and contained a quantity of *Discoaster brouweri.* In a kind of postscript we had noted that they were peculiar; many had only five, four, or three rays. But if one of the discoaster zones was common to the two cores, how about the others?

As usual, we could not find the flashlight, but one of our assistants had left her cigarette lighter on her desk. Down we went to the core storage room, managed to open the combination lock by the flickering light, and found the core from the Blake Plateau. After years of storage, the core was as dry as a bone, but that did not matter. We took samples, moistened them, and made up a set of slides. It took patience to wait for them to dry. At last we had them under the microscope, and we found what we had hoped for. There were the same three zones of discoasters that we had found only half an hour before in the core from the equatorial Atlantic. Needless to say, we had that "disappointing" core sampled for foraminifera at ten-centimeter intervals, and we were delighted to find a cross-correlation of foraminiferal zones between the two cores. To explain the faunal change in the two cores on the basis of slumping, which would have removed a section of sediment, it was now necessary to suppose that almost exactly the same stratigraphical thickness of sediment had been lost at both locations. This seemed very improbable; yet the possibility of such a coincidence did exist. To eliminate every vestige of doubt, we needed more cores with the same faunal changes. With something tangible to look for, we began a thorough search of the collection of cores, and ended with seven cores that contained the same faunal change, the same succession of species of discoasters, and zones of foraminifera that could be correlated. We now felt that coincidence had been ruled out; accumulation of sediment across the boundary had certainly been continuous.

A prime factor that led to our conviction that the boundary was not a depositional hiatus due to loss of a part of the sedimentary record by slumping was the thinness of the layer that contained the discoasters with five, four, and three rays. The layer varied from about fifty centimeters, or twenty inches, to no more than twenty centimeters, or eight inches, depending presumably on the local rate of sediment accumulation. If this restricted thickness in all seven cores from stations scattered over a distance of 14,500 kilometers, or 8,000 nautical miles, was due to slumping, this random process would have had to lay bare almost exactly the same stratigraphical level at each coring station. We submit that the probability of such a coincidence is so small it is almost nonexistent.

In February 1963, we published our findings in a paper we wrote in association with Maurice Ewing. For the paper we added an eighth core to the suite, because it contained the boundary. However, the pre-Pleistocene section in this core was too thin to include the succession of discoasters and some of the lower zones of foraminifera.

To our knowledge, no one had ever before defined the Pliocene–Pleistocene boundary by means of planktonic organisms. Because of the broad geographical distribution of most planktonic organisms, the paleontological criteria defining the boundary should be almost universally applicable to marine sediments. The paper, published in *Science,* presented for the first time multiple, and therefore widely applicable, criteria for defining the boundary, and evidence that the transition from the conditions of the Pliocene to those of the Pleistocene was abrupt. This was at variance with earlier thinking, which had assumed, on theoretical grounds, that the change had been gradual.

The boundary is defined by a faunal change which takes place

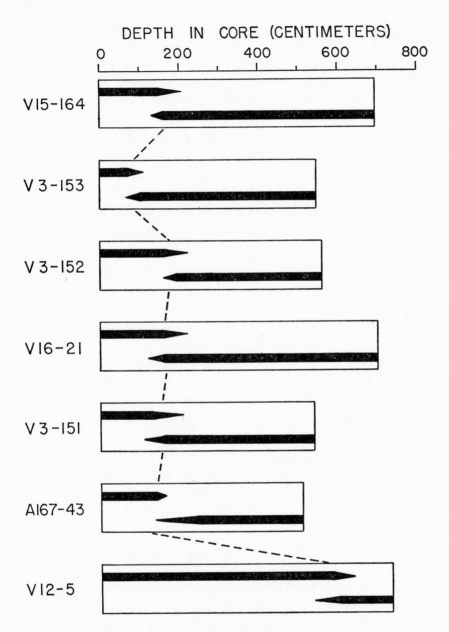

FIGURE 13   *Pliocene-Pleistocene boundary as indicated by the disappearance of discoasters and the abrupt appearance of* Globorotalia truncatulinoides *in seven sediment cores from the Atlantic. The dashed lines connect the boundary in the various cores. The core sections to the left of the dashed lines are Pleistocene; the sections to the right are Pliocene. The upper solid bar in each core represents* G. truncatulinoides; *the lower solid bar, discoasters. The thickness of the solid bars indicates abundance.*

within a thickness of sediment of no more than ten to fifteen centi-meters. From the nature of the sediment at the boundary, we estimate that this thickness represents a time interval of no more than about 5,000 years. Since vertical mixing of the microfossils by mud-eating burrowers must have caused an increase in the apparent thickness of the transition zone, the real time interval represented by this zone was probably somewhat shorter.

The contrast between the planktonic assemblage above and below this zone indicates that the change in living conditions must have been such that it had a profound effect on the evolution of plank-tonic organisms. The eight cores provide a rare opportunity to follow the evolutionary reactions of populations of foraminifera and individual species which lived at various latitudes during the rela-tively long climatic deterioration of the Pliocene and during the sudden onset of the severe Pleistocene climate, and thereby to gain an insight into the process of speciation.

No mineralogical, chemical, or physical change occurs in the sediment at the boundary in any of the cores. The purely paleonto-logical criteria which define the boundary are as follows:

1) Extinction of the Discoasteridae.

2) Change in the coiling direction of members of the *Globoro-talia menardii* complex from right coiling among ninety-five per-cent below the boundary to left coiling among ninety-five percent above it.

3) Appearance of *Globorotalia truncatulinoides* in abundance above the boundary.

4) Disappearance of *Globigerinoides sacculifera fistulosa* above the boundary.

5) Reduction of the *Globorotalia menardii* complex to a single fairly uniform race above the boundary.

6) Increase in the average diameter of the shells of *Globorotalia menardii* and reduction in their number with respect to the total population of foraminifera above the boundary.

From the magnitude of the faunal change at the boundary, we conclude that it records a climatic event of a different order from the climatic fluctuations which seem to have occurred repeatedly

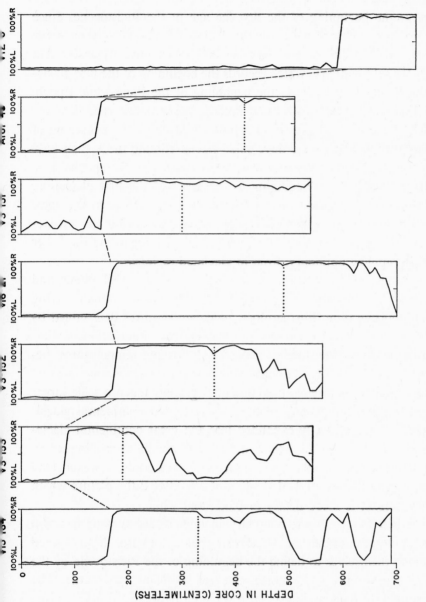

FIGURE 14 The Pliocene-Pleistocene boundary, as indicated by changes in the coiling directions of Globorotalia menardii in samples from seven cores at ten-centimeter intervals. The dashed lines connect the boundary in the seven cores. The scale of coiling is from a hundred percent left at the left margins to a hundred percent right at the right margins. The horizontal dotted lines in six of the cores mark the level at which Globigerina nepenthes, a species of planktonic foraminifera, became extinct. The core at the right, V12-5, does not reach the G. nepenthes zone. Left coiling remains dominant in the part of the Pleistocene not present in these cores.

during late Pliocene time. This is why we believe that the boundary marks the beginning of the first ice age of the Pleistocene. Since periodic glaciations most clearly distinguish the Pleistocene from the earlier epochs of the Cenozoic Period, we have suggested that this faunal boundary, which records the beginning of the first glaciation, be chosen to denote the beginning of the Pleistocene Epoch.

The crux of the problem of finding the complete record of the Pleistocene has been to find tangible evidence of the beginning of the epoch. Since, as we have said, glacial climate more than anything else sets the Pleistocene apart from the earlier epochs, it is logical to define its beginning as the onset of the first glaciation. Unfortunately, students of the Pleistocene disagree as to the number of continental glaciations which occurred during the Pleistocene. Consequently, there is still no unanimity regarding the lower stratigraphical boundary, even in glaciated regions.

Changes in the geographical distributions of fossil plants and animals yield evidence of a gradually deteriorating climate during late Pliocene time. Furthermore, paleotemperatures determined by the oxygen-isotope method show that climatic fluctuations similar to those of the Pleistocene, but of less extreme temperatures, occurred during the late Pliocene. Under such a climatic regime, one can envision a succession of mountain glaciers, each a trifle larger than the preceding one, followed by restricted continental glaciations, which gradually expanded into the great continental glaciations of the classic Pleistocene. In such a gradually expanding series, "first glaciation" would have no meaning. The cores, however, lend no support to this gradual shading of conditions; the picture which they present is more nearly in black and white.

Search for a natural boundary in unglaciated regions has also encountered difficulties. Vertebrate paleontologists have agreed among themselves to define the beginning of the Pleistocene by the first appearance of the horse, the true elephant, and cattle. The invertebrate paleontologists have wavered between the first appearance of the cool-water clam, *Cyprina islandica,* and the considerably later first appearance of the bottom-dwelling species of foraminifera, *Anomalina baltica,* in the marine sediments of the Mediterranean

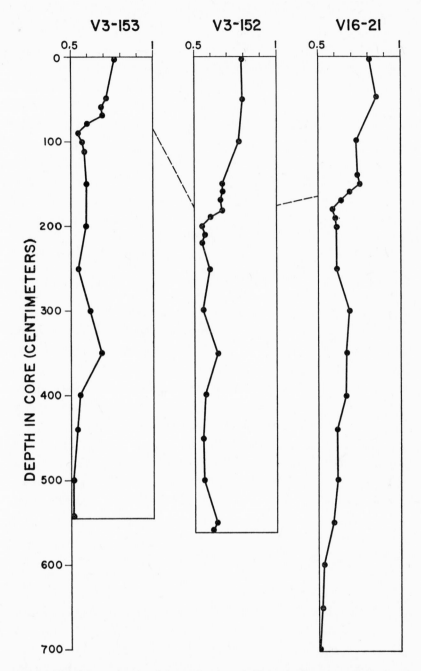

FIGURE 15   *Curves showing increase in size of* Globorotalia menardii *at the Pliocene-Pleistocene boundary in three cores. The dashed lines connect the boundary in the three cores. The average diameter of the shells is shown in millimeters in the scale at the top of each diagram.*

region. To end the indecision, a commission of the Eighteenth International Geological Congress recommended in 1950 that the Pliocene–Pleistocene boundary be defined by the first appearance of *Anomalina baltica*.

Official approval notwithstanding, this definition is not fully satisfactory. There is no compelling evidence that the first appearance of *Anomalina baltica* in the Mediterranean marks the onset of the first glaciation. Neither is it clear that this definition of the boundary coincides with that of the vertebrate paleontologists. In any case, these paleontological criteria, we believe, are valid only locally— that is, within the Mediterranean region. These difficulties have prompted not only us but also other scientists to search for a natural Pliocene–Pleistocene boundary in deep-sea sediments.

Among the sediment cores raised in the Pacific by the Swedish Deep-Sea Expedition of 1947–8, Gustaf Arrhenius found two which in his opinion included sediment representing all of the Pleistocene Epoch and part of the Pliocene. He based his conclusion on variations in carbonate content from layer to layer, on the theory that layers containing abundant carbonate secreted by planktonic organisms represented times of rapid oceanic circulation, which, in turn, corresponded to ice ages. He suggested that the first ice age, the Nebraskan, started at a level above which there was a marked increase in carbonate, about five hundred centimeters below the tops of the cores. He estimated an age of about 500,000 years for the beginning of the first ice age. His evidence was geochemical rather than paleontological, and it was inapplicable outside of the equatorial Pacific.

Because of the difficulty of recovering cores much longer than about twelve meters in calcareous sediment of slow accumulation, we have not yet found any core which in our opinion includes a continuous record of all Pleistocene time. In our search for the Pliocene–Pleistocene boundary, we have found the results of slumping helpful. Slumping is normally a nuisance, but it has reduced the thickness of the Pleistocene section at the expense of its continuity and has thus brought the basal boundary within reach of the coring tube.

Four of the cores that contain the boundary were obtained from the western Atlantic north of the Bahama Islands, two from about halfway between Cuba and western Africa, one from the equatorial Atlantic near South America, and one from the Indian Ocean south of Madagascar. The depths of water at the points where the cores were raised range from 970 meters to 3,795 meters, and the lengths of the cores, from 510 centimeters to 1,108 centimeters.

The sediment of the seven cores from the Atlantic is an unsorted foraminiferal clay ranging from a burrow-mottled tan to a light tan. In physical character, these cores are indistinguishable from thousands of others from the Atlantic and adjacent seas. The sediment of the core from the Indian Ocean is a lutite, or clay—silty, burrow-mottled, and grayish-tan to light buff—and contains abundant shells of foraminifera and radiolaria. From the top down to 850 centimeters, the sediment contains scattered heterogeneous mineral and rock fragments. This land-derived detritus is indicative of rafting by drifting ice.

None of the cores, with one exception, contains a sharply defined change in physical character or an abrupt increase in state of compaction such as one would expect if a considerable thickness of sediment had been removed by slumping. In one core, a sharply defined change in color occurs within the Pleistocene section, sixty centimeters from the top of the core. In spite of the absence of similar clearly defined discontinuities in the other cores, we realize that the Pleistocene sections are incomplete because of loss of sediment through slumping. The restricted thicknesses of the Pleistocene sections, which range from ninety-five to six hundred centimeters, are sufficient evidence of that.

The fact that the faunal zones in the Pleistocene sections of the eight cores fail to correlate with the standard sequence of late Pleistocene faunal zones which we have found in thousands of other cores is additional evidence of discontinuity and indicates that, except for a little sediment near the tops of the cores, the Pleistocene sections represent deposition during the earliest part of that epoch.

Not content with this evidence, we submitted to radiocarbon dating a sample of between thirty to forty centimeters from the core with the longest Pleistocene section. Sediment from that level in a normal core in which sediment accumulation has been continuous would be about 15,000 years old. The chemist who made the radiocarbon assay knew this. When he found that the age of the sample exceeded the range of the radiocarbon method, about 35,000 years, he was sure that we would be upset by the result. He broke the bad news to us as gently as he could; we surprised him with a triumphant cheer!

In four of the cores, there is a gradual increase upward in the percentage by weight of material coarser than 74 microns. In the others, irregular minor variations occur, but no consistent trend is discernible. Since the measurements were made at ten-centimeter intervals in all the cores, it is unlikely that any abrupt change in this parameter was overlooked.

In two cores we found a similar gradual small increase in carbonate content. Although the carbonate measurements were made at wider intervals, it is improbable that any large and abrupt change in carbonate content occurs in these cores. Such changes are almost always accompanied by conspicuous changes in color; as we have pointed out before, no such changes in color occur at the boundary or below it. In short, the evidence of an important time boundary in these eight cores is purely paleontological; in physical and chemical properties, the cores appear to be as uniform from top to bottom as deep-sea cores ever are.

Extinction of the Discoasteridae is a biological event of particular significance. As we have said, the first discoasters appear in sediments that are known to be about 75 million years old, according to radioactive dating. During all of the pre-Pleistocene part of the Cenozoic Era, the so-called Age of Mammals, the Discoasteridae must have flourished mightily in equatorial and mid-latitude waters, judging from the vast numbers of discoasters that we find in the older sediments among the cores in the Lamont collection. Then, at the end of the Pliocene Epoch and the beginning of the Pleistocene, something happened, something that had not happened before during all the preceding 75 million years of the Cenozoic— and it brought the Discoasteridae to a sudden end. Most probably it was a fall in temperature of a greater severity than any previously experienced during the earlier Cenozoic. Among the planktonic foraminifera we also see evidence of this severe test. But the foraminifera are a highly diversified group; some particularly sensitive races succumbed, but many others survived.

For example, striking changes took place in the group of related forms which for convenience we call the *Globorotalia menardii* complex, the members of which are variations on a single theme exemplified by the still living species, *Globorotalia menardii*. Immediately below the boundary, the complex includes two forms in about equal numbers. One is similar to what has been called *Globorotalia menardii* variety *miocenica,* first found in the Miocene sediments of Jamaica. The other resembles *Globorotalia menardii multicamerata,* also found in Jamaica, but differs a little in that it has a thin rim around the shell instead of a "very heavy" one. In addition there is a third form, which is essentially similar to the race of *Globorotalia menardii* now living in the Atlantic. This last is very much subordinate in numbers to the other two. Close biological relationship between these three forms is shown by the presence in the population of some individuals with intermediate characters. Apparently some crossing between members of the complex was possible.

Out of this complex of races, only one survived the trial of the first ice age. That was the race which was least numerous below the boundary and probably least well adapted to the conditions of the late Pliocene.

But the boundary is marked by more than extinctions; at least one newcomer, *Globorotalia truncatulinoides,* is conspicuous above the boundary. Very probably its appearance in these cores from low latitudes is due to the southward shift of a preexisting population. *Globorotalia truncatulinoides* is a well-defined species without any close relatives. Its degree of differentiation bespeaks fairly long selection acting upon a whole series of mutations. Almost certainly, the time interval represented by the transition at the boundary would not have been sufficient for such an accumulation of mutations. On the other hand, the absence of the species from the waters in these low latitudes during the Pliocene is in keeping with what we know of the behavior of the species during the late Pleistocene. We know from the study of many other cores that at times of exceptionally warm climate during the late Pleistocene it disappeared from the equatorial Atlantic and took refuge in more northerly waters. Upon the resumption of more nearly normal climate, it returned.

In four of the cores, shifts to dominance by left-coiling members of the *Globorotalia menardii* complex determine correlating zones in the lower part of the Pliocene sections. These zones are absent in the other cores from the Atlantic, probably because the cores are not long enough to reach the zones. In four of the cores, the ratio of abundance among members of the *Globorotalia menardii* complex varies from level to level and defines correlation.

In all of the Atlantic cores, but not in the core from the Indian Ocean, *Globigerinoides sacculifera fistulosa* appears for the first time about a half meter below the boundary and disappears just above it. The thin zone defined by this race is particularly strong evidence for depositional continuity; it is fantastically improbable that slumping or any kind of subsea erosion could have taken place at seven widely scattered places in such a way as to have left at each so nearly the same restricted thickness of sediment containing this distinctive subspecies.

In six of the cores from the Atlantic, *Globigerina nepenthes* is abundant in the lower parts of the pre-Pleistocene sections but disappears below the boundary at depths varying from 100 to 325 centimeters. It is entirely absent from the core which fails to reach the zone of *Discoaster challengeri*, probably because the core is too short.

Correlation between the Atlantic cores and the one from the Indian Ocean rests upon extinction of the Discoasteridae and the appearance of *Globorotalia truncatulinoides* in abundance above the boundary. *Globorotalia menardii*, *Globigerina nepenthes*, and *Globigerinoides sacculifera fistulosa* do not occur in the core from the Indian Ocean. It would be surprising if they did, because they are warmth-loving species and the core taken at 42° 39′ south latitude contains ice-rafted detritus.

In summary, the faunal evidence points to a gradually deteriorating climate during the Pliocene Epoch, which culminated in the drastic and sudden change indicated by the extinctions at the boundary. It seems to us highly improbable that a comparable climatic change could have occurred at the boundary between the Miocene and Pliocene epochs, or, for that matter, anywhere else within the Cenozoic Era. The extinction of the Discoasteridae, as we have pointed out, is an indication of the severity of the climatic change. They had swarmed in the oceans for about 75 million years; only a worldwide deterioration of climate of a degree unprecedented in all the earlier Cenozoic can explain their sudden disappearance.

In addition to evidence of a gradually deteriorating climate during Pliocene time, there is some indication that climatic fluctuations of about the same duration as those that occurred in the Pleistocene, but of less severity, were superimposed on the gradual trend toward cooler climate. We believe this because at lower levels in some of the eight cores we find zones in which the left-coiling race of *Globorotalia menardii* is dominant. But the ability of the left-coiling race to survive the trial by temperature at the boundary is good evidence that it was better adapted to withstand low temperatures than its right-coiling relatives. This makes us think that the lower zones, in which left coiling is dominant, represent times of cooler climate, but not so cool as that of the zone directly above the boundary, because both the right-coiling races and the Discoasteridae survived them.

The species *Globorotalia menardii* is particularly sensitive to temperature. A marked decrease in the frequency-to-weight ratio of *Globorotalia menardii* occurs just above the boundary. The close approach of this ratio to zero between 590 and 330 centimeters in the core with the longest Pleistocene section is particularly striking. This drop in the ratio of *Globorotalia menardii* just above the boundary is completely in keeping with its behavior in the sediment layer in the north Atlantic which accumulated during the last ice age. From this we conclude that the layer between 590 and 330 centimeters records a time of glacial climate, the first ice age.

The interrelationship between variation in the dominant coiling direction of certain species of planktonic foraminifera and variations in the environment presents a tantalizing problem. In almost all species of planktonic foraminifera, the shells, or tests, develop from the embryonic form by the addition of progressively larger chambers arranged in a conical spiral. This arrangement makes the tests superficially similar to snail shells, and like snail shells, the tests coil either to the right or to the left. In some way, temperature plays a part in determining the preferred direction of coiling. We admit that we cannot imagine how the geometry of the test can have any direct influence on the tolerance of a species to temperature. Probably the interrelationship is indirect, through gene linkage; the gene or genes that determine the direction of coiling are so linked with those which determine tolerance to temperature that they are transmitted from generation to generation as a group. However that may be, the change in the *Globorotalia menardii* complex at the boundary is an interesting example of the stabilizing effect of drastic selection upon a highly variable population. Under the easygoing conditions of the equatorial Atlantic in late Pliocene time, a series of closely related forms were able to coexist. But with the onset of the first ice age, selection must have set in with a vengeance. It weeded out completely the two races that had previously flourished, *Globorotalia menardii miocenica* and *Globorotalia menardii multicamerata,* and it decimated the population of the third race, leaving to survive into Pleistocene time a group almost entirely, if not quite, composed of the descendants of those Pliocene dissenters which coiled to the left.

Independent studies by C. L. Bandy and ourselves have shown that the left-coiling race of *Globigerina pachyderma* is tolerant of temperatures down to the freezing point. With rising temperature, the right-coiling race takes over, to the exclusion of the left coilers. Variation in the ratio of abundance of these two races in the core from the Indian Ocean indicates that the climate of that region became milder above the Pliocene–Pleistocene boundary. This is supported by the frequency-to-weight curve.

Ice-rafted detritus in the core from the Indian Ocean supports the faunal evidence of climatic deterioration during the final phase of the Pliocene Epoch. Presumably, the drifting ice originated on the Antarctic continent. The fact that the detritus first appears at about 850 centimeters, or 580 centimeters below the Pliocene–Pleistocene boundary, indicates that the climate of Antarctica had become glacial some 250,000 years before the drastic climatic change that marked the end of the Pliocene Epoch.

This is really not so paradoxical as it may seem at first glance. Evidence of gradual cooling during the Pliocene is afforded by the gradational reduction in number of species of discoasters and by the disappearance of species of foraminifera at levels well below the Pliocene–Pleistocene boundary in the eight cores. Furthermore, paleobotany has provided evidence of an increasingly intensified latitudinal zonation of climate during the latter part of the Cenozoic. The implication is that at some point in late Pliocene times glacial conditions could very well have developed at the poles, as at least one paleobotanist has suggested. The complete independence of the paleobotanical evidence gives the evidence from the cores particularly strong support.

Another pertinent consideration is the well-known quantity of ice on Antarctica today. Even though the present climate may not be quite as warm as that at the height of the interglacial, the fact remains that during the last 11,000 years the former continental glaciers of the northern hemisphere have melted, yet the ice on Antarctica has diminished very little. Probably, therefore, Antarctica was glaciated, though a little less heavily, even during the warmest times of the Pleistocene interglacials. Since there is no reason to suppose that the climate of the late Pliocene was warmer than that of the interglacial glaciation of Antarctica in late Pliocene time becomes highly probable on theoretical grounds. But conditions in Antarctica cannot have had much, if any, influence on the course of organic evolution. In contrast, the influence of the continental glaciations in the northern hemisphere must have been powerful. Since a better understanding of the tempo of organic evolution is an important reason for studying the chronology of the Pleistocene, it seems to us most logical to define the beginning

of the Pleistocene Epoch by the onset of the first continental
glaciation in the northern hemisphere.

When we were satisfied that the boundary was indeed a record
of climatic change, we looked into its bearing on Pleistocene chronology. We had an early Pleistocene section of sediment which extended upward from the boundary and which in one of the eight
cores was 600 centimeters thick. We also had, among the many
cores in the Lamont collection, a continuous section that extended
downward from a surface layer of recent origin. In our longest
core this section was 1,200 centimeters thick. Our first thought was
that the two sections might overlap and thus provide us with the
long-sought complete record of the Pleistocene. But, on comparing
the sections, we could find no evidence of overlap; the foraminifera
in the bottom of the upper section were as different from those in
the top of the lower section as Pleistocene foraminifera ever are.
That these sections did not overlap did not cause us much unhappi-
ness. A few years before, we had published an estimate of the
duration of the Pleistocene based on our interpretation of the late
Pleistocene record in the cores. We had decided then that the duration of the Pleistocene could not have been much less than about
1,200,000 years. Had the sections overlapped, this span of time
would have been considerably reduced.

However, we could at least use the sections to estimate the
minimum duration of the Pleistocene. The texture of the sediment
above the boundary was essentially similar to normal late Pleistocene sediment in the North Atlantic, and from radiocarbon dating
we knew that this sediment accumulated at the rate of three
centimeters in a thousand years. Dividing the thickness of the section, 600 centimeters, by three gave us 200—200,000 years for
the amount of time represented by the section. The texture of
the sedimentary section extending down from the surface was also
quite normal. Its thickness, 1,200 centimeters, by the same arithme-
tic gave us 600,000 years for the time span it represented. Since
the sections did not overlap, the age of the boundary could not be
less than the sum of the time intervals represented by the two
sections, that is, 800,000 years. Because of the improbability that
the upper section began just where the lower one left off, we felt

fairly sure that there was a gap of unknown thickness between the two—or, what amounted to the same thing, a time gap whose duration we had no way of estimating at that stage of our study.

To summarize, we found a remarkable faunal change in eight cores from points scattered over a distance of 14,500 kilometers. The vertical uniformity of sediment in these cores suggested continuous accumulation across the faunal change, but we could not accept this as satisfactory proof of continuity. The possibility remained that the abrupt faunal change was due to a depositional hiatus brought about by loss of some part of the section by slumping. However, examination of the foraminifera, and particularly the discoasters, below the faunal change revealed a series of zones which correlated through the suite of eight cores. The probability was extremely slight that the uppermost of these zones, whose thickness varied from fifty to only twenty centimeters, would have been left at all eight widely scattered points on the ocean floor as a result of slumping, which is purely random. Slumping would most likely have removed the entire zone at one or more of the coring stations. Accordingly, we concluded that sediment accumulation had been continuous across the faunal change. The faunal change, which includes the extinction of the Discoasteridae and several races of planktonic foraminifera, indicates a sudden and drastic change in living conditions. We believe that the environmental change that accompanied the onset of the first ice age of the Pleistocene is responsible for these abrupt extinctions. This is in harmony with the unquestionably Pleistocene age of the foraminifera above the faunal change and the Pliocene age of those below it. We believe, therefore, that the faunal change marks the beginning of the Pleistocene Epoch.

An important by-product of the discovery of the lower boundary of the Pleistocene is the evidence it gives us regarding the nature of the climatic change that initiated the Pleistocene. Evidently there was no transition period of long duration between the Pliocene and Pleistocene epochs. When the curtain rose on the drama of man's evolution, it rose with a bang. Let us hope that it will not fall with an atomic bang!

10

CLOSING THE GAP

Now it was a question of closing the gap. Our record of the Pleistocene extended from the present through postglacial time back into the latter part of the second or great interglacial age. In addition, we had discovered the lower boundary of the Pleistocene —the record of the first ice age and the lower part of the first interglacial age. The combined thickness of sediment in the cores that contained this record added up to about twenty meters. On the assumption that this thickness of sediment had accumulated at about the same rate as similar late Pleistocene sediment layers which had been dated by the radiocarbon method, we estimated that the combined thickness represented some 800,000 years. The missing section of the record included a large part of the second interglacial age, all of the second ice age, and part of the first interglacial age. How thick the missing section of sediment might be or how long a time interval it would represent, we did not know. Nor had we any idea of how it might look. Furthermore, we could

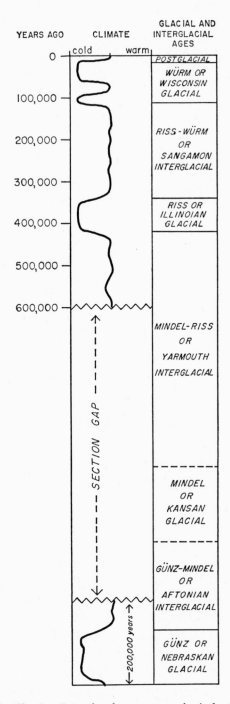

FIGURE 16   *The "gap" in the deep-sea record of the Pleistocene.*

not be sure that we had any cores which contained a record of
the gap in time. All we could be sure of was that when we found
cores containing the missing section we would be able to fit them
into the sequence by correlating the parts of these cores which
overlapped with the already known record.

What we planned to do, if we could find suitable cores, was
borrow a trick from the dendrochronologists, who piece together
records of past climates based on studies of tree rings from many
trees, each older than the preceding. Thus they build up a composite record which goes much farther back in time than the life-
time of any single tree. As we explain in Chapter 5, this is possible
because tree rings are variable in thickness. Unique sequences of
thick and thin rings can be recognized in trees of about the same
age in the same general region. When such a characteristic sequence
of several rings near the center of a living tree can be correlated
with or matched by the same sequence in the outer part of a tree
trunk used to hold up the roof of an Indian pueblo, it becomes
possible to push the record back beyond that of the oldest living
tree. But near the center of the tree trunk from the pueblo is another distinctive group of rings which can be correlated with a
corresponding group in a log from a still older pueblo, and so on,
as long as the dendrochronologist can find older and older logs.
In a way, the layers of sediment on the ocean floor are not unlike the
growth rings of a tree. In correlating the layers of sediment from
core to core, however, we do not need to rely upon matching thin
and thick layers. In Chapter 5, we have described our method of
correlating zones containing distinctive groups of foraminifera from
core to core.

Statistically, the probability of finding the complete record of
the Pleistocene seemed quite good. We knew that slumping was
a common occurrence and that it was capable of removing thicknesses of sediment varying from a fraction of a meter to tens of
meters. Our hope lay in finding cores in which the top section of
sediment deposited during roughly the last 500,000 years had
been removed. The existence of such cores in the Lamont collection was, we had to admit, a question of chance, but the chance

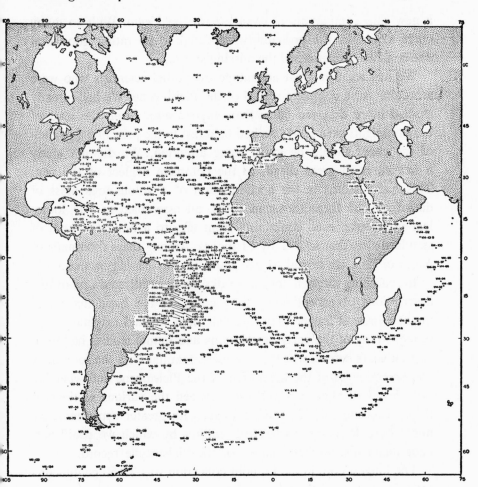

FIGURE 17 *Locations from which the majority of the deep-sea sediment cores in the Lamont collection were taken. The collection contains more than 3,000 cores from all the oceans, obtained in forty-four expeditions.*

improved as the number of cores available for study increased. In that respect, we were in a favorable position; we had at our disposal by far the largest collection of deep-sea cores in the world— more than three thousand, obtained in more than forty expeditions. And more cores were constantly being added. In fact, at about this time, toward the end of 1962, the rate of growth of the collection doubled as a result of the addition to the Lamont fleet of a new ship comparable in efficiency to the *Vema*. With so many cores available, the probability appeared to be rather good that one or more encompassed the missing section.

We had another great advantage over other scientists who were searching for a complete record of the Pleistocene. We had already studied more deep-sea cores than anyone else. From the start of the investigation in 1947, we had held fast to the principle that each of the cores should be given some attention. We did not study a few cores in great detail, to the complete neglect of the rest. This had resulted in the accumulation of a voluminous mass of data from the three thousand cores, all assembled in 107 loose-leaf notebooks, each containing from fifty to a hundred pages of standard size, that is, 8½ by 11 inches. Among these thousands of pages of data we hoped to find clues to the missing section.

In searching through our notebooks, we concentrated first on the descriptions of exceptionally long cores, in the hope that some might represent longer time intervals than we had originally supposed. Many of the early descriptions and faunal studies had been written years before, when we were less familiar with the foraminiferal assemblages of the latter part of the Pleistocene and when we were less well able to distinguish between the various sections of the Pleistocene. We felt that in 1962, with greater experience, we might be able to spot distinctive features by which we could perhaps distinguish earlier sections of the Pleistocene record.

The longest core in the Lamont collection was 2,360 centimeters long. It was one of the three or four longest cores of deep-sea sediment in the world. In addition, twenty-five other cores exceeded fourteen meters in length. We concentrated on these cores. But long as they were, it seemed that only one, 1,755 centimeters long, included the zone corresponding to the third ice age, the Illinoian; the rest stopped somewhere in sediment deposited during the third interglacial age, the Sangamon.

Our criteria for distinguishing the zones in these cores and our reasons for correlating them with particular climatic events of the Pleistocene are, very briefly, as follows. The uppermost and thinnest layer contained the species of foraminifera which are living in the

Atlantic today, as we knew from living specimens caught in nets. Among these, *Globorotalia menardii* was particularly abundant and conspicuous. From radiocarbon dates, we knew that this layer of sediment had accumulated during the last 11,000 years.

In the next zone below, *Globorotalia menardii* was rare or absent; instead, there were various species which now live farther north. Radiocarbon dates show that the upper part, which is within the range of radiocarbon dating, was deposited during the Main Wisconsin Ice Age. Since the lower part contained the same kind of cool-water foraminifera, we could only suppose that that part had also been deposited during the Main Wisconsin.

The third zone again contained *Globorotalia menardii* in abundance, together with the racial variant, *Globorotalia menardii flexuosa*. We correlated this zone with the minor interglacial or interstadial separating the Main Wisconsin from the Early Wisconsin Ice Age, which was represented in the cores by the fourth zone, in which *Globorotalia menardii* is rare or absent.

The fifth and thickest of the zones contained *Globorotalia menardii*, among which *Globorotalia menardii flexuosa* was very abundant in the upper two thirds but nearly absent in the lower third. On the evidence of the thickness of this zone, or the length of time it must represent, and the prevalence of warm-water species of foraminifera in it, we assigned it to the third interglacial, the Sangamon.

And finally, in only one of the cores, we found a sixth zone in which *Globorotalia menardii* was almost absent and the population of *Globorotalia truncatulinoides* had a tendency to coil to the left. From the basic similarity of the foraminifera in this layer to those in the layer corresponding to the Main Wisconsin Ice Age, we concluded that the sixth zone represented the third ice age, the Illinoian.

As we went down these zones, our familiarity with them decreased. We had seen the upper three in hundreds of cores. We were less familiar with the upper part of the zone corresponding to the Sangamon Interglacial, and much less so with its lower third. The Illinoian section we had encountered only rarely before.

The longest core, with its 2,360 centimeters, did not reach the Illinoian layer for a good reason. All the overlying layers in this core were unusually thick, which meant that sediment accumulation had been unusually fast at the point on the ocean floor where the core had been taken. That this longest core had been taken in an area of rapid accumulation was not mere coincidence. In Chapter 5 we mentioned the influence of deep and continuous currents on the rate of accumulation and the texture of sediments. The finest particles, most of which are clay minerals, are swept together and concentrated in depressions in the ocean floor. The resulting sediment is particularly soft and slippery and therefore offers little frictional resistance to the core barrel. We have learned, to our chagrin, that the very long cores, which can be taken so easily in depressions of rapid accumulation, rarely contain long sequences of climatic zones.

To be doubly sure that the time intervals represented by these long cores did not extend back more than about 200,000 years, we reexamined selected samples and in some cases had new samples taken and washed.

To the uninitiated, washed coarse fractions of deep-sea sediments look very much like ordinary beach sand. But, except for the fact that the sizes of the particles fall within the size range of "sand," the material is very different from the kind of sand which has made some beaches famous. To appreciate this, one must look at the "sand" with a microscope. Then one enters a new world. At a magnification of thirty diameters, the particles of mere "sand" undergo an astonishing change into the chambered shells of planktonic foraminifera, microscopic shells which make up more than ninety percent of the coarse material of most deep-sea sediments. Many thousands of samples of these coarse fractions have been prepared and stored in vials in the sediments laboratory at Lamont.

Over the years, many laymen have visited the laboratory and have looked at samples of foraminifera with a microscope for the first time. The normal reaction at the first glance is an exclamation of surprise and pleasure. Apparently there is something about the proportions of the chambers, the pattern of their arrangement, and the surface texture of these little shells which appeals to an innate sense of form possessed by most people. The same pleasure in form must have prompted ancient men to carry the shells of snails and clams long distances to their caves, to string them together as necklaces and to adorn their dead with them. However, despite a superficial similarity to mollusk shells, the shells of foraminifera are basically distinct. Perhaps this is why at first sight they often evoke surprise; nothing else in the organic world is quite like them.

Our reexamination of the foraminifera in the exceptionally long cores was disappointing; none yielded new information or helped to bridge the gap.

There was one long core, however, which had not been examined by us. In fact, it was still sealed in the galvanized gutter pipes in which it had been stored after having been taken more than a year before. It had been obtained by a new kind of coring apparatus which had been developed in the hope of taking much longer cores than could be taken with the conventional piston corer. Its inventor and designer was Stephen Chelminski, an engineer employed by Lamont for that specific task. In attempts to take long cores, the most difficult problem has been to provide enough energy to overcome the resistance of the sediment, particularly the frictional resistance of calcareous sediments containing abundant shells of foraminifera. The conventional coring tube is driven into the sediment by the kinetic energy of the falling lead weight attached to the top of the tube. In theory, the energy can be increased by adding more lead, but in practice a limit is soon reached; it is imposed by the lifting power of the winch on board the ship. At depths of several thousands of meters in the oceans there is, however, an ample source of energy in the water pressure. Accordingly, Chelminski dispensed with the lead weight and designed a corer that utilized the hydrostatic pressure through an ingenious piston system to drive the coring tube into the sediment. The apparatus was tested only once, at a depth of 4,275 meters. At that depth the available power was enormous, and its effect upon the mechanism was quite unpredictable. Under the circumstances, it would have been almost miraculous if something had not gone wrong with the first trial.

When brought back to the surface, some parts of the apparatus were found to have been torn to pieces by the violence of the reaction of the apparatus to the great pressure. The report made at the time, perhaps overly influenced by the mishap to some parts of the corer, gave the impression that the experiment had been a complete failure. This cast discredit on the principle on which the corer was designed, with the result that it has never again been tested. On the evidence of this single trial, it was decided that longer and better cores could be taken with the conventional piston corer, which is cheaper to build and easier to use. Actually, the Chelminski corer had taken a very long core. But the scientists who examined it on board the research ship reported that it was too badly disturbed to be of any interest. Accordingly, we had neglected to do anything with what was presumably a worthless core. But now, as we were systematically reexamining all long cores, we decided to take a look at this one, which had been reported to be as much as twenty-three meters long.

When the sections of the core had been taken out of the gutter pipes, unwrapped, and sliced lengthwise, our first impression was that the sediment had not been too badly disturbed. Admittedly, there was some disturbance of the stratification within a section three meters long near the middle of the core, and then the last meter of the core was completely disturbed, but the rest seemed to be in fairly good condition. We took samples for preliminary microscopic examination of the coccoliths and to see if any part of the core contained discoasters that would indicate a pre-Pleistocene age. In the samples we found evidence that seemed to show that the part of the core between about eight and eleven meters was much older than the lower half of the core. Either the core sections had been misplaced or the sequence of microfossils had been reduced to complete confusion by the violence of the coring process. We carefully checked the possibility that the sections were in the wrong order—that they had been mislabeled on the ship— but this possibility had to be ruled out. Reluctantly we concluded that the core, badly disturbed by the coring process, was of no use to us.

Again we went through the notebooks and picked out for further study those cores which lacked the normal upper faunal zones representing late Pleistocene time. We felt fairly sure that the absence in the upper section of the core of the familiar late Pleistocene zone was due to slumping, which had uncovered earlier parts of the Pleistocene record. We excluded cores which consisted mostly of pre-Pleistocene sediment; although the upper parts of some of these cores did contain short Pleistocene sections, we felt that the task of fitting such short sections into our composite sequence would be hopelessly difficult.

Examination of the coccoliths in some of these cores aroused a hope that they might provide a relatively easy and fast way of distinguishing between sediments of early, middle, and late Pleistocene age. The ease with which they can be prepared for study favors their use, but their exceedingly small size has discouraged detailed study. In consequence, the geographical and time ranges of the various kinds of coccoliths are not well known. In examining our slides with a polarizing microscope at a magnification of six hundred diameters, however, we found well-defined differences between the samples. In the late Pleistocene sediments we found vast numbers of a form that was so small as to be quite unresolvable at our highest magnification. Only by looking at them with polarized light was it possible to distinguish them from tiny particles of detrital calcite. In such light, each little plate showed a characteristic swastika-like figure. In the sediments which we believed to be of middle Pleistocene age we found larger elliptical coccoliths with a central slot and a border ornamented with curving radial striae. Still larger circular coccoliths with strongly defined radiating striae and a circular central opening seemed to be confined to sediments of early Pleistocene age.

On the evidence of the coccoliths, we found about twenty cores which gave promise of containing sediment deposited between the first and the third ice ages. We felt sure that among these we could find some which would close the gap, but the final test would have to depend upon detailed study of the foraminifera. Only in that way could we expect to discover zones that overlapped with the Pleistocene sequence we already knew. With the help of our laboratory assistants, we worked up such faunal variables as the coiling direction of *Globorotalia truncatulinoides* and the relative abundance of *Globorotalia menardii*, and evidences of climatic change as recorded by variations in relative abundance of warm-water and cold-water species of foraminifera at ten-centimeter intervals in the cores.

The first results were discouraging. Only one of the cores correlated with a part of our composite section and at the same time filled a part of the gap. But we persevered, and after months of more detailed study of the foraminifera, we found two more cores that overlapped with the old sequence and filled in a little more of the gap. However, the final result was not nearly as rewarding as we had hoped it would be. From the study of the foraminifera, it appeared that most of the cores that we had thought were of early and middle Pleistocene age on the evidence of the coccoliths, were in reality of late Pleistocene age. Why had the coccoliths led us so far astray? Probably because of redeposition of old coccoliths in younger sediments—what is known, among micropaleontologists, as "reworking." The coccoliths are so minute that the slightest current flowing over the bottom of the sea is sufficient to dislodge them and carry them at least short distances. Our first impression that the large and clearly ornamented species no longer live in the equatorial Atlantic is probably basically correct. The absence of large, ornate species in a sediment sample may well be a reliable indication that the sample is no older than the late Pleistocene. Unfortunately, however, the presence of the large species in some other sample may mean nothing more than that a portion of the fine material of the sample has been transported by current scour from some nearby exposure of sediment of earlier Pleistocene age. Very probably when more is known about the distribution of coccoliths they will prove to be useful in stratigraphy, but for our particular purpose they were more misleading than helpful.

The reworking, or displacement of microfossils, is a problem with which we have had to contend from the start of our study of the cores. Many samples of foraminifera from sections known to be of Pleistocene age have contained some specimens of species which certainly became extinct as long ago as the Cretaceous period. In the majority of cases, this kind of mixing of the foraminifera has been the work of turbidity currents, which flow with sufficient velocity to erode older sediments and transport particles as large as the shells of foraminifera. But in some other cases of reworking, evidence of the action of turbidity currents was lacking. This left us no alternative but to suppose that under certain circumstances currents connected with deep oceanic circulation are capable of transporting the shells of foraminifera. In all our earlier experience, the reworked species had been of pre-Pleistocene age. Not until we had systematically studied the coccoliths did we realize that the reworking of earlier Pleistocene microfossils into younger sediments may occur fairly often. Here is a moral for geochemists. Where reworked microfossils can be recognized in Pleistocene sediments, one may be sure that fine inorganic components of earlier sediments have accompanied the microfossils. This may have a particularly misleading effect on methods of dating which depend on the decay of radioactive substances held on the surfaces of clay particles.

Our study of the coccoliths did not turn out to be as useful as we had expected, but it had at least helped us find three cores that narrowed the gap. Furthermore, having discovered the limitations of the coccoliths, we were in a better position to use them successfully in the future.

Two of the newly found cores correlated with the cores that contained the lower boundary of the Pleistocene; these contained sections extending upward into the second ice age, the Kansan or Mindel. The third core was helpful too, but it presented a puzzle. It was a rather long core, 1,380 centimeters, from the equatorial Atlantic. The geographical position of the coring station was 60° 54′ north and 35° 28′ west. At the top it started in the interstadial of the last ice age, the Wisconsin or Würm. Then, going back in time, it passed through the early Wisconsin, the third interglacial age, the third ice age (the Illinoian or Riss), and then through eight meters of sediment deposited during the second interglacial age, the Yarmouth or Mindel-Riss.

The upper three meters of the Yarmouth section correlated excellently with the sections we had discovered before. It was the lower five meters of the core that puzzled us. Instead of containing a fauna dominated by warm-water foraminifera, this zone contained a mixture of both warm-water and cold-water species. Furthermore, *Globorotalia truncatulinoides*, whose coiling dominance had always been strongly to the right in sections of interglacial age, here coiled to the left fifty to seventy percent of the time. In this section, the clear-cut segregation between right- and left-coiling races, so evident in the Pleistocene sequence above, had broken down. True, this lower part of the core at two different levels contained populations of *Globorotalia truncatulinoides* which were decisively dominated by right coilers, and there were some variations in the relationship between numbers of warm-water and cold-water species of foraminifera. But we decided that the sediment of the lower five meters must have been thoroughly mixed by a process we call "flow-in," and was, therefore, without stratigraphical significance.

We have mentioned three processes that may cause confusion in the interpretation of the climatic record. Turbidity currents may interpose meters of sediment deposited almost instantaneously and quite without climatic significance; slumping and submarine erosion due to deep currents may remove parts of the section; and deep-current scour may transport and redeposit both organic and inorganic components of older sediments. More often than not, cores from the deep ocean basins contain evidence of the effect of one or more of these confusing processes. However, as if these were not enough, we have had to contend with still another cause of confusion, one which is a consequence of the coring process. "Flow-in" occurs when the coring tube is dropped into compact sediment containing abundant shells of foraminifera. Because of the resistance of this kind of sediment—the very kind which yields the best climatic records—the coring tube very often comes to rest before having penetrated to its full length and before the piston in the tube has reached the shoulders near the top of the tube. But the cable from the ship's winch is attached to the piston, and as soon as the winch starts to heave in the cable, the piston rises in the tube and sucks sediment into the tube. The sediment that has flowed into the tube by suction is thoroughly mixed; it is not core in the proper sense. As a rule, one can easily tell where good core ends and "flow-in" begins. Undisturbed sections show horizontal layering and mottling due to the burrowing of mud-eating animals; in contrast, sediment mixed by flowage normally displays distinct vertical streaks. However, it is not always so simple. When the original sediment is quite homogeneous and lacks easily recognizable structures, it is difficult to distinguish undisturbed sediment from that which has flowed. In these cases, the only way of distinguishing between the true and the false is to study the foraminifera. Absence of clear-cut changes in the foraminifera from level to level is normally a good indication of mixing by flow.

In our puzzling core, however, the foraminifera did not give us a decisive answer. In some respects the assemblages seemed to be mixed; yet there seemed to be evidence of stratification. Of one thing we were sure; the lower five meters were more uniform than any other section of comparable thickness that we had seen up to that time. This was damning enough to induce us to put the core aside as probably containing "flow-in," in spite of our feeling that there was something not quite right about it all. For this reason we kept it in mind, in the hope that we might eventually be able to check it against new information.

At this stage of our exploration, we were bothered by the problem of distinguishing between sections representing the Sangamon and the Yarmouth interglacials. In both, the assemblages of foraminifera were dominated by *Globorotalia menardii*. When the overlying section was complete, we could identify the Yarmouth by its position below the section that represented the Illinoian, but we realized that we could hope to find a complete Yarmouth section only in cores from which much of the late Pleistocene section had been removed by slumping. Without the late Pleistocene section to guide us, would we be able to distinguish the Yarmouth from the Sangamon? We were haunted by the fear that we could not do so, and that perhaps we had overlooked Yarmouth sections for that reason.

Then one day in the late summer of 1963 we found what we thought was a reliable way of making the distinction. A certain species of foraminifera, apparently not previously described, occurred throughout all the Yarmouth sections, but it seemed to disappear near the middle of the Sangamon.

Again we went through the data, which we had accumulated in the more than one hundred notebooks. For reexamination we selected cores that contained long sections which we had assigned to the Sangamon but which, on reexamination, might prove to belong to the Yarmouth Interglacial. For a time it seemed that we were on the right track. After carefully checking through the notebooks, we found a couple of cores that helped to narrow the gap still more. But then, to our disappointment, we discovered after further investigation that the unnamed species occurred throughout some Sangamon sections. We had overrated its reliability; it was helpful in some cores, but it could not be depended upon in all. Apparently it was useful only for the correlation of cores from limited areas.

We now turned our attention from the old data to the study of cores that had been obtained recently; by that time cores taken with the specific purpose of reaching sediment of early Pleistocene age were coming into the laboratory. These had been taken in the equatorial Atlantic and Caribbean, on topographical features which we believed offered the most favorable conditions for reaching sediments of middle and early Pleistocene age. Previous cruises in these same regions of gently uneven bottom topography had proved that small-scale slumping had occurred frequently within them; at the same time, sediment had accumulated at a very slow rate in these areas—another condition essential for success in reaching sediments of earlier Pleistocene age. Every effort to obtain long cores—fifteen meters or longer—had been made during the recent cruises.

Again the results were discouraging. Our preliminary survey of more than a hundred of these cores left no doubt that none of them would help us to discover the whole of the Pleistocene. None contained long sections of middle or early Pleistocene age. As is so often the case, the shipboard descriptions of the lengths of the cores proved to be much exaggerated. Most of the lengths as measured on the ship fell between fifteen and twenty meters. In reality, few of them contained as much as ten meters of undisturbed sediment; a great deal of "flow-in" had unwittingly been included in the measurements. As a rule, the cores are not split on the ship because of the difficulty of storing them after splitting, but without splitting, it is almost impossible to tell where good core ends and "flow-in" begins.

As we snapped off the microscope light after returning the last samples from these cores to the steel cabinet in which the washed samples are kept, we looked up at the wall in front of us, where a graphic picture of the results of our analyses was hanging. The gap, an empty space on the diagram, seemed larger than ever before; evidently, the problem of closing the gap was much more formidable than we had thought.

In order to keep constantly before our eyes the progess of our effort to close the gap, we had tacked up on the wall diagrams of selected cores to which we had applied our three methods of faunal analysis. On the righthand section of the wall were the curves that represented variation in relative abundance of warm-water and cold-water species. The middle section was covered by curves that traced variations in the ratio between right- and left-coiling shells of *Globorotalia truncatulinoides,* and on the lefthand section of the wall were curves that represented vertical change in the frequency of *Globorotalia menardii.* Since the scale of the diagrams was fairly large, and the cores relatively long, mostly between ten and seventeen meters, the diagrams covered almost the whole wall. They reached from near the ceiling down almost to the middle of the wall and from close to the floor upward nearly to the middle. With the diagrams displayed in this way, the excellent correlation provided by the three methods singly and in combination made an impressive showing. To that extent, this exhibition afforded us

a good deal of gratification. Unfortunately, our enjoyment of
the show was marred by that dismal void along the middle of the wall
where the diagrams failed to meet.

Additional diagrams lay stacked up on the drawing board. These
represented the results of other methods that we had tried out.
Among them were curves showing variation in the coiling direction
of *Globorotalia hirsuta*, and others tracing the variation in abundance of *Globorotalia truncatulinoides* and *Sphaeroidinella dehiscens*. These data had proved useful in a very limited way.

Whether we looked at the wall with its void or at the drawing
board with its stack of unavailing diagrams, the view only heightened
our depression. We turned to stare instead at the bookshelves where
row upon row of our notebooks were assembled. Was the solution to
our problem still buried among those thousands of pages of data?
Had we failed to discover it in spite of our careful and repeated
reviews of the notes?

Next to the bookshelves stood a row of large steel cabinets with
the doors ajar. These cabinets were filled with more than a hundred
thousand vials, each containing a washed sample of sediment.
Every one of these samples from various levels in more than three
thousand cores had been studied by us at some time during the
past sixteen years. Very probably among those samples were a
few hundred that could give us the information we needed to close
the gap, if only we knew how to find them.

Shaking off the paralyzing gloom that had settled over the
laboratory, we went to one of the cabinets and took out the samples
from our standard section of the Sangamon Interglacial. We looked
over these samples once more, as we had done so often before, and
the solution dawned on us. All at once it seemed so simple that
we could not understand why we had not discovered it before.
The answer to the problem of distinguishing between the Sangamon
and the Yarmouth interglacial sections lay in the racial variations
of the *Globorotalia menardii* complex. We knew that the subspecies,
or race, called *Globorotalia menardii flexuosa* occurred sporadically,
and at some levels in great abundance, throughout most of the

Sangamon section, but had we ever found it in the Yarmouth? Now that we thought of it, we felt fairly sure that we had not. Or would we be disappointed again?

There was just one thing to do—get out the samples of the Yarmouth sections in the cores that contained both Sangamon and Yarmouth sections in sequence. In such cores we were certain of the identification of the Yarmouth because of its position beneath the Illinoian and the overlying Sangamon. These cores had been raised from points ranging from the eastern part of the equatorial Atlantic to the western part of the Caribbean, as well as from points in the North and South Atlantic. Our reexamination of the Yarmouth samples proved that at last we had found a reliable crite-rion by which to distinguish the sediments of the two interglacial ages; *Globorotalia menardii flexuosa* did not occur in any of the samples from the Yarmouth! By the application of this criterion, we soon found more sections of Yarmouth age where we could not previously have recognized them. In addition, we found more cores that went from the Yarmouth through a zone representing the Kansan Ice Age and into sediment deposited during the Aftonian Interglacial Age. This led to the crucial discovery that two of the Yarmouth sections, which contained unmistakable evidence in the form of burrow-mottling that they had not been disturbed, correlated with the core section which had puzzled us and which we had finally condemned as being nothing but meaningless "flow-in." In these newly discovered Yarmouth sections we found the same seemingly anomalous mixture of cold-water and warm-water species and the same lack of clear-cut segregation between right- and left-coiling populations of *Globorotalia truncatulinoides*. We had no choice but to conclude that these characteristics were not an indication of "flow-in" but instead were the real nature of the major part of the Yarmouth section.

Now, with abundant Yarmouth material, we were able to work out the zonation of the section in greater detail. As a result, we found evidence of four minor cold intervals within the Yarmouth interglacial. This was particularly interesting because as recently as

1961 S. Z. Rózycki[1] had reported to the Sixth Congress of the International Association for the Study of the Quaternary, in Warsaw, that he had found evidence of four minor cold intervals in continental deposits in Poland which belonged to the second interglacial age, the equivalent of what we call the Yarmouth in America.

This, however, did not explain the intermingling of right- and left-coiling races of *Globorotalia truncatulinoides* or the association of mild- and cool-water species of foraminifera which occurred in the Yarmouth section of the cores.

However, the important thing was that the gap was now almost closed. In fact, it was possible that we would be able to close it completely when we had made a detailed study of all of the Yarmouth sections. But before we could be really sure that we had the complete record of the Pleistocene, we needed to find a core which contained a long Yarmouth section that correlated with the overlapping shorter sections and bridged the gap near the beginning of the Yarmouth to near its end. There was still a chance that we could find such a core; in the group of cores we had selected for reexamination after having found a reliable way of distinguishing the Yarmouth and the Sangamon sections, there were four that remained to be reexamined. Admittedly, we were scraping the bottom of the barrel; if we did not find what we needed among those four cores, we would have to wait until new cores had been obtained, and that could easily mean a delay of years since the chances of obtaining the right kind of cores had proved to be so small.

Our results after having studied three of the four cores were disappointing, to say the least. They contained long Sangamon sections only—long because the sediment had accumulated at a relatively fast rate. Our spirits were probably lower than at any other time of stagnation and frustration in all the sixteen years we

---

[1] Rózycki based his conclusion on a study of forty transverse sections of the valleys of the Vistula and several other Polish rivers. The climatic evidence consisted of four cycles of sediment accumulation, each beginning with gravel and ending with fine sediment, and pollen profiles that record changes in vegetation alternating between species adapted to cool climates and species adapted to warm climates. These cycles occurred within a sedimentary section assigned by Polish geologists to the second, or Mindel-Riss, interglacial.

had spent searching for the complete record of the Pleistocene. Our gloom was made deeper by the fact that our only hope now lay in the long core which had been taken with the Chelminski corer, and the results of the preliminary examination of that core had been discouraging. In fact, the results had been so negative that we had not bothered until then to study the foraminifera in it.

But at last the sun came through the clouds. It really seemed too good to be true that after having exhausted every other recourse we should find the missing link in that long-neglected core. To our astonishment and unbounded pleasure, we found that it contained a Yarmouth section almost twenty meters long. When we looked again into the notes describing the coring operation as observed on board the ship, we understood what had happened. Because of the violence of the action of the corer under the enormous pressure, the core barrel had been shot into the sediment as powerfully as if impelled by a charge of dynamite. As a result, and perhaps also because of some miscalculation in the positioning of the piston, the core barrel had penetrated some twelve meters of sediment *before taking any core*. We found confirming evidence for this when we compared this core with one obtained at the same place with a conventional piston corer.

When detailed study of the core taken with the Chelminski corer indicated that the results would correlate to the degree we had hoped, we plotted the data on diagrams of the core and added them to our exhibit on the laboratory wall. The gap had finally been closed. We now had before us a complete record of the Pleistocene, the epoch of earth history in which occurred that momentous step in organic evolution which led to the emergence of man. The record indicated that the Pleistocene spanned a period of about 1,500,000 years.

It was a cold night in the middle of December 1963 when we put up on the wall the diagrams of the data from our study of the Chelminski core. That night we celebrated the occasion by drinking hot glögg, a Swedish Christmas drink, followed by hot buttered rum. It was an early start to the celebration of a most enjoyable Christmas.

11

THE PLEISTOCENE RECORD

Two investigators of deep-sea sediments, Gustaf Arrhenius and Cesare Emiliani, have reported that they have found the complete record of the Pleistocene. They published their conclusions in the early 1950's, about ten years before we reported our discovery.

Gustaf Arrhenius, of the Scripps Institution of Oceanography, estimated that the first ice age, the Nebraskan or Günz, began about 500,000 years ago. He inferred that a series of layers distinguished by large differences in calcium-carbonate content represented the climatic zones of the Pleistocene. He based his chronology on the rate of accumulation of titanium oxide in the sediment as determined in the upper parts of the cores by radiocarbon dating. He concluded that two cores, one about fifteen meters long and the other about ten meters long, from the eastern Pacific included the complete record of the Pleistocene.

Cesare Emiliani, of the Marine Laboratory of the University of

Miami, estimated that the Günz Ice Age began about 300,000 years ago. He based his interpretation of the climatic record in several sediment cores from the Atlantic and the Caribbean on ratios of oxygen isotopes in the calcareous shells of certain species of planktonic foraminifera, and estimated the ages of the various climatic zones from rates of accumulation as determined by radiocarbon dating of the upper layers of sediment. Later he confirmed the essential correctness of the ages of the various zones by dates independently determined by the protactinium-ionium method, which we describe in Chapter 8. In reaching his conclusions about Pleistocene chronology, Emiliani relied to some extent on evidence from a series of samples from a core, 930 centimeters long, from the Lamont collection, which we have included among the cores selected to support our long chronology of the Pleistocene. The protactinium-ionium method was applied to two samples from this core. The first, from a level of ten to seventeen centimeters, gave an age of 9,000 years; the second, from a level of 230 to 237 centimeters, gave an age of 97,000 years. Accordingly, the date of 97,000 applies to the lower part of the zone, which we correlate with the minor interglacial or interstadial of the last ice age. However, according to Emiliani this zone should be equivalent to the last interglacial, the Riss-Würm.

We have no quarrel with the ages in years assigned by Emiliani to the various zones in this core; it is his correlation of the zones with the climatic events of the Pleistocene that we do not accept. We believe that the record in this core goes back from the present to a time no earlier than the beginning of the third ice age, the Illinoian or Riss.

Our record of the Pleistocene is the result of piecing together correlating and overlapping sections from twenty-six cores ranging in length from 545 to 2,190 centimeters. These cores were obtained from various localities in the Atlantic extending from 4° west to 79° west and from 28° south to 28° north latitude. The depths of water at the locations of the cores vary from 1,250 to 4,800 meters. The latter depth is close to the lower limit of legible records of climatic change; at greater depths the cold[1] abyssal water dissolves the carbonate shells of the planktonic foraminifera and thereby obliterates the climatic record. The remaining insoluble residue, the so-called "red clay," or brown lutite, the characteristic sediment of the deepest parts of the ocean basins, consists essentially of clay particles and very finely divided quartz derived from the continents. Thick sections of this kind of sediment are monotonously uniform and consequently devoid of interest for students of past climates.

All the cores included in our composite record consist of foraminiferal lutite, that is, a mixture of fine mineral particles from the continents and particles of calcium carbonate secreted by planktonic organisms, particularly the Coccolithophoridae and the foraminifera. Except for minor variations in color in some of the cores, the sediment is uniform from top to bottom; the climatic zones are not distinguished by any discernible changes in the physical character of the sediment.

The cores we have selected for our interpretation of the climatic history of the Pleistocene contain undisturbed foraminiferal records. By "undisturbed" we mean that the shells of the planktonic foraminifera settled to the bottom one by one from the water above and have remained in place ever since. However, because of the large differences in size of the particles of the various components of normal deep-sea sediment, a given component may be undisturbed but an important part of some other component may have been transported horizontally by current scour from some exposure of older sediment. A deep current that can easily transport clay particles from one place to another on the sea floor may have no disturbing effect upon the shells of foraminifera, which are about five hundred times as large as the clay particles. This differential

---

[1] Carbon dioxide activates the solution of calcium carbonate, and cold water, as a rule, contains more carbon dioxide than warm water does. However, various conditions other than low temperature probably influence the amount of carbon dioxide and therefore the solution of lime in deep oceanic water. One is production of carbon dioxide by the oxidation of organic matter raining down from the photic zone; another may be the slow movement along the deep parts of the oceanic basins of water coming from high latitudes in which the carbon dioxide has been increased by oxidative processes. Actually, the theory of the solution of lime at abyssal depths is not satisfactorily understood; all we really know is that it happens.

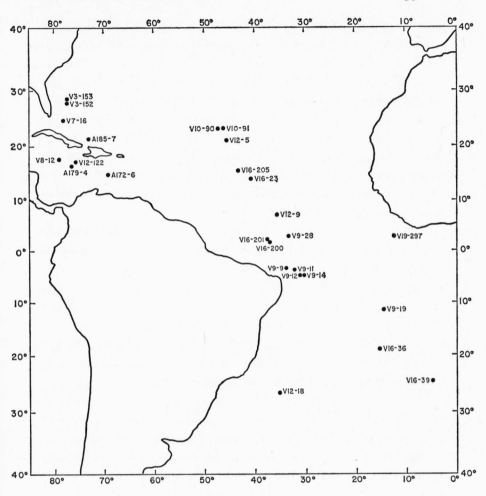

FIGURE 18 *Sections of cores taken from these locations, when pieced together, add up to a complete record of the ice ages and interglacials of the Pleistocene.*

disturbance can cause confusion when two different methods of dating are applied to a core. If one method depends on the decay of a radioactive substance adsorbed on clay particles, it may give a quite different "age" from that given by the radiocarbon in the shells of the foraminifera. Even the radiocarbon method may yield different "ages," depending on whether it is applied to the foraminifera or to the coccoliths, which are very much smaller and easily shifted about by gentle currents. The processes that most often disturb the foraminiferal record are turbidity currents, scour by deep currents, and removal of layers of sediment by slumping. Transportation and emplacement of foraminifera by turbidity currents or deep oceanic currents gives rise to abrupt and easily recognizable changes in texture. In none of the twenty-six cores selected for our study are there any such changes in texture. Slumping, of course, has no effect on texture. Deletions in the record due to slumping can be detected only by careful cross-correlation between two or more cores. Such cross-correlation has been one of our chief concerns in this study.

The best places on the ocean bottom to core for undisturbed sections are the tops and flanks of gentle rises. Of the twenty-six cores, those which contain continuous records from some time in the past up to the present were taken on gentle rises. As we have mentioned, slumping has been very useful to us because it removed sediment of Late Pleistocene age, thereby bringing older sediment within reach of the coring tube. Slumping is confined to relatively steep slopes; the cores containing the middle and early Pleistocene sections were taken on such slopes.

Our investigation of more than three thousand cores of deep-sea sediment has clearly shown how difficult it is to find areas of the ocean floor where the foraminiferal record has not been disturbed in some way. To find cores in which all the sedimentary components are undisturbed is even rarer. Since the finest fraction of the sediment, which is mostly clay, is used for dating by the protactinium-ionium method, we had to exercise the utmost care in selecting cores for dating. We believe that the cores dated by this method were in all respects undisturbed.

Most of the data on the Pleistocene which have come from deep-sea sediments are based on study of the planktonic foraminifera. This has been essentially the case with our own results, but although the foraminifera have provided the climatic record, we believe we could not have obtained reliable results if we had not also carefully examined the physical aspects of the cores. The sea floor is a far more dynamic environment than was realized only

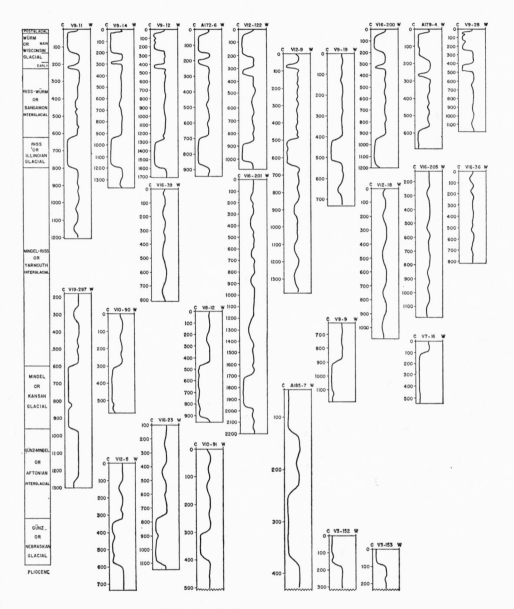

FIGURE 19 *Curves of climatic change, based on study of the planktonic foramini-fera in samples taken at ten-centimeter intervals in twenty-six cores, correlated with the glacial and interglacial ages of the complete Pleistocene. C indicates cold climate and W warm climate. Present climate is plotted midway between C and W and inferred past climates are plotted with respect to present climate. Numbers to the left of the columns are depths in the cores in centimeters.*

a few decades ago; truly quiet areas of the sea floor, where sediment, once having come to rest, can remain undisturbed for millions of years, are exceptional. In view of the prevalence of disturbing processes, we have felt it necessary to check carefully the continuity of our Pleistocene sections by cross-correlation. To be doubly sure, we have correlated the cores by climatic zones and also by changes in coiling direction of *Globorotalia truncatulinoides*.

The most important criteria which distinguish Pleistocene sediments from those of earlier epochs of the Cenozoic Period are absence of discoasters; the dominance of left coiling, from ninety to a hundred percent, in *Globorotalia menardii*; the general occurrence of *Globorotalia truncatulinoides* in abundance; and the absence of certain species, or more probably subspecies, closely related to *Globorotalia menardii,* with consequent reduction of the *Globorotalia menardii* racial complex to a much more homogeneous group.

Although the earliest Pleistocene assemblages of foraminifera are essentially "modern" in aspect, some extinctions and evolutionary changes have taken place within Pleistocene time. For our purpose the most useful of these is the appearance of the subspecies, *Globorotalia menardii flexuosa,* within the zone corresponding to the Sangamon Interglacial. It first appears just above the lower third of the Sangamon section and rapidly becomes very abundant and even dominant over its cousins, *Globorotalia menardii menardii* and *Globorotalia menardii tumida* at some levels. At the top of the Sangamon section the members of this racial group disappear or become rare in the Atlantic; all three reappear again in great abundance in the warm interstadial of the last ice age. Wherever *Globorotalia menardii flexuosa* occurs in the section, it is accompanied by its two cousins together with intermediate forms. In the light of Mendelian genetics, there should be nothing anomalous about the coexistence of several genetically different phenotypes. To deny such phenotypes the taxonomic status of subspecies or races merely because of their coexistence is unrealistic, and would in this case be inconvenient. In the long run, selection will tend to reduce a highly polymorphic population to more or less uniformity by weeding out forms less well adapted

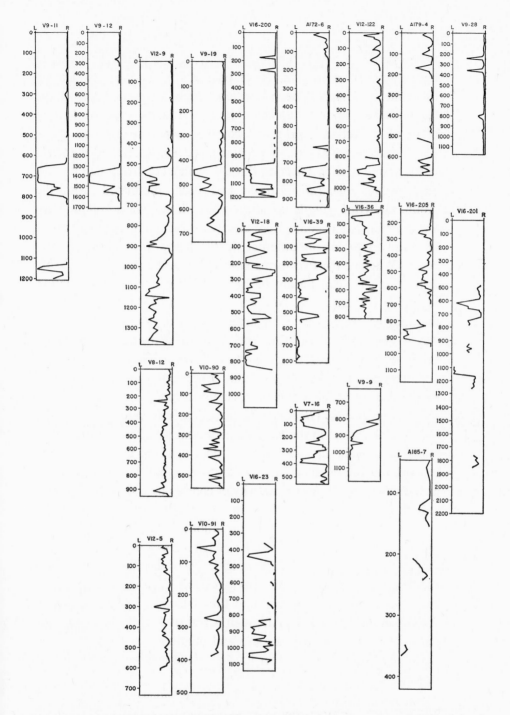

FIGURE 20 *Correlation of twenty-two of the twenty-six deep-sea cores which include the Pleistocene section. The correlating levels are defined by changes in the coiling direction of* Globorotalia truncatulinoides *in samples taken at ten-centimeter intervals. The scale of coiling runs from a hundred percent left at the left margins of the columns to a hundred percent right at the right margins. Numbers to the left of the columns are depths in cores in centimeters.*

to the particular environment. Actually, this is just what seems to have happened during the latter part of the last ice age. During that time, on the evidence of the core record, the members of the *Globorotalia menardii* complex in the Atlantic tottered on the brink of extinction. The racial complex which reappeared about 11,000 years ago, as climate became more genial, showed the effect of the severe trial by selection through which the group had passed. *Globorotalia menardii flexuosa* had been eliminated from the group; and *Globorotalia menardii menardii* and *Globorotalia menardii tumida* had become more clearly distinct, probably as a result of adaption to life at different depths below the surface of the ocean. Whether the two forms now living in the Atlantic are truly distinct species can hardly be decided without more information regarding the creatures' habits and ability to hybridize. However that may be, we can say with some confidence that they are on the way to becoming two distinct species adapted to different environments. For some reason, *Globorotalia menardii tumida* is strongly dominant in the lower half of the postglacial zone; *Globorotalia menardii menardii* is dominant in the upper half.

Another species, *Globorotalia hexagona,* still lives in the Pacific but became extinct in the Atlantic about halfway through the warm interstadial of the last ice age. This does not help us in our efforts to work out the sequence of the Pleistocene, but it is of interest as an indication of the greater severity of conditions within the Atlantic region, as compared with those in the Pacific.

Further evidence of less trying conditions in the Pacific is provided by the survival of *Globoquadrina conglomerata* in the Pacific, although this species is absent from all levels of the Pleistocene of the Atlantic. Another species of *Globoquadrina* is common in the lower half of the Sangamon section and then becomes less frequent and smaller in the upper half. Although it still lives in the Atlantic and the Caribbean, its dwindling size and numbers suggest that it will not be able to survive another ice age in the relatively inhospitable Atlantic region.

The distinction in the sedimentary record between the interglacial and glacial ages is for the most part quite well defined. The most

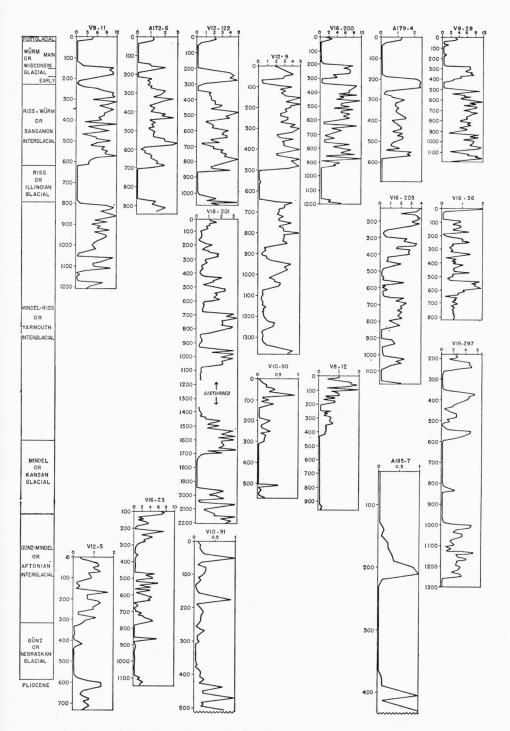

FIGURE 21   *Curves indicating variations in abundance of* Globorotalia menardii *in samples taken at ten-centimeter intervals in seventeen of twenty-six cores which include the Pleistocene section. Numbers to the left of the columns are depths in cores in centimeters. The curves are correlated with the glacial and interglacial ages of the Pleistocene.*

striking difference is in the abundance of the large and conspicuous forms of the *Globorotalia menardii* complex. These are very abundant in the zones that correspond to interglacial ages and are absent or rare in those which correspond to ice ages. However, in this respect the great interglacial, the Yarmouth, is a little different from the others. The form representing the *Globorotalia menardii* in the Yarmouth section is a trifle smaller, shows less individual variation, and plays a more subordinate role in the total population. This, together with evidence of short periods of cold climate, and a tendency to left coiling on the part of *Globorotalia truncatulinoides* even in cores from the equatorial Atlantic, strongly suggest that the climate of the great interglacial differed from that of the other two interglacials. It is also suggestive of cyclical change—that is, of two cycles, each consisting of two ice ages separated by a warm interglacial, in turn separated by a long interglacial of a climatic character distinctly different from the other climatic phases of the Pleistocene.

Another interesting feature of the climatic record is the abruptness of the faunal changes, in spite of more or less postdepositional mixing of the shells of the foraminifera at the boundaries by burrowing animals. In most cases the faunal change is complete within a thickness of ten to twenty centimeters. Even the basal boundary of the Pleistocene is only a little more drawn out; the transition zone is hardly more than about thirty centimeters thick.

Through the years, since about 1950, a considerable number of radiocarbon-age determinations have been made on samples from the cores. Thirteen of these were made on samples from the cores selected by us to show the complete record of the Pleistocene. The great shortcoming of the radiocarbon method is its limitation to material no older than about 35,000 years. To estimate the ages of zones farther down in the cores, one must assume a reasonably constant rate of sediment accumulation. In dealing with sediments deposited in shallow water, there would be no justification whatever for assuming a constant rate of sediment accumulation. Fortunately, the situation is somewhat different in deep ocean sediments. Our study of such sediments has shown that there is great variation in the rate of accumulation from place to place, but such variations are always accompanied by obvious differences in texture. Sediments of abnormally slow accumulation are distinguished by large numbers of the shells of foraminifera, whereas sediments of rapid accumulation contain large proportions of fine material. Since the sediments of the cores selected for this study are quite uniform in texture from top to bottom, we infer that the sediments have accumulated at correspondingly uniform rates.

But during the last five years of our investigation new methods of dating have been developed which extend the range back some 200,000 years. Samples from two of the cores that make up our composite record of the Pleistocene have been dated by the Th^{230}/Th^{232} method and the Pa^{231}/Th^{230} method. The first of these depends on change in the ratio of two isotopes of the chemical element thorium. Clay particles wafted from the continents in the general oceanic circulation adsorb these isotopes in a ratio which is in equilibrium with their relative abundances in sea water. In this way the radioactive clock is set at time zero. After some time, possibly some years, the clay particles come to rest on the floor of the ocean and are covered up. From that time on, the ratio of the isotopes slowly changes through radioactive decay.

The second method, similar in principle, differs in that it makes use of the slow change in the ratio between an element called protactinium and an isotope of thorium which is also called ionium. This method was developed by W. M. Sackett and H. A. Patratz in 1958. The datings were done by Elizabeth Rona of the Oak Ridge Institute of Nuclear Studies, and by J. N. Rosholt, C. Emiliani, J. Geiss, F. F. Koczy, and P. J. Wangersky of the Marine Laboratory of the University of Miami.

However, the dates obtained by the two methods did not agree. The ratio of thorium isotopes gave dates which were consistently older than those determined by the protactinium-ionium method. Perhaps this ought not to be too surprising; the theory on which the thorium-isotope method is based has several weaknesses. The concentration of thorium-230 in sea water, and consequently in the sediment, is dependent on factors which have very probably varied

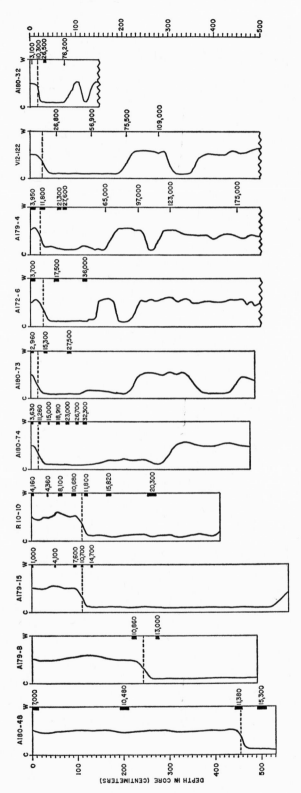

FIGURE 22 Curves of climatic change based on relative numbers of cold-water and warm-water species of planktonic foraminifera in samples taken at ten-centimeter intervals in ten deep-sea cores. C indicates cold climate and W warm climate. Present climate is plotted on the midpoint between C and W, and inferred past climate is plotted with respect to it. Dashed lines indicate the end of the last ice age. The black boxes indicate the sections of the cores that were used for dating, and the numbers to the right of the black boxes are radiocarbon ages in years before present (B.P.). Numbers to the right of the lines in core A179-4 are dates determined by the protactinium-ionium method; numbers to the right of the lines in cores V12-122 and A180-32 are dates determined by the protactinium method, with the exception of the radiocarbon date of 26,500 in core A180-32. The lines indicate the midpoint in the samples dated by the protactinium-ionium method and by the protactinium method. Three of the cores (A172-6, A179-4, V12-122) are included in the twenty-six selected to show the complete record of the Pleistocene.

in the past. Determination of the ratio, Th^{230}/Th^{232}, instead of Th^{230} alone, is an attempt to correct for this variation, but on theoretical grounds it is not likely to be successful because the geochemical history of Th^{230} differs from that of Th^{232}.

Since the dates obtained by the protactinium-ionium method agreed with the radiocarbon dates and with those estimated from the rates of sediment accumulation determined by the radiocarbon method, we consider them to be essentially correct. The protactinium-ionium method is based on the assumption that the ionium and protactinium are precipitated in a constant ratio. This assumption is plausible because ionium and protactinium, although they are not isotopes of the same element, have similar chemical properties. Such being the case, the ratio of protactinium to ionium after a given time should be a function of the age only.

Another method of dating recently developed by W. M. Sackett is based on the decay of unsupported protactinium-231. Sackett regards this method as particularly reliable because apparently protactinium does not migrate vertically in the sediment as some other radioactive substances seem to do.

As yet, the method has been applied to only two cores, one of which is among the twenty-six that we have included in our composite record of the complete Pleistocene. We chose this core because we judged from the chronology we had established that the rate of accumulation of the sediment was about 2.5 centimeters in a thousand years, which is about the normal rate for the Atlantic. In spite of our confidence in our estimate of the rate of accumulation, we confess that we felt some suspense while waiting for the dates. After all, the method was being tried out for the first time. It was a happy day for us when Sackett announced the results; he had dated several levels going back as far as 109,000 years. These dates gave an average rate of accumulation of 2.6 centimeters in a thousand years, an excellent confirmation of our original estimate of the rate.

We selected the other core for dating because correlation of its faunal zones indicated unusually slow accumulation—that is, at a rate somewhat less than one-half of the normal rate. Once again, Sackett had good news for us; the protactinium age of the level 75

centimeters below the top was 76,200 years, which meant that the
rate of accumulation was about one centimeter in a thousand years
—in good agreement with what we had expected from the correlation of the faunal zones.

Thus the protactinium-ionium, the protactinium, and the radiocarbon dates provided us with an absolute time scale extending from
the present back to about 175,000 years ago. These dates indicated
that the average rate of accumulation of sediment in the twenty-six
cores was on the order of two and a half centimeters per thousand
years. On the basis of this average rate of accumulation and the fact
that the average thickness of the whole Pleistocene section was about
thirty-eight meters, we could, by extrapolation beyond 175,000
years, establish a time scale for the entire Pleistocene Epoch. Our
time scale pushes the beginning of the Pleistocene, as defined by the
onset of the first ice age, the Nebraskan or Günz, to about 1,500,000
years ago. This age is rather startling when compared with the
generally accepted estimates of the duration of the Pleistocene, which
range from about 300,000 to about 1,000,000 years.

As we have said, we have maintained from the very beginning
of our studies of the climatic record in the sediment cores that the
duration of the Pleistocene Epoch was on the order of a million
years. Although a great amount of literature presenting arguments
in favor of the shorter chronologies has been published, we have
steadfastly refused to accept the arguments as valid. We have stated
our belief and presented evidence for it in scientific reports published
during the 1950's and the early 1960's.

To our great satisfaction, important new evidence supporting our
chronology has been published by other investigators in the last
couple of years. This new evidence has come to light through the
application of the potassium-argon method of dating to Pleistocene
deposits on the continents. The age of an early glaciation of the
Sierra Nevadas, correlated with the Kansan by Eliot Blackwelder,
has been determined to have been greater than 980,000 years but
less than 3,200,000 years by J. F. Evernden, D. E. Savage, G. H.
Curtis, and G. T. James, using the potassium-argon method. This
harmonizes with our chronology, according to which the Kansan

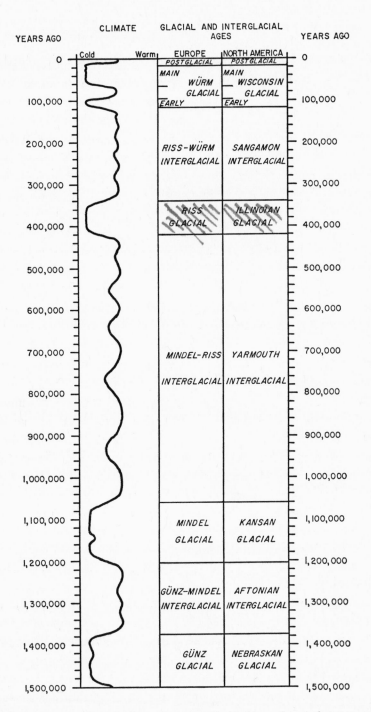

FIGURE 23 *Generalized climate curve based on the study of deep-sea cores, correlated with Pleistocene time scale. In this book, the Pleistocene is considered to begin with the onset of the first glaciation, the Nebraskan, or Günz.*

Ice Age began 1,205,000 years ago and ended 1,060,000 years ago.

Evernden and Curtis have also estimated the age of *Zinjanthropus,* the australopithecine hominid from Olduvai Gorge in East Africa, at 1,750,000 years. The layer of sediment containing the bones of *Zinjanthropus* contains the bones of certain genera of mammals as well. These same genera also occur in the famous Villafranchian deposit in Villafranca d'Asti in Italy. For many years the Villa-franchian, with its assemblage of mammals, was assigned to the final phase of the Pliocene, the epoch directly preceding the Pleisto-cene, but more recent opinion regards it as representing the early Pleistocene. This re-evaluation has been made because the mammals of the Villafranchian give some evidence of a change toward cooler climate. However, there is no evidence that this cooling was connected with an ice age. In consequence, Pleistocene geologists are in complete disagreement regarding the relationship between the first ice age and the Villafranchian. Some speak of the Villa-franchian as "preglacial Pleistocene"; others believe that the first ice age occurred toward the end of the time represented by the Villafranchian deposits; and still others place the first ice age at the beginnings of Villafranchian time. According to our chronology of the Pleistocene and the age of the Villafranchian deposit in East Africa as determined by Evernden and Curtis, the first ice age occurred immediately or soon after the close of Villafranchian time. It should be added here that the materials from Olduvai which were dated by Evernden and Curtis were volcanic ash beds, one of which was beneath and the other above the layer of sediment containing the Villafranchian bones. The ages of the ash beds were 1,550,000 and 1,850,000 years. From these two dates Evernden and Curtis estimated the age of *Zinjanthropus.*

On the evidence of these dates, the Villafranchian is "preglacial Pleistocene," if it is Pleistocene at all. There is abundant evidence of a trend toward cooler climate during the Pliocene. Therefore, similar evidence in the Villafranchian is not a valid reason for placing it within the Pleistocene. It would be more logical to define the beginning of the Pleistocene by the onset of the first ice age. This definition would return the Villafranchian to its original posi-tion at the end of the Pliocene.

On the basis of our time scale, the last ice age, the Wisconsin or Würm, falls between 11,000 and 115,000 years ago; accordingly, it spanned a time interval of 104,000 years. Our faunal evidence indicates that the Wisconsin was separated into two parts, a Main Wisconsin and an Early Wisconsin, in turn separated by a warm interstadial. According to the core record, the Main Wisconsin was longer and colder than the Early Wisconsin. The Main Wisconsin falls between 11,000 and 65,000 years before present; the interstadial falls between 65,000 and 95,000 years before present; and the Early Wisconsin between 95,000 and 115,000 years before present. Our chronology gives the Sangamon or Riss-Würm Interglacial Age a duration of 225,000 years; that is, from about 340,000 to about 115,000 years ago. The Illinoian or Riss Ice Age lasted some 80,000 years; that is, between 420,000 and 340,000 years ago. The Yarmouth or Mindel-Riss Interglacial extended from about 1,060,-000 to about 420,000 years ago, and lasted some 640,000 years. The Kansan or Mindel Ice Age lasted about 145,000 years, or from 1,205,000 to 1,060,000 years ago. The Aftonian or Günz-Mindel Interglacial lasted 170,000 years; that is, from 1,375,000 to 1,205,-000 years ago. The first ice age, the Nebraskan or Günz, we place between 1,500,000 and about 1,375,000 years ago; accordingly, it had a duration of about 125,000 years.

12

NEW TIME SCALE FOR

EVOLUTION

ONE of the most important results of the new record of the Pleistocene is that it provides a definite time scale, not only for the various climatic events, but also for the evolution of man. With a fairly accurate calendar of the Pleistocene, we can put the chronology of human evolution in order, for the rise of new types of early men and their migrations are connected with the glacial and interglacial ages. Man is a product of the climatic changes of the Pleistocene; these provided the rigorous selection necessary for his emergence. About thirty percent of the surface of the earth was buried under ice during the ice ages. At the same time, climatic change in varying degrees of severity spread to every part of the world. As the continental glaciers waxed and waned, arid regions received increasing rainfall, rivers flowed anew, and previously empty basins became lakes; luxuriant vegetation took over where dust storms had prevailed; with abundant fodder, animal life teemed. But the Pleistocene was preeminently an epoch of change.

Before long, geologically speaking, reversion set in. Evaporation exceeded rainfall; the levels of lakes fell below their outlets; their water became salty, and at last mere salt flats remained to mark their former presence. Once again the dust storms gained control. A pluvial cycle, corresponding to an ice age in higher latitudes, had completed a full turn.

While climatic change proceeded in its cyclical course, sea level rose and fell by a hundred and fifty or even two hundred meters. As the continental glaciers encroached upon the former northerly ranges

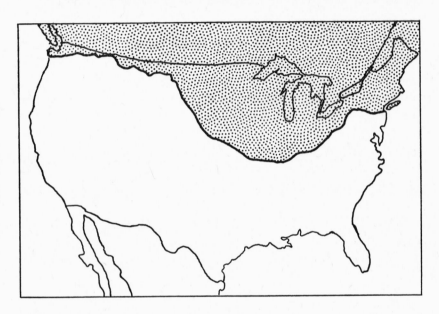

FIGURE 24   *Map showing the southern margin of the North American ice sheet at its maximum extent during the last ice age.*

of plants and animals, they depleted the water in the ocean basins, and sea level fell, uncovering new land areas farther south. Much of the bottom of the Adriatic Sea must have been dry land during the last ice age. Almost certainly, late Pleistocene men and their game lived there while the Alpine glaciers were at their height. Emergent continental shelves not only around the Mediterranean but also on the Atlantic coast of Europe and off Africa and Asia must have supported populations of early men attracted by the more genial climate near sea level and the nearby supply of fish and clams.

That men and mammoths roamed what is now the bottom of the North Sea, we know with certainty. Thousands of teeth of mammoths as well as the bones of elephants, bears, hyenas, horses and bison, shells of fresh-water clams, together with flint tools and harpoons embedded in masses of peat, have been dredged up by fishing boats off the coasts of Germany, England, and Holland and as far out as the northern edge of the Dogger Bank, which is near the center of the basin. The plant remains include stumps of trees rooted in the underlying glacial deposit.

But "Doggerland" cannot have been open to colonization for long. At the height of the last ice age, the basin of the North Sea was covered by an extension of the great Scandinavian ice sheet. This is shown by the glacial till, or ice-deposited material, beneath the peat of the Dogger Bank and by the presence in eastern England of rocks which occur in place only in Scandinavia. When the ice melted, sea level was already on the rise. Presumably, "Doggerland" was dry only during a relatively short period immediately after the local ice cover had melted and before the rise of sea level which accompanied the complete deglaciation of the continents.

Much valuable archaeological and anthropological material must lie beneath shallow seas, possibly more[1] than has been found on land. Just as we have gone to sea to find a complete record of Pleistocene climates, so students of early man may have to go to sea to solve some of the problems of man's early development. Already some of the shallower sites are accessible to skin divers and scuba divers; soon, no doubt, even the deepest sites will be visited by seagoing archaeologists and paleontologists working from underwater vehicles.

However, the land areas uncovered by lowered sea level did not begin to make up for the land lost to the ice sheets. Each time the

---

[1] Because of the probability that coastal regions were particularly popular as camp sites on account of the food available nearby in the form of mollusks, fish, and seals, and because, once covered by the rising sea, these sites would be protected from natural erosion as well as from erosion by unarchaeologically-minded men.

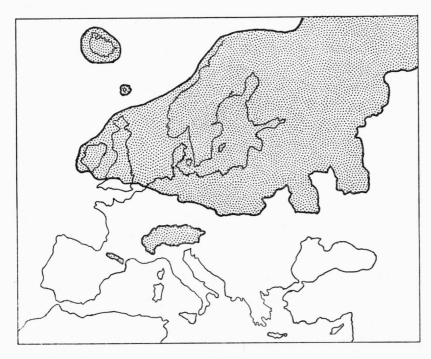

FIGURE 25 *Maximum extent of the European ice sheet during the last glaciation. The Alpine glaciation is also shown.*

continental glaciers spread, the plants, animals, and early men of Europe were forced to retreat into the narrower quarters of southern Europe. At such times the competition between species and within species, particularly between tribes of men, must have been intense. There was no opportunity for biological stagnation. To survive and leave descendants in those days, one needed to excel the average in physical stamina and mental alertness. When climatic amelioration came, the elite few who had been retained by the sieve of natural selection were able to expand their range northward and there increase in numbers.

Lowered sea level also had a direct effect on biological and cultural evolution. It opened temporary land bridges and coastal migration routes by which floras and faunas from widely separated regions came into contact. Intensified competition resulted when closely related species met and fought for living space and sus-

tenance. When races of the same species met, hybridization was a
possibility, particularly among early men. This is more than a
probable conjecture; what is believed to be good evidence of crossing has been found in the morphology of skulls and other bones of
late Pleistocene men. Such crossing would lead to genetical instability—that is, to wider variability of heritable physical and
mental traits, the raw material for selection to work on.

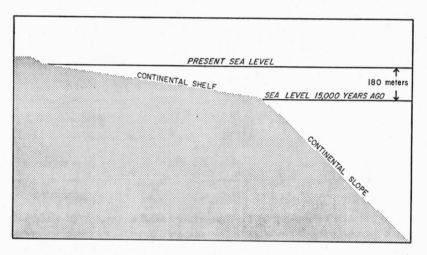

FIGURE 26   *Lowered sea level during the last ice age. The amount of lowering was
sufficient to uncover most, if not all, of the continental shelf.*

In the final analysis, selection is the molder of new races and new
species. An environmental change in itself cannot effect a genetical
change in an individual or, for that matter, in a single generation of
a population. Genetical change, which is the only kind of truly
evolutionary change, takes place only when a given environment acts
selectively on a whole population and over many generations. This
presupposes that there is variation among the individuals of the
population. Had our primate ancestors been really "equal" among
themselves, Darwinian evolution by natural selection could not have
taken place, and we have no evidence that there is or ever has been
any other process of evolution. In short, the environment cannot
determine what kind of variants may appear within a population;

all it can do is favor the survival with offspring of certain variants and weed out the rest.

Since, as a rule, one particular type is better suited to cope with a given environment than all others, rigorous natural selection tends to reduce the variability within populations. A result is the extraordinary uniformity of some populations of wild animals. And yet, in spite of superficial uniformity, each individual is unique. Certain species of antarctic penguins provide an interesting example. The individuals of a rookery appear to an outsider, in this case an experienced ornithologist, to be quite identical. The penguins know better. Mates recognize each other instantly after being separated for months, and parent birds can single out their chicks from among hundreds of others.

That no group of organisms will ever run out of variability, however drastic the selection, is ensured by the mechanism of inheritance. The particles of genetical material, the genes, are constantly subject to mutation, or change in their complex chemical structure. When such a change occurs, it gives rise to some abnormality in the development of the individual carrying the mutant gene. Since these mutations are quite random and purposeless, their effect is almost always disadvantageous,[2] and consequently their carriers are eliminated from the population by natural selection. Much more rarely, a mutation has no appreciable effect on the survival of its carrier in the existing environment, in which case the mutuation may be transmitted through many generations, until in a changed environment it may turn out to have some survival value. There are also the rare mutations which are advantageous. Through preferential survival of their carriers, these transformed genes tend to permeate the group of organisms in which they occur. But this takes time, and still more time for a whole series of mutations to accumulate, until their combined effect is enough to set the group of organisms apart

[2] Let us use computing machines as an example, to show by analogy why random mutations are more likely than not to be disadvantageous. Suppose that a mischievous person without knowledge of the anatomy of computers should make some small change in the circuitry of such a machine. Clearly, a change made in that way would almost certainly impair the usefulness of the machine, if it did not destroy it entirely. However, the remote possibility exists that the change might by pure accident improve the efficiency of the machine.

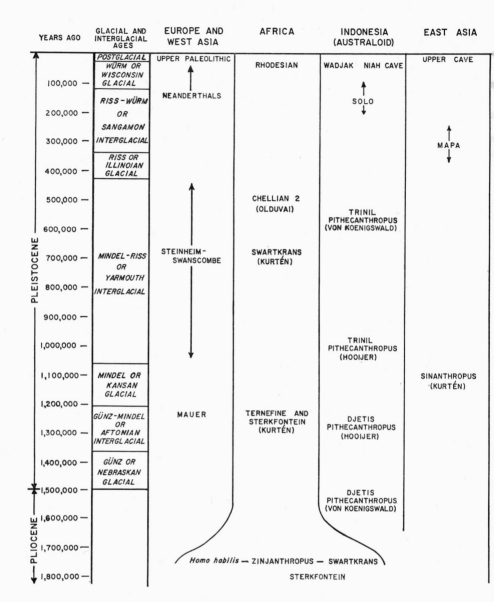

YEARS AGO	GLACIAL AND INTERGLACIAL AGES	EUROPE AND WEST ASIA	AFRICA	INDONESIA (AUSTRALOID)	EAST ASIA
	POSTGLACIAL	UPPER PALEOLITHIC	RHODESIAN	WADJAK NIAH CAVE	UPPER CAVE
100,000 —	WÜRM OR WISCONSIN GLACIAL				
		NEANDERTHALS		SOLO	
200,000 —	RISS – WÜRM OR				
300,000 —	SANGAMON INTERGLACIAL				MAPA
400,000 —	RISS OR ILLINOIAN GLACIAL				
500,000 —			CHELLIAN 2 (OLDUVAI)	TRINIL PITHECANTHROPUS (VON KOENIGSWALD)	
600,000 —					
700,000 —	MINDEL – RISS OR	STEINHEIM – SWANSCOMBE	SWARTKRANS (KURTÉN)		
800,000 —	YARMOUTH INTERGLACIAL				
900,000 —					
1,000,000 —				TRINIL PITHECANTHROPUS (HOOIJER)	
1,100,000 —	MINDEL OR KANSAN GLACIAL				SINANTHROPUS (KURTÉN)
1,200,000 —					
	GÜNZ–MINDEL OR	MAUER	TERNEFINE AND STERKFONTEIN (KURTÉN)	DJETIS PITHECANTHROPUS (HOOIJER)	
1,300,000 —	AFTONIAN INTERGLACIAL				
1,400,000 —	GÜNZ OR NEBRASKAN GLACIAL				
1,500,000 —				DJETIS PITHECANTHROPUS (VON KOENIGSWALD)	
1,600,000 —					
1,700,000 —					
1,800,000 —		Homo habilis — ZINJANTHROPUS — SWARTKRANS STERKFONTEIN			

(left margin: PLEISTOCENE, PLIOCENE)

FIGURE 27   *Placing the fossil remains of early man and his antecedents in glacial or interglacial eras is subject to differences of opinion among physical anthropologists. This chart is a summary of the dating of major hominid or human remains. Where the location of the fossil in the glacial sequence is widely accepted, there is no attribution to the specialist. In cases involving a difference of opinion, however, the fossil's location in terms of glacial or interglacial ages is attributed to the scientist who dated it. In two instances—Trinil Pithecanthropus and Djetis Pithecanthropus—we have given both Hooijer's and Von Koenigswald's placings. Although the discoverers of Swartkrans and Sterkfontein place them before the first glacial age, Kurtén dates Swartkrans a full million years later and Sterkfontein a half million years later.*

as a new species. How much time? No one really knows. It has been estimated that the evolution of a new species requires about half a million years, but this is little more than a reasonable guess. On the other hand, we know that the duration of the Pleistocene was sufficient for the evolution of distinct species, one of which was *Homo sapiens.*

Speciation among the elephants of Europe is also known to have taken place within the time span of the Pleistocene. The ancestor of the European Pleistocene elephants was *Elephas meridionalis,* the southern elephant, whose bones occur in the Villafranchian deposits. For a long time, vertebrate paleontologists regarded the Villafranchian as part of the late Pliocene, but because some of the species of mammals in the Villafranchian assemblage give evidence of a cooler climate than one would expect during the Pliocene, geologists now agree that the Villafranchian represents the earliest phase of the Pleistocene.

However that may be, *Elephas meridionalis* should be thought of as a survivor from the Pliocene which lived on into the early Pleistocene. At the end of the Lower Pleistocene, the end of the second ice age, about 1,060,000 years ago, *Elephas meridionalis* disappeared, at least as a recognizable species. But it left descendants. The original species separated into two groups which had survived in two different environments and which in consequence had been subjected to different kinds of selection. One of these, *Elephas antiquus,* became adapted to woodlands and a temperate or warm climate; the other, *Elephas primigenius,* was adapted to open steppe and tundra, harder food, and a colder and more continental climate. The divergence shows particularly clearly in the teeth, which were influenced through selection by the different diets of the animals. Fortunately for paleontologists interested in evolution, the teeth are particularly durable and consequently occur in great numbers. With such abundant material available, it has been possible to follow in detail the gradational changes in the teeth of the elephant lineage.

The fossil remains of the ancestral form, *Elephas meridionalis,* show considerable variation. With this variability, it was the kind of species on which selection can most effectively work. It is significant that a race called *Elephas meridionalis nestii,* which succeeded the original *Elephas meridionalis* and was directly ancestral to *Elephas primigenius* and *Elephas antiquus,* was even more variable than its predecessor. Apparently the rate of mutation in the racial group was high; at the same time, strong selective pressure was absent. However, as the herds betook themselves to more specialized environments, selection came into play, and from the variable original stock two distinct species emerged. This happened soon after the first cold phase of the Pleistocene, that is, during the first interglacial, between about 1,375,000 and 1,205,000 years ago. However, even at that time most specimens were of intermediate form and classifiable as *Elephas meridionalis nestii.* During the second ice age the differences became more marked. By the end of the middle Pleistocene and the beginning of the last interglacial, about 340,000 years ago, the intermediate forms had disappeared almost everywhere, leaving two morphologically distinct species adapted to distinct environments. Since the environment suitable to *Elephas primigenius* spread periodically over Central and Western Europe during the ice ages, whereas that favorable to *Elephas antiquus* prevailed during the temperate interglacial phases, the two species alternate stratigraphically in the later Pleistocene successions of Central and Western Europe. Presumably *Elephas primigenius* retreated to the northeast in times of mild climate, and *Elephas antiquus* went south during times of cold climate. Where their ranges met or overlapped, their remains occur together in one deposit, but as quite distinct species. No intermediate specimens have been found in deposits of Upper Pleistocene age. This strongly suggests that the two forms were truly distinct species and not races of a single species which could cross and produce hybrids.

The conclusion that this instance of divergent evolution was causally related to the peculiar climatic conditions of the Pleistocene is inescapable. The mechanism was that of an overall environment which was highly variable in time and in geographical latitude, working through selection upon an ancestral population, *Elephas meridionalis,* which was unusually variable in its genetical makeup. It has been estimated, on the basis of the generally accepted chro-

nology of the Pleistocene, that the time required for the emergence
of these two species from their common ancestor was about 500,000
years, counting from the first evidence of divergence in the Villafranchian to the clear establishment of two independent species in
the last interglacial age. However, according to our chronology, the
time required was about 1,400,000 years.

Species other than the elephants have developed in the course of
the Pleistocene, probably in response to the selective pressure of
the climatic fluctuations and repeated displacements of the main
environmental zones. Examples are two closely related European
species of crows, the carrion crow and the hooded crow, and two
species of grasshoppers in Europe which evolved from two groups
of an ancestral species which were separated and confined to refuge
areas by advances of the continental ice sheets. However, so far as
is known, no species has evolved more rapidly than the elephant
lineage of our example.

The most accurate way to date the stages of human evolution
would be to determine the ages of the fossil bones directly by measuring the decay of some radioactive substance in them. Unfortunately,
the only such substance which occurs in bones is radioactive carbon,
and its rate of decay is so fast that it is useless for dating objects
older than about 35,000 years.

Another way of attacking the problem is to determine the duration of the Pleistocene and its subdivisions. Previous estimates of
the duration of the Pleistocene—from 300,000 to about 600,000
years—created a dilemma. There was no doubt that man had
evolved during the Pleistocene, but 300,000 years seemed altogether too short a time for the emergence of a new species. It was
hardly any easier to reconcile 600,000 years with the slow pace of
evolution which Darwin had assumed. Now, however, this dilemma
vanishes; according to our time scale, the Pleistocene spanned a
period of about 1,500,000 years.

Let us adventure on a journey backward in time according to our
calendar, and follow in retrospective order the antecedents of *Homo
sapiens* as we know them by some of their most important fossilized
relics.

Careful and systematic comparisons have made clear that *Homo sapiens* existed during the last glaciation. According to our time scale, this glaciation took place between 115,000 and 11,000 years ago. During the time when the Upper Paleolithic culture known as the Magdalenian flourished in Western Europe, the local population, judging from their bones, was composed of people who were similar in physical character to modern Europeans. They have left us a few sketches of themselves, but their drawings of each other are mostly rude caricatures. In contrast, they were quite serious when they depicted the animals they hunted; on the walls of the cave at Altamira in Spain are paintings in several colors done by Magdalenian artists. In these masterpieces, bison and boars seem to come to life before our eyes. The Magdalenians lived during the latter phases of the last glaciation, the Würm. Dating by radiocarbon gives them an age of about 15,000 years before present.

The Aurignacian period immediately preceded the Magdalenian. These people, according to their bones, were essentially similar to the Magdalenians and ourselves. They are set apart only by their culture, that is, their tools, weapons, and art. They were particularly fond of making things out of bone, and their art was sculpture rather than drawing. In reality the two cultures merge into each other; they are merely stages in the steady evolution of Upper Paleolithic industry. A radiocarbon date of 27,000 years has been reported for the period.

In the meantime, *Homo sapiens* was moving about in the world. He had certainly reached Australia some 10,000 years ago, and North America probably somewhat earlier.

One important question is, of course, whether there is any concrete evidence from the fossil record that *Homo sapiens* was actually in existence before the last glaciation. Preceding the Aurignacian industry in Europe, there was a prolonged cultural period of the Paleolithic called the Mousterian. For convenience, this has been divided into two phases, the Early and the Late Mousterian. The Early Mousterian is generally considered to have covered the last interglacial period, the Riss-Würm, and to have extended into the onset of the last glacial period; the Late Mousterian coincided with the climax of the first part of the last glaciation.

A fairly large number of bones of Mousterian men have been found in Central Europe and in the Near East and Russia. On the evidence of the skulls from Central Europe, Marcellin Boule and Henri V. Vallois (1957) concluded that Mousterian man was a distinct species, *Homo neanderthalensis,* not to be confused with *Homo sapiens.* In support of this opinion, they cited the morphological homogeneity of the bones. But Carleton S. Coon (1962), with data on a larger series of skulls from more widely scattered sites, has insisted that there was really much variation among the Mousterian people and that they overlapped morphologically with *Homo sapiens.* Coon sees them as a race, or subspecies, of *Homo sapiens.* If so, *Homo sapiens* appeared during the last interglacial, that is, about 115,000 to 340,000 years ago, according to the new time scale, and not 70,000 to 100,000 years ago, as has been generally believed on the basis of the time scale most widely accepted for the last ten years.

We now come to the problem of "pre-Mousterian man." A fairly complete and well-preserved skull found at Steinheim in Germany probably dates from the third glacial period, the Riss Ice Age. It closely resembled the Early Mousterians. Two fragments of skulls found at Fontéchevade in France, also reckoned to be of pre-Mousterian age, show a much closer resemblance to modern *Homo sapiens.* In this regard, the discovery at Swanscombe in England in 1935 was most important; important because the age of the skull could be assigned with considerable assurance to the second interglacial period, the Mindel-Riss, which according to our time scale encompassed the interval between 1,060,000 and 420,000 years ago. Various features of the Swanscombe skull prove that its owner did not belong to the Neanderthal race. Except for the very great thickness of the bones, the skull is essentially similar to that of a modern woman; the skull is evidently that of a woman of about twenty. There can no longer be any doubt that men who already possessed the general characteristics of the modern *Homo sapiens* were living during the second interglacial.

We have now traced primitive representatives of *Homo sapiens,* or at any rate, the immediate precursors of this species, to the second interglacial period. Moreover, there is no structural break in continuity in the gradational series through which these early types are linked with modern *Homo sapiens*. If we now continue our journey still further into the past, we come to the second glacial period, the Mindel Ice Age, which we reckon to be included between 1,205,000 and 1,060,000 years ago. A much more primitive type of hominid was distributed over relatively wide areas of the Old World at that time. So different from *Homo* was this primitive type, and so ape-like in certain features of the skull and jaws, that it was originally put into a separate genus, *Pithecanthropus,* the ape-man. Today, however, anthropologists regard *Pithecanthropus* as a race belonging to the species *Homo erectus.*

The first relics of this race, which for convenience we will call *Pithecanthropus,* were found in Java in 1891. For many years after, in spite of expeditions designed to search for more remains, nothing else was found. Then, in 1937 and the following years, additional fossils were brought to light. These consisted of a few skulls, some jaw fragments, and a number of teeth. In the meantime, from 1921 on, excavators of caves near Peking in China had been finding extensive remains of hominids. Confusingly enough, these finds were assigned to a new genus and a new species, *Sinanthropus pekinensis.* But in reality *Sinanthropus* was merely another example of *Pithecanthropus,* though probably a trifle younger than the Javanese representatives, which are in several respects more primitive in anatomical structure.

The members of this group were rather small-brained individuals with retreating forehead, beetling brows, and big jaws, but with limbs fashioned like our own. In spite of their small brains, they were not without culture; we know from the refuse left from their feasts and the traces of their cooking hearths that those which lived in China were skilled hunters and knew how to use fire. They were also capable of fabricating stone implements, though of a rather crude kind. According to one scientist who studied a cast of the inside of the best of the Chinese skulls, *Sinanthropus* must have been right-handed and must have had an articulate language. An important point that bears on whether *Pithecanthropus* could have provided the ancestral stock for the subsequent evolutionary development of *Homo* is the fact that his remains, as found in the Far East, show a fairly wide range of variation. The cranial capacity, at its upper limit, reaches close to the mean value for *Homo sapiens,* and there are similar degrees of variability in the size of the jaws, the development of the forehead region, and so forth. In fact, at one end of the range, *Pithecanthropus* approaches quite closely to the Early Mousterian or pre-Mousterian populations, and many authorities believe that the morphological "gap" between them is almost insignificant.

Thus far, it seems, we have a fossil record which does suggest that very probably from the second glacial period, about 1,150,000 years ago, onwards there has been a progressive sequence of hominid types leading almost insensibly from the primitive, small-brained *Pithecanthropus* through pre-Mousterian and Early Mousterian man to *Homo sapiens* as this species exists today. If Darwin's line of reasoning, from the indirect evidence at his disposal, is sound, one might predict that *Pithecanthropus* would itself have been preceded by a type showing even more ape-like features, such as a still smaller brain and jaws of more simian dimensions.

In 1924 Raymond A. Dart found at Taung in Bechuanaland an extraordinarily fine and well-preserved skull of a new type of hominid. Since then quantities of the fossilized remains of these creatures have been collected from cave deposits at widely scattered sites in Africa, so that it is possible to speak with considerable assurance about their anatomical features. Undoubtedly the most striking is the size of the brain case; it is not only much smaller when compared with that of *Pithecanthropus,* but it actually overlaps the range of the modern large apes. The small brain case, combined with huge jaws, gives the whole skull a very simian appearance indeed; for this reason, upon first being discovered, these remains were given the name *Australopithecus,* which means the "southern ape." Now it has been realized that they were not apes in the strict sense of zoological nomenclature. They were exceedingly primitive hominids which in a number of fundamental features had already developed a considerable way along the direction of hominid evolution, quite opposite to the direction of evolution which the anthropoid ape family followed.

On the basis of the early discoveries, it had been inferred from some features of the base of the skull that the australopithecines were erect bipedal creatures. Since then four different specimens of the australopithecine pelvis have been found at different sites in South Africa; all conform in their fundamental characters to the hominid pattern of construction. There can be no reasonable doubt, therefore, that the australopithecines had already achieved an erect, bipedal posture.

Stone tools occurred in association with the remains of *Australopithecus*. The inference that the australopithecines had made the tools seemed obvious. However, some anthropologists questioned whether creatures with such small brains could have had enough intelligence to make tools. These scientists suggested that some more advanced hominid had not only made the tools, but had also preyed upon the australopithecines.

In 1961 Louis S. B. Leakey made a discovery at Olduvai Gorge, in Tanganyika, which provided a clue to the origin of the tools. Leakey had already found a wealth of bones at Olduvai, including excellent specimens of *Zinjanthropus,* a late australopithecine. The new finds consisted of the greater part of a juvenile hominid mandible and some fragments of a skull vault. Leakey attributed these juvenile remains, not to an australopithecine, but "to a very remote and truly primitive ancestor of *Homo.*"

In 1963 more bones of outstanding importance were uncovered at Olduvai Gorge. On the basis of this material, L. S. B. Leakey, P. V. Tobias, and J. R. Napier published in 1964 in *Nature* the description of a new species of the genus *Homo,* which they called *Homo habilis,* or the "able, handy man." Possibly *Australopithecus* and *Homo habilis* both made stone tools, but very probably *Homo habilis,* with a larger skull capacity, was the more advanced toolmaker.

From the association of the remains of *Australopithecus* and *Homo habilis* it is clear that two different branches of the family Hominidae were evolving side by side in the Olduvai region.

Eventually *Australopithecus* became extinct without evolving into a higher form. Presumably the more able *Homo habilis* carried on; judging from what is known of his anatomy, he may well have been ancestral to *Homo erectus*.

We know that *Homo habilis* lived before *Homo erectus*. By a lucky chance, the layer of sediment which contains the bones of *Homo habilis* lies sandwiched between two layers of volcanic ash, or fragmental material strewn over the former land surface by the explosive eruptions of an ancient volcano. As a result of recent advances in radiochemistry, volcanic deposits of this kind can now be dated. The method depends on the fact that a radioactive isotope of potassium decays into calcium and an isotope of the gas argon. The method is applicable only to igneous rocks, the potassium-bearing minerals of which are devoid of argon when they first crystallize. Since the generation of argon is constant with time, its abundance in certain minerals of an igneous or volcanic rock provides a measure of the time elapsed since the rock solidified. By dating the volcanic ash layers above and below the layer of sediment containing the bones of *Homo habilis,* Jack F. Evernden and Garniss H. Curtis have estimated that the sediment was deposited about 1,750,000 years ago.

The genera of the mammals whose bones are associated with *Homo habilis* indicate that the stratigraphical position of his resting place is equivalent to the faunal zone known as the Upper Villafranchian. Because some of the species of mammals in the Villafranchian assemblage indicate a drop in temperature, geologists by general consent regard the Villafranchian as representing the earliest phase of the Pleistocene. However, as we point out in Chapter 9, there is good evidence in a suite of sediment cores of falling temperature before the drastic faunal change that we believe records the onset of the first ice age. This is particularly clear in a core from the Indian Ocean which contains ice-rafted detritus probably from Antarctica, below the faunal change. We cannot help wondering, therefore, whether the evidence of cooler climate in the Villafranchian is a sufficient reason to assign it to the Pleistocene. On the evidence of the ages of the layers of volcanic ash, the Villafranchian at Olduvai antedates the onset of the first ice age.

We have now traced in retrospect a graded morphological series, arranged in an ordered time sequence, which links *Homo sapiens,* through Early Mousterian man, pre-Mousterian man, and the small-brained *Pithecanthropus*, with the still smaller-brained *Homo habilis*. This sequence comprises a remarkable confirmation of the connecting links postulated and predicted, almost entirely from observations of living organisms, in Darwin's hypothesis of the descent of man, at any rate as far back as the beginning of the Pleistocene. There is no conspicuous gap in the sequence.

Man is still evolving by natural selection. But today, in the midst of the latest toolmaking revolution, man has achieved the capacity to mold his environment to his needs and impulses. The impact of human works on the environment is so strong that it has become very difficult to make out the forces to which the human species is now adjusting. Man is the only product of biological evolution who is aware that he has evolved and will keep on evolving. He should be able to replace the blind process of natural selection by conscious direction, based on his knowledge of nature and on his values.

13

APPLYING THE TIME SCALE TO PLEISTOCENE CULTURES AND MAMMALIAN SUCCESSION

MANY years ago we, together with a distinguished old geologist and a local guide, were walking across the nearly level bottom of a broad valley in eastern Turkey. The guide, a Kurd, was supposed to be leading us to an oil seep, or spring of petroleum. As we plodded along in the intense heat, our companion in science lectured on his favorite topic, his theory of the origin of petroleum.

Then, all at once, we saw something, and exclaimed. The lecturer broke off in the middle of a sentence, halted by the former presence of Paleolithic man. There at our feet was as beautiful a flint hand ax as we have ever seen in any museum. We believe we have never come closer to shaking hands with a ghost than during those seconds as we grasped the flint by its blunt end just as its maker must once have done.

Probably the hand ax had been washed out of the stream terrace which bordered the valley, but its edge, still almost as sharp as when it was first chipped, showed that it had not traveled far. As archaeological hunting ground, the valley could hardly have been improved upon. Cliffs of limestone containing layers of flint formed the walls of the valley; the country abounded in caves, some large enough to shelter flocks of sheep; and in our hands we held the proof that men of the stone age had lived nearby.

Excited by the discovery, we declared the necessity of exploring the valley for the remains of ancient man. For a while we discussed how it might be done—until present-day technology drew us back to reality. It was getting late and we had not found the oil seep. We turned indignantly on our guide. Why was he standing there, instead of leading us to the oil seep? The poor man knew no English and little Turkish, but he got the idea and pointed back in the direction from which we had come. We discovered to our painful embarrassment that we, the petroleum experts, had walked over the seep without seeing it. Such is the power of an eloquent tongue! As for our guide—he had been much too awed by our friend's "lecture" to interrupt. And, anyway, he had led us to the seep; if the Efendiler chose to walk on without stopping, that was none of his business. When we got back to our camp, we gave him an extra tip; had he tactlessly stopped us at the seep, we would have missed our close brush with Paleolithic man.

Did we explore the valley? No. At the camp we found that other plans had been made; a group of mounted police had arrived to escort us to the banks of the Tigris, where there was a bigger and better oil seep. Since then, our friend the petroleum geologist has died and fate has tumbled us along hither and thither. In spite of our vow to return to the valley of Hermis, we have never done so.

Anatomically, man has never been a distinguished creature. Other animals can run faster, bite harder, swim better, or fly by means of their own bodily equipment. In many places the fossil bones of other animals occur in profusion, but the bones of ancient men are so fragile that after long and patient search by paleo-anthropologists we are only now just beginning to find out what manner of men our ancestors were.

The profound difference that sets man apart from the rest of the organic world is his brain. It gives him the ability to develop a culture, a faculty which depends upon manual dexterity and the use of symbols by which ideas can be transmitted from one mind to another. By virtue of his culture, he leaves his mark on his environment as no other creature can. One can tell with certainty where he has been without having to find his bones. More than that, one can estimate the degree of his physical and mental development from the products of his culture. Thus human industries provide a time sequence for the Pleistocene, one for which there is no equivalent in the deposits of the earlier epochs.

It must have begun as a chance mutation which favored a tendency to rise on the hind legs and thereby to free the forelimbs. In most animals, such a mutation would come to an evolutionary dead end. To cite an extreme example, the same innate and heritable tendency in a hoofed animal would be disadvantageous; selection would soon eliminate it from the population. But the prehuman primate had already passed through a stage of tree-climbing during which selection had strongly favored the ability to grasp. Thus by pure chance the mutant gene which favored the freeing of the forepaws, or hands, of a certain primate fell on fertile ground. It was a portentous event and has had repercussions throughout the world of living things.

This primate who could get about on his hind legs could not only use sticks and long bones as clubs and stones as hammers; he could also carry them about as he hunted. In this he possessed a decisive advantage over all other animals, including his closest relatives, who could do nothing better with their forepaws than to walk on them. Inexorably, selection favored the survival of every mutation, however small, which enhanced manual dexterity in its carrier. The result was a powerful interaction between the use of tools and the anatomical evolution of early man.

Until fairly recently, it has been rather generally held that man evolved almost to his present structural state and then discovered tools and the new ways of life to which they are the keys. In this, one can discern a vestigial idea, the mental analogue of a vestigial organ like the vermiform appendix. Although those who hold this belief have discarded the Adam and Eve hypothesis, they seem to have been unconsciously influenced by that story to such an extent that they still think man arrived on the scene almost fully evolved physically and mentally, and yet naked and without knowledge of tools. More than anything else, the discoveries of the Leakeys in East Africa have destroyed the last vestige of that myth. The evidence that a hominid as anatomically primitive as *Homo habilis* could fabricate tools was fatal to it. Of course we are influenced by hindsight, but as we see the matter now, it seems obvious that the mechanical perfection and fine nervous control of the hand could not have evolved without long and powerful selective pressure—something which only the use of tools could provide. Charles Darwin realized this; more than a hundred years ago he suggested that the use of tools was both the cause and the effect of bipedal locomotion. As he saw it, the evolutionary process was a closely meshed interaction between innately determined behavior and innately determined change in anatomical structure, as, for example, the gradual shortening of the pelvic bones, which permitted a more fully upright posture.

For a long time, early hominids must have used stones as hammers only. Then one day a hammer user carrying a unique combination of genes broke a hammer stone by accident. It had happened often before to hammer users, but this one was a little different. The sharp edges of the broken stone made it into a cutting tool. His chance combination of genes had given rise to a brain that could follow through from accidently broken stone to stone broken by design. He proceeded to do what no other primate had ever done before; he deliberately broke more stones in order to develop more and better cutting edges. Here was a new ability that had survival value. It made him a better provider; his offspring, who received genes from him, were less likely to go hungry and consequently had a better chance to reach maturity and perpetuate the genetical strain of a hominid who could form a mental image, for the mental image of a stone broken by design must have taken form in his head before he struck two flints together with a purpose.

But what of fire? Striking flints together makes sparks which can accidently ignite dry leaves. In the course of hundreds of thousands of years of flint chipping, some fires must have been started by accident, but one can imagine that for *Zinjanthropus* an accidental fire would be a terrifying experience, something to be avoided by all means. At any rate, all available evidence indicates that neither *Zinjanthropus* nor his cousin *Australopithecus* ever used fire. Apparently they were not quite bright enough to discover its usefulness. More permutations of new genes and more selection had to occur before a hominid emerged with less timidity, more curiosity, and the ability to put two and two together.

Such a hominid, perhaps hard pressed by a damp cave and a winter that was colder than usual, may have discovered the pleasant sensation of warming his hands over an accidently kindled fire. Once again a hominid struck two flints together with a purpose; this time to start the most fundamentally useful chemical reaction known to man. However, this crucial event could never have occurred without the additional spark of intelligence. Here once more was survival value. The children of the firemaker had a better chance to survive in a warm, dry cave, and consequently the genes that made a better brain became a part of the genetical pool of the species.

Stone tools were known in Europe long before it was generally realized that primitive men had existed. In medieval Europe, stone tools were regarded as thunderbolts, allegedly produced or hurled by lightning. With the Renaissance, their real nature dawned upon a few wise men. But the idea of a stone age was scorned by most people until travelers in America returned with accounts of stone tools and weapons used by the Indians. By the beginning of the eighteenth century, this evidence had won the day. No one any longer doubted that the "thunderbolts" were anything but the tools of ancient men; still, there was no realization of how ancient they really were. Thinking was still closely confined by Biblical chronology.

In the nineteenth century, the new sciences of geology and paleontology began to shed light on the antiquity of man. It became evident that many implements of primitive design occurred in deposits which also included the bones of animals that no longer exist today. A Frenchman, Édouard Lartet, deeply impressed by this association, expressed the thought in 1858 that the history of man, like that of other animals, is a continuous story which calls for a chronological method, that is, the establishment of a temporal succession of events. Accordingly, he put forward a provisional chronology based on the succession of extinctions of Pleistocene mammals. On the basis of this, he could classify the strata in which traces of primitive men had been found. This was a realistic way of dealing with the problem in those days, when geology had no means of measuring time intervals in years.

Another way of establishing a temporal sequence is by the archaeological method based on the evolution of cultures. This is practicable because the traces of man's industry, particularly in the form of dressed flints, are so much more enduring than his bones that they may be found by thousands where there is no trace of the bones of the makers.

Having recognized that a stone age had preceded the age of metals, the early prehistorians soon realized that the stone age as well could be subdivided into a more recent Neolithic phase during which men shaped implements by grinding and polishing, and a more primitive phase, the Paleolithic, during which they fashioned their tools by chipping only. In Europe, archaeologists distinguish a third and intermediate phase, the Mesolithic, which includes cultures showing the first uncertain attempts to finish tools by grinding the edges. The relationship between deposits that contain articles of Mesolithic and Neolithic cultures and the deposits laid down during the last ice age shows that both of these phases of culture flourished within the Holocene, or postglacial time. In fact, the change-over from the Paleolithic to the Mesolithic industry coincides fairly closely with the end of the last ice age. Since that climatic event occurred about 11,000 years ago, archaeological sites which belong to these phases can be dated by the radiocarbon method. For this reason, our chronology of Pleistocene climatic events has no useful bearing on these most recent stages in the cultural development of man. Furthermore, although some physical evolution must have taken place, particularly in the nervous system, there is no evidence of evolutionary change in the bones of the men of those times. Physically, they appear to have been similar to modern men. The great importance of our chronology lies in its ability to provide a time scale for the vastly longer Paleolithic phase, during which most of man's physical evolution took place. In that respect, it is by far the more fascinating and significant phase.

In broad outline, the sequence of cultural phases as worked out in Europe can be applied to other parts of the world, but strict contemporaneity of similar cultural levels in remote parts is improbable. According to one theory of cultural development, every change occurred at a unique center, from which the particular innovation diffused to all parts of the world. But even if this is a correct interpretation, the rate of diffusion must have been extremely slow, particularly in crossing from continent to continent. According to a more plausible theory, cultural advances were often due to independent discoveries, which need not have occurred simultaneously. The fallacy of the assumption that similar cultures occurred contemporaneously is clear when one considers that the natives of Tasmania were in a paleolithic cultural stage thousands of years after Europeans had discovered the use of metals. Our chronology, therefore, applies most particularly to the subdivisions of the Paleolithic as it developed in Europe, where the stages have been correlated with the advances and retreats of the continental glaciers. When the chronology is applied to cultural development on other continents, some allowance should be made for possible cultural lags, though in view of the long time intervals involved, the errors of timing should not be serious.

The Paleolithic phase may be divided into three parts. The Lower Paleolithic spanned the period extending from the onset of the first ice age to the end of the third ice age, and according to our chronology lasted from about 1,500,000 to about 340,000 years ago. The Middle Paleolithic comprises the last interglacial and the first half of the last ice age, that is, from about 340,000 to about 95,000 years ago, according to our time scale. The Upper Paleolithic consists of the latter half of the last ice age, from about 95,000[1] to 11,000 years ago.

[1] This date, 95,000 years before present, for the beginning of the Upper Paleolithic requires comment. The Upper Paleolithic begins in the early part of a mild interstadial during the last ice age. It is recognized in Europe as the Göttweig Interstadial. On the evidence of the correspondence between the position of the Göttweig within the Würm and the stratigraphical position of our warm interstadial, the two should be equivalent. However, a series of radiocarbon datings of samples from peat deposits of Göttweig age are in serious dis-

The Lower Paleolithic industry includes only a few types of tools. However, toward the end of this period and in the beginning of the Middle Paleolithic, the number rises markedly and the record becomes relatively complex. In the Upper Paleolithic the diversification of tool forms increases greatly, although the time interval was less than a fifth of the duration of the Middle Paleolithic. This was probably due not so much to rapid evolution of culture as to a diversity of styles of toolmaking among tribes which were constantly on the move.

According to a popular school of thinking, this acceleration of cultural development should reflect the influence of a particularly favorable environment. Admittedly, at times and under certain circumstances the effect of environment on cultural development can be profound. For example, Western technology and science within the last hundred years have created an artificial environment which is highly favorable to the further development of technology and science. But the environment of the Upper Paleolithic was that of an ice age. It is not clear to us how such an environment could promote an acceleration of cultural development in a genetically static population. However, the stormy, cold climate of an ice age would intensify selective pressure. Accordingly, it seems to us more probable that an increase in genetically controlled and heritable ability to perceive connections and follow logical trains of thought from premise to conclusion was the primary factor behind the innovations which archaeologists find in the industry of this period. Very probably man's thinking was becoming logical in the original sense of the word. The Greeks realized the importance of words in maintaining a train of thought, and accordingly they called sequential thinking logical or, in effect, verbal. It seems to us a safe guess that the men of the Upper Paleolithic were making

agreement with our estimate of the age of the warm interstadial in the cores. According to the radiocarbon dates, the Göttweig extended from 42,000 to 31,000 years ago. We question these dates. Wood and peat samples are easily contaminated. The method of concentrating the radiocarbon used in dating these old samples is open to the criticism that it necessarily increases the error due to contamination and thereby may yield a spurious finite "date" for a sample which is really older than the limit of the method. Unfortunately, no attempt to repeat the datings of the Göttweig samples has been made since the original investigator died about six years ago.

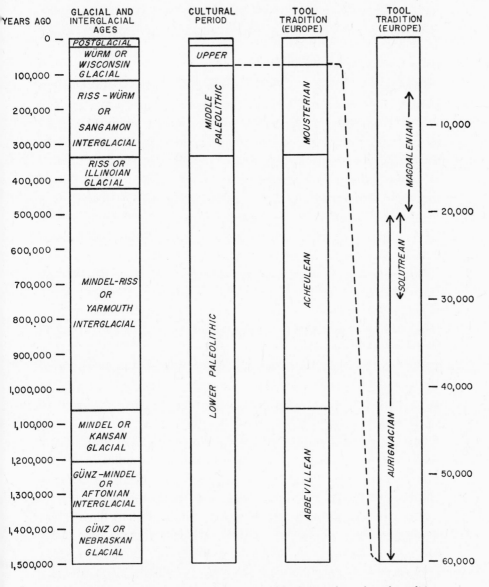

FIGURE 28 *Time scale and correlation of cultural periods and tool traditions with the glacial and interglacial ages of the Pleistocene.*

rapid strides in their ability to think with the symbols we call words. According to our chronology, the duration of the Upper Paleolithic was some 50,000 years, a sufficiently long time interval to allow significant genetical change.

During this period, man's first artistic creations—paintings, engravings, and sculptures—enter the record. This was the prelude to the Mesolithic and Neolithic cultural phases, from 11,000 to about 5,000 years ago, during which culture rapidly advanced to the invention of ceramics, the use of metals, and the development of writing, which opened the door on the historic period. From then on, a chain reaction set in. The recording of facts, conjectures, or mere idle thoughts on clay tablets, papyrus, or sheepskins created the intellectual environment which has finally culminated in the technological explosion of the twentieth century.

But to return to the earlier days—during the Lower and Middle Paleolithic there were at least two distinct cultural cycles. These were the flake culture and the hand-ax culture, each made up of a greater or smaller number of differing, though allied cultures. The Upper Paleolithic saw the addition of a third cultural element, the blade industry, essentially an industry of long, narrow flakes of flint adapted to many purposes—knives, scrapers, piercers, gravers, and saws. These implements have been found by the thousands in the Dordogne region of France.

The most important cultures of the Paleolithic have been named after particular caves or sites in France where examples of the industries were first found. These are the Abbevillean, Acheulian, Mousterian, Aurignacian, Solutrean, and Magdalenian.

The Abbevillean culture is generally considered to have lasted through the first ice age, the first interglacial, and the second ice age, which according to the new chronology would be from about 1,500,000 to 1,060,000 years ago, or for about 440,000 years. The Abbevillean tools, which were worked on both faces, generally by a hard hammer stone or on a fixed stone anvil, are more or less pear-shaped, with deep-biting flake scars and with a fair proportion of the original crust or cortex of the flint retained on or near the butt. Fitted to the hand or used as wedges, these tools could serve the purpose of ax, saw or chisel, but probably they were used mainly for cutting, scraping, and skinning game. Abbevillean implements are widely distributed; like the succeeding Acheulian, the Abbevillean entered Europe from Asia.

The Acheulian culture is generally correlated with the second interglacial period and the third ice age, that is, from about 1,060,-000 to 340,000 years ago, according to the new time scale. The dominant tools were the hand ax with a pointed or rounded edge and the "cleaver," which has a straight and sharp cutting edge. Several Acheulian traditions developed in Europe, Africa, and Asia. Their characteristics depended on the assemblages of bifaces, some of which were made from large pebbles and others from flakes struck from virgin rock. The men who made these implements knew how to kindle fires; traces of hearths occur at Acheulian sites in Germany. They must necessarily have worked and utilized wood extensively, and probably they also used bone.

The extraordinarily conservative character of this long-enduring culture led F. E. Zeuner, one of the foremost students of Pleistocene chronology, to remark that "this conservatism of the Acheulian is one of the most striking phenomena in the chronology of the Pleistocene." Yet Zeuner was thinking in terms of a "short" chronology according to which the Acheulian culture lasted some 300,000 years. Now we know that it lasted more than twice as long, about 720,000 years.

The Mousterian cultural period started at the beginning of the last interglacial, which we date at about 340,000 years ago, and ended in the middle of the last ice age, about 60,000 years ago. The tools of this period are more complex than those of the preceding culture. They represent a flake industry of highly developed technique. The flake was worked on one side only; the sloping lateral retouch is typical of the period. The culture also includes a microlithic industry, that is, a complex of miniature blades which may have been used as fine gravers or perhaps more often were set in rows in slots carved in wooden or bone handles. The Mousterian culture was distributed over all Europe south of the former ice sheets. Its source was doubtless in Asia.

The Upper Paleolithic, which we date from 60,000 to 11,000 years ago, was a time of rapid invention. It includes the Perigordian, Aurignacian, Solutrean, and Magdalenian industries. The Aurignacian, the most important of the four, extended over Europe, Asia and Africa. An important cultural advance was signaled by the general use of bone from horses and reindeer. The use of mammoth ivory is particularly characteristic of the period. The Middle Aurignacian culture, with its characteristic technique, statuettes, and bone tools, may have been intrusive into Europe, having sprung from an Asian source, possibly in the Iranian Plateau.

The Solutrean, though of very short duration, marks the culmination of the art of flint working. The flakes of this industry are flat and remarkably thin, sharp-edged, and perfectly symmetrical. They are distinguished by the beauty of their secondary or ripple flaking, which was achieved by a new technique. Small flakes were sprung from the first rough edge by pressing a piece of bone or wood against the edge instead of striking it with another flint. This made possible a control and precision of the final retouching that could be achieved in no other way.

The Magdalenian flint implements, often made from material badly selected and poor in quality, were less elaborate and less complex in style than the Aurignacian and Solutrean, and they display a minimum amount of finishing and dressing. Magdalenian man was more at home in working in reindeer and deer horn, or even in amber. He developed a high degree of skill and artistry in the fabrication of quantities of tools of bone, horn, and mammoth ivory. Bone needles, which are sparse in the Upper Aurignacian and Solutrean industries, became abundant in the Magdalenian. Arrowheads and spearheads of bone were adorned with incised designs. Multibarbed harpoons, the earliest known, were used for fishing. The Magdalenian developed in what is now France. It had its origin in the Pyrenees and spread into northern Spain, central France, Switzerland, Germany, Austria, and Czechoslovakia. It occurs less frequently in Belgium and atypically in England. It is unknown in Eastern Europe, in southern Spain, Italy, or anywhere in Africa. During the Magdalenian, migration, or transmission of culture on a wide scale, gave way to local variations of the already established culture.

The application of our time scale to prehistoric archaeology makes it possible to view the cultural evolution of man in proper perspective. The beginning of man's cultural evolution took place much farther back in time than has been generally realized. Instead of having originated some 600,000 years ago, or even no more than 300,000 years ago, as an estimate based on oxygen-isotope paleotemperatures would have it, the cultural evolution of man stretches back about 1,500,000 years, according to the new chronology of the Pleistocene.

Though man was the chief actor in the evolutionary drama of the Pleistocene, he was not alone; other animals were also evolving. The now more correctly estimated dates of events during the Pleistocene, even if only approximate, will enable paleontologists to see biological changes against their true chronological background. Scientists will thus be in a better position to deduce from these changes some of the hidden rules of life.

One of the methods used to establish a relative chronology of Pleistocene events is based on the study of fossil bones of animals other than man; during the Pleistocene striking changes took place among land animals, particularly among the mammals. Unfortunately, one cannot find anywhere a complete succession of beds containing a continuous procession of mammals starting with the first ice age. But by piecing together many incomplete sections, vertebrate paleontologists have been able to build up a composite stratigraphical section which is essentially complete and which can be applied with confidence to deposits within a geographical unit such as Western Europe. The method is also used to correlate deposits in Africa and Asia with the glacial events in Europe, but the equivalence in time of similar groups of animals in such widely separated regions is probably true only in a broad sense.

The usefulness of the method depends on the fact that bones of large mammals are vastly more abundant and widespread than the bones of hominids. To establish a stratigraphical sequence by means of the bones of hominids alone would be quite impossible, but when hominid bones are found, their relative position in the sequence of events can usually be determined on the basis of the mammal bones associated with them.

The broad divisions of the Pleistocene—Lower, Middle, and Upper—are readily recognizable by their distinctive assemblages of mammals. By convention, the Lower Pleistocene is understood to include the first ice age, the first interglacial, and the second ice age. The Middle Pleistocene includes the second or great interglacial and the third ice age. And the Upper Pleistocene comprises the last interglacial and the last ice age. The Lower Pleistocene mammalian fauna consisted of survivors from the Pliocene, along with primitive elephants and small horses; the Middle Pleistocene is distinguished by true Pleistocene elephants and large horses; and the Upper Pleistocene begins with the extinction of many of the preceding large mammals. It is marked by the appearance of species adapted to cold, such as the woolly mammoth and the woolly rhinoceros. The mammoth of the Upper Pleistocene was a clearly defined species of elephant, peculiar in the shape of its skull, its dentition, the loss of a toe, and a hairy coat.

The widespread faunal changes of the European Pleistocene consisted of the extinction of old forms, the immigration of new forms, and the evolution of more primitive species into advanced species. Animals appeared and disappeared after time intervals which varied with the species and with the region. Thus *Trogontherium cuvieri,* a large beaver, did not outlive the first interglacial age, the Günz-Mindel, in Central Europe, but in Western Europe its range straddles the second interglacial age, the Mindel-Riss. The hippopotamus appeared suddenly as an immigrant into Europe in the Lower Pleistocene. It disappeared from Europe before Mousterian or Aurignacian time, as did *Elephas antiquus,* the straight-tusked elephant. The panther lived at Mosbach and Mauer in Germany in the Lower Pleistocene and was widespread during the Mousterian but apparently failed to survive the Aurignacian. The mammoth, *Elephas primigenius,* probably lasted into the earliest part of postglacial time.

The Pleistocene mammals of North America are a combination

of faunas from different latitudes; immigrants from Eurasia and South America are included. This assemblage died out gradually and at different rates in different places. The vast area of the southern part of the North American continent provided safe refuges during the continental glaciations, in contrast to Europe at these times. Consequently, the clearly defined faunal changes which characterize the Pleistocene succession in Europe are absent in North America. However, the work of B. Brown, E. D. Cope, J. Leidy, W. H. Hall, W. D. Matthews, and H. F. Osborn has established three successive Pleistocene mammalian faunas in North America. These are a Lower Pleistocene fauna, which includes a short-jawed mastodon, several mammoths, a tapir, puma, camel, and several species of horses; a Middle Pleistocene fauna, from which the short-jawed mastodon is absent and to which the Canadian elk and moose have been added; and an Upper Pleistocene fauna, which includes the musk ox, the caribou, or American form of reindeer, the woolly mammoth, and the black bear.

The horses, of which there were at least ten species, grew fewer as the Pleistocene advanced, and failed to survive through the last ice age, the Wisconsin. One species of camels, the western camel, occurs in deposits of the last ice age, but it became extinct before the end of the ice age. Remains of mastodons have been found associated with late Wisconsin glacial deposits on Long Island and Staten Island. There is evidence that they, together with elephants, musk oxen, moose, peccaries, and the giant beaver, survived into postglacial time.

Many groups and families, such as the ground sloths, the California lion, the mastodon, and the mammoth, and certain peccaries, camels, musk oxen, bison, and giant beavers lived on in America after they had become extinct in Europe. It is at least possible that they owed their survival to the late arrival of man in America; their extinction at about the time of man's arrival in America suggests that he had a hand in their disappearance.

The paleontological chronologies that we have outlined are of course strictly relative. They tell us that certain groups of animals are older than certain other groups—but how much older? Yet, to the student of organic evolution, the time intervals, in years, which separate the stages of the great procession are of fascinating interest and importance. Now, thanks to the new chronology of Pleistocene climatic events, it will be possible to evaluate the rates of evolution of the animals in Europe and North America, and wherever else assemblages of fossil mammals can be tied in with the climatic sequence.

But what of our globe, the scene of this biological pageant— has it been quite passive all the while? It has, in fact, shown not a trace of old age. Apparently it is still full of energy, as indicated by volcanic activity and mountain building in all regions during the Pleistocene. Many volcanoes were active in the Mediterranean region; Vesuvius and Etna were born during this epoch; and in Italy, Upper Paleolithic men dug shelters in beds of volcanic ash.

Volcanic eruptions were frequent in the Central Plateau of France, and the great basaltic volcanoes of the Laacher See district of the Eifel were active during the Riss-Würm Interglacial. In the Atlantic basin, the volcanic rocks of Iceland are interbedded with glacial deposits. Pleistocene vulcanism also occurred in the Cape Verde and Canary Islands. Volcanic activity was widespread in Asia, in Africa, and in Australia. Even in Antarctica, volcanoes burst forth in the region of the Ross Sea, on Deception Island, and on Kerguelen.

In America, volcanoes were active from Alaska through the Sierra Nevadas, through Central America, and down the entire length of the Andes, and an eastward extension of this activity took in the islands of the West Indies. Evidence of this volcanic activity in the form of layers of finely divided particles of volcanic glass occurs in cores of sediment from the bottom of the Caribbean, the Gulf of Mexico, and above all from the Pacific off the coast of South America.

But volcanoes were not the only kind of mountains that came into being during the Pleistocene. It has been said that the Pleistocene represents one of the crescendos in the structural history of the earth. Pleistocene fracturing, uplift, and crustal warping have been proved for almost all regions of the globe. Mountain-making forces were at work in the Alps, particularly during the great interglacial of the Mindel-Riss. In Russia, the Ural Mountains rose at this time while other structural elements, such as the Caspian region, subsided.

In Asia, a structural discontinuity of Middle Pleistocene age has been traced from the Caucasus to Central and Eastern Asia. At this time the fault troughs of the Dead Sea, the Red Sea, the Gulf of Aden, the Persian Gulf, and the Arabian Sea took on their present form. The height of the Himalaya increased by some two thousand meters.

In China as well as in Burma and northwestern India, an abrupt uplift, more clearly defined than that at the base of the Pleistocene section, took place in the Middle Pleistocene.

In America the Appalachians rose to their present altitudes during the Pleistocene. Uplifts of thousands of meters occurred in western North America. Similar mountain-making activity, with uplifts of as much as 2,700 meters, affected the whole of the Andes. As in many other places, the deformation was most pronounced during the Middle Pleistocene.

Confronted by so much crustal unrest, it is hardly surprising that Pleistocene geologists working only with continental deposits have had difficulty piecing together a complete sedimentary sequence for the Pleistocene. That some unrest has extended to the ocean floor is certain; and fortunately so, for Pleistocene chronology. Had the accumulation of sediment continued uninterruptedly everywhere on the ocean floor throughout the Pleistocene, the relatively short coring tube could not have reached the layers of sediment which represent the earlier divisions of the Pleistocene. Thus, the geological unrest of the Pleistocene has contributed to our success in discovering the complete chronology of that epoch. Now, by applying the new time scale to the extraordinary biological and geological phenomena of the Pleistocene, we may hope to gain a clearer insight into the exciting chapter of earth history, which includes the evolution of man.

14

THE CAUSATION OF
THE ICE AGES

THE discovery of the complete stratigraphical section of the Pleistocene and a record of the major climatic events with a chronology has an important bearing on the long-debated question of the cause of the ice ages.

The cause of the extraordinary climatic changes of the Pleistocene has been the happy hunting ground of a large tribe of theorists. Some of the best minds, and many more fantastical minds, have played with this problem. It has been estimated that a new theory to explain continental glaciations has been published for every year that has passed since the first recognition of the evidence for past glaciation in the second quarter of the nineteenth century. Theories have been championed by some and denounced by others with the fervor that marked the religious controversies of earlier centuries. The enthusiasm of many ingenious and imaginative people has generated a throng of theories running the gamut from the possible but unprovable to the internally contradictory and the palpably inadequate.

To anyone unfamiliar with the history of the earth, the ice ages may suggest a late stage of a gradually cooling earth. Very probably the earth in its development passed through a molten state. However, this is purely conjectural. It is not registered in the record of the rocks; the oldest known rocks are not igneous, that is, rocks which froze from a molten state, but instead they are much altered sedimentary rocks. Since some or all of these accumulated under water, it is clear that the surface of the earth cannot have been very hot even in those primeval days. Furthermore, some of these sediments contain quantities of carbon scattered through them, an indication of abundant aquatic life of some sort. Evidently water temperatures then were not much different from those of present-day lakes and seas. Apparently the temperature of the surface of the earth had become stable long before the beginning of the Cambrian Period, some 600 million years ago, when the first recognizable forms of life appeared.

Since then, the earth has lost a vast amount of heat by radiation from its surface. However, this is not residual heat left over from the earth's molten state; it is heat continually generated by the decay of radioactive substances within the earth, such as, for example, the radioactive potassium by which geochronologists can tell the age of rocks. Presumably this heat will be with us for a long time to come, though until we learn to use it as a source of energy, it has no direct effect on our lives, and certainly none on climate, which is determined by interaction between energy from the sun and the earth's atmosphere, the oceans, and the topographical features of the surface of the earth.

But may not the ice ages of the Pleistocene be a result of a decrease in the sun's energy? On this question we find some evidence in the record of the rocks. It seems that intervals of glacial climate have occurred from time to time long before the Pleistocene. The thickest and most widespread deposits of ice-transported rock detritus are associated with pre-Cambrian sediments, which the radioactive clock shows to be older than 600 million years. If the sun is expiring, then truly, like a certain king of England, it has been taking an unconscionably long time about it.

Rather surprisingly, the great majority of theories of glaciation assume a constant output of energy from the sun and look elsewhere for the cause of refrigerations. Most of them are based on some event or change in conditions on the earth or in its atmosphere. One theory relates ice ages to changes in the amount of carbon dioxide in the atmosphere. Carbon dioxide is transparent to short-wave radiation from the sun. The earth's surface, having been heated by this solar radiant energy, reradiates long waves, but carbon dioxide is opaque to long-wave radiation. Thus, heat energy is trapped by the atmosphere very much as it is trapped by the glass roof of a greenhouse. However, the possibility that variations in the carbon-dioxide content of the atmosphere occurred repeatedly and at the tempo demanded by the climatic record of the sediment cores presents as much of a problem as the problem it is intended to solve. The carbon dioxide in the atmosphere is in equilibrium with that in solution in the oceans; carbon dioxide removed from the atmosphere would at once be replaced by carbon dioxide from the oceans. Accordingly, the problem is not merely the reduction of the carbon-dioxide content of the atmosphere, but rather the reduction of the carbon-dioxide content of the entire system of atmosphere and ocean—a problem of quite a different order.

Fine mineral particles in the atmosphere have the opposite effect; they reflect short-wave radiation from the sun but permit long heat waves to escape into space. These particles would have an even more important effect as centers on which water vapor could condense. Unquestionably, copious precipitation is necessary for the spread of continental glaciers, but the condensation of water vapor to form rain or snow will not occur without mineral particles to act as centers. This is the principle on which "rainmakers" work when they scatter crystals of silver iodide in the upper atmosphere. Fine particles of volcanic ash, which may be thrown to great heights by explosive volcanic eruptions like that of Krakatoa, may also act to effect precipitation.

Water vapor, like carbon dioxide, is opaque to long heat waves. Reduction of water vapor in the atmosphere through the influence of particles of volcanic ash should lead to cooler climate. Consequently, frequent volcanic eruptions should have two effects: first, to increase precipitation; and second, to increase the probability that the precipitation should fall in the form of snow. This theory has been rather popular with nongeologists. To geologists, it is not acceptable. It is true that there were many active volcanoes during the Pleistocene, but there were as many or more during various earlier times when there were no glaciers. Evidence from the cores of deep-sea sediment is entirely negative. Most cores from the Atlantic Ocean contain no evidence of explosive vulcanism in the form of windblown particles of volcanic glass or ash. Cores from the neighborhoods of volcanic islands and from parts of the Pacific, particularly off the west coast of South America, contain thin layers of volcanic ash as well as scattered particles of volcanic glass. But these are so distributed through the sequence of faunal zones as to leave no doubt that explosive vulcanism was as frequent during the interglacials as during the glacial ages, a circumstance which leaves the theory without support.

Local conditions, such as a submerged Sahara region which might have provided moisture for the glaciers of the Alps, or sudden irruptions of vast masses of floating ice into the North Atlantic as a result of earthquakes in the polar regions, or the opening and closing of sea connections, are quite inadequate to explain general refrigeration. J. W. Charlesworth pointed this out in 1957 in his magnificent work *The Quaternary Era,* an outstanding landmark in literature about the Pleistocene. A global phenomenon requires a global cause.

J. Esmark in the 1820's ascribed glaciation to the supposed resemblance of the earth's orbit to that of a comet; at times, according to Esmark, the earth was very distant from the sun. This was taking altogether too much freedom with celestial mechanics, but the underlying principle has some merit. Actually, the shape of the earth's orbit changes periodically so that the annual variation in the distance from the earth to the sun itself varies. These changes in the eccentricity of the orbit are rather complicated, but astronomers can calculate their timing with reasonable accuracy. The periodicity varies from 60,000 to 120,000 years.

Two other variations in the motion of the earth may also have an influence on climate. Because of precession of the earth's axis of rotation, the northern and southern hemispheres take turns in being tilted toward the sun at the time of year when the earth is nearest to the sun. At present, the northern hemisphere is tilted away from the sun at perihelion, or while closest to the sun, but in about 13,000 years the relationship will be reversed. Then the northern hemisphere will have hotter summers and colder winters. The other variation involves the angle between the earth's axis of rotation and the plane of its orbit. This is subject to cyclical changes with a period of about 40,000 years. These geometrical changes are independent of each other and have different periods, but they sometimes coincide and mutually reinforce their effect on climate. At other times they fall out of phase and tend to cancel each other's effect.

Very probably these changes have some influence on climate, but is it sufficient to cause glaciation? On this point there is complete disagreement. Some scientists are convinced that the so-called astronomical theory is the final answer to the problem of the ice ages; others are equally sure that the effect on climate is too small to bring about glaciations.

An attractive aspect of the astronomical theory is that it allegedly provides a fairly precise chronology, not only of past climatic events, but of those to come as well. At least this claim is made; the reader may judge for himself. According to one popular interpretation of the curve of climatic change based on the astronomical chronology, the first ice age, the Nebraskan, began 600,000 years ago. On the other hand, another investigator finds a correlation between the astronomical chronology and temperature zones in deep-sea cores which proves that the first ice age began 300,000 years ago.

For our part, we can see no agreement whatever between our chronology of the Pleistocene, which is based on the record in the sediment cores, and the chronology derived from the astronomical theory. We believe that our chronology disproves the validity of the astronomical theory. Or does it? If the elastic chronology of the astronomical theory can be stretched from 300,000 to 600,000 years, why not draw it out to 1,500,000 years? The answer is, it will be—but not by us.

Beginning shortly before Pleistocene time and continuing into it, the earth has been in the throes of a major crustal revolution. Mountains and other continental areas were raised high. The snow line enveloped many mountain ranges and high plateaus. Ice from these high places spread across the plains, and an ice age was in full swing. Many believe that in this way the Pleistocene got off to a start. Although elevated continents and high mountains predispose and favor cold winters and precipitation, however, they are not in themselves sufficient to cause the spread of continental ice sheets. The proof of that is before our eyes; our landscape is as mountainous as ever, but the continental glaciers of the last ice age have gone. Furthermore, our study of the oceanic record shows that the onset of the Pleistocene was sudden and that the subsequent climatic changes came in abruptly; mountains simply cannot rise and fall at such a preposterously rapid rate. Nevertheless, the present topographical state of the earth—marked by strong contrast between continents and ocean basins, by absence of shallow seas covering broad areas of the continents, and by long ranges of lofty mountains—is very probably essential to the spread of continental ice sheets, though it is evidently not the sole cause. The cause was probably a combination or coincidence of some other factor of fluctuating effect acting in conjunction with exceptional topography.

The simplicity of the theory that explains glaciations on the basis of polar wandering has attracted some adherents; to bring on the glaciations, one has only to put the North Pole in Greenland. As in other simple theories, the interglacial ages present a serious difficulty; to account for them, we must suppose that the Poles shifted once for every climatic change. In addition to the theoretical improbability of so many and, geologically speaking, such rapid polar shifts, there is no supporting evidence for sufficiently large shifts. Perhaps the most serious theoretical objection is that at each

shift the shape of the whole earth would have to change. Because
of the so-called centrifugal force, the earth is flattened at the Poles
and bulges at the Equator. Any shift in the axis of rotation would
be followed immediately by a shift in the position of the equatorial
bulge. It is true that the Pleistocene was a time of exceptional
mountain-building and volcanic activity, but these were not on the
scale or of the nature to be expected from the rapidly repeated polar
shifts demanded by the theory.

Possibly the secret of the ice ages lies in the minor climatic
changes which have taken place during the past 10,000 years, and
even more recently, within historical time. These changes are going
on before our eyes, as it were. In many places, students of past
climates have found evidence of a period of climate considerably
warmer than the present. During this time, which extended from
7,000 to 4,500 years ago, most mountain glaciers receded greatly
or even disappeared altogether. Then climatic deterioration set in;
old glaciers came to life and new glaciers appeared in valleys from
which the old glaciers had completely disappeared. This time has
been called "the little ice age." Most glaciers of the present day
came into existence then; they are not remnants of the last ice age,
as one might think. Glaciers continued to advance until about a
hundred and fifty years ago. The Scandinavian glaciers reached
their greatest size between 1740 and 1825. Since then, all over the
world glaciers have been melting rapidly, though they are still larger
than they were during the Middle Ages. The cause or causes of
these recent climatic changes must have been the same, though on a
different scale, as those which brought about the continental glaciations. Exactly what they were we do not know, but we can rule out
with some certainty just about all theories save one; that is the
theory which attributes climatic changes to variations in the output
of radiant energy from the sun.

Accordingly, we are strongly inclined to the theory that the ice
ages were due to the coincidence of the extraordinary topographical
conditions of the Pleistocene with fluctuations in energy from the
sun. About the first condition there is no disagreement among geologists; about the second there is no agreement among any group of

scientists. Some astronomers assert that appreciable variation in the sun's output of energy within the short time span of the Pleistocene is utterly impossible. Others are not so sure, and at least one eminent astrophysicist has postulated a model of the sun's internal workings which he believes can satisfactorily account for fairly rapid and significant changes in the output of energy from the sun.

We are not overly impressed by assertions that the output of energy from the sun cannot vary; they remind us of the assertions of the opponents of the glacial theory to the effect that continental glaciation was impossible. Just as the evidence for glaciation can be explained in no other way than by the former presence of continental ice sheets, the recent climatic changes appear to be inexplicable except in terms of a variable sun.

Attempts are being made to detect by direct measurement variations in the energy coming from the sun. However, variations in atmospheric conditions introduce so much uncertainty into the measurements that as yet nothing very convincing in the way of evidence one way or the other has emerged.

At first thought, the cause and effect sequence of the solar-emission theory appears to be childishly simple. The interglacials were times of great emission of energy; the ice ages were times of reduced emission. But in this crude form the theory leaves the problem of precipitation unanswered. Would a drop in temperature by itself suffice to bring on an ice age? Many meteorologists and students of Pleistocene climates think not. This difficulty prompted Sir George Simpson to equate ice ages with times of greater emission of radiant energy from the sun. This paradoxical scheme of Simpson's has much plausibility. The effect of increased radiation would be to heat the earth more at the Equator than at the Poles. Such differential heating would increase the rate of atmospheric circulation. Higher temperatures and stronger winds then bring about greater evaporation in equatorial regions, which in turn leads to increased cloudiness and heavier precipitation.

Thus, times of increasing solar radiation would be times of heavy rainfall, or pluvials, in relatively low latitudes, but in high latitudes, where the incidence of radiant energy per unit area would be less on account of the shape of the earth, precipitation would still be in the form of snow. Winters in high latitudes are so cold under present conditions that even with a moderate rise in temperature, precipitation during most of the winter would be in the form of snow. As the quantity of snowfall increased due to the copious supply of moisture from lower latitudes, a time would come when melting during the summers would fail to remove all of it. From then on, net accumulation from year to year would lead to the formation of glaciers, which would themselves have an influence on climate.

But now let us suppose that the intensity of solar radiation increases still more. Eventually, even high latitudes will receive so much heat that snowfall will change to rain. As the glaciers melt, the ice age comes to an end and a warm and wet interglacial age follows. In time solar emission decreases, rain changes to heavy snow, glaciers reappear, and once again the earth is in the grip of an ice age. But as the heat from the sun falls below a certain level, evaporation decreases and poleward circulation decreases. Now the glaciers dwindle because of lack of nourishment as snowfall during the winters fails to replace loss by melting during the summers. The consequence is a cold, dry interglacial age, which completes the cycle. Evidently two such cycles could explain the four ice ages of the Pleistocene.

An important implication of this scheme is that a marked difference in climatic character should distinguish the middle interglacial from the first and last interglacials. Evidence from the continents seems to show that all three interglacials were on the whole similar, but evidence from the continents is really not very complete, particularly as regards the earlier phases of the Pleistocene. On the other hand, the core record strongly suggests that the middle, or Yarmouth, interglacial was distinctly different from the other two. Not only was it much longer, but apparently the climate of the equatorial Atlantic on the average was much less warm than during the other two interglacials.

Also, the coiling behavior of *Globorotalia truncatulinoides* during the middle interglacial is significant; the clear-cut segregation between the right- and left-coiling races, so evident at other times, seems to have broken down. Was this a consequence of poorly defined circulation, and that in turn a consequence of decreased energy from the sun? We think that this is a very reasonable interpretation. Moreover, the race of *Globorotalia menardii* which oc-

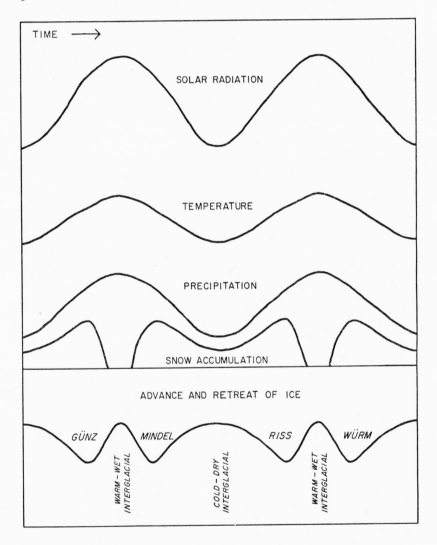

FIGURE 29 *Effect of two cycles of fluctuation of solar radiation on temperature, precipitation, snow accumulation, and glaciation, according to Simpson's hypothesis. The curves are qualitative only.*

curs in the middle interglacial is somewhat different from that of
the dominant forms in the other interglacials. It is more similar to
the form which is prevalent today in the Sargasso Sea, a hint perhaps that oceanographic conditions throughout the Atlantic during
the middle interglacial were more nearly like those of the Sargasso
Sea today—a part of the Atlantic which is characterized by feeble
circulation.

Undoubtedly, the middle interglacial included minor climatic
fluctuations; in fact, evidence of these appears more conspicuously
in the faunal record of this interglacial than in any other section
of the Pleistocene. In part these may be due to variations in the
geometry of the motion of the earth about the sun, superposed on
the controlling effect of emission of radiant energy. Or, more probably, they are an indication of a flickering sun. The Simpson scheme
leaves the tempo of climatic change entirely open. In presenting
his hypothesis, Simpson drew a smooth, symmetrical curve to represent variation in energy from the sun, but the course of variation
may equally well have been fitful and irregular. As yet no one knows
enough about the internal workings of the sun to be able to say
which kind of solar variation is the more probable. A complicating
factor which may have introduced irregularities was the rise of
mountains here and there during the Pleistocene, particularly during
the long middle interglacial.

But if the ice ages were due to increased energy from the sun, how
does it happen that in the cores of sediment from the Atlantic the
zones that correspond to ice ages contain species of foraminifera
adapted to cooler rather than warmer water? Simpson has an
answer; he supposes that the waters of the Atlantic were cooled by
enormous quantities of ice discharged from the Arctic Ocean
through the Norwegian-Greenland Sea. In fact, the distribution of
ice-rafted detritus on the floor of the Atlantic as known from dredging and coring shows that a great deal of ice was drifting about in
the North Atlantic during the last ice age and that some pushed its
way to the south of the track of the present Gulf Stream.

Evidence that drifting ice crowded the Norwegian-Greenland Sea
is provided by a nearly black carbonaceous sediment containing

fossils dating back to the Mesozoic Era, the age of medieval life. That the material was not originally deposited where it was found, but has been redeposited by drifting ice, is proved by Pleistocene foraminifera mixed in with the older fossils. We are fairly sure that the black sediment came from the north, probably from the general vicinity of Spitsbergen, because the particles of sediment are coarsest and the shell fragments largest and there is the least admixture of other kinds of detritus in a core from a station north of Norway and south of Bear Island. This redeposited sediment occurs in the eastern half of the Norwegian-Greenland Sea where now a current sets to the north. Unless the current here was different during the last ice age, which seems improbable, we suppose that the ice carrying the black sediment was pushed against the current. This implies that the Norwegian-Greenland Sea was crowded with bergs funneling through from the Arctic Ocean, where they were being carved from glaciers on the surrounding continents and islands, very much as Simpson has suggested. Such a massive influx of ice into the Atlantic could certainly have caused the southward displacement of the boundary between right- and left-coiling races of *Globigerina pachyderma,* as recorded in the cores, and may very well have been sufficient in cooling effect to have brought about the marked faunal changes of the equatorial cores.

At first glance, the cooling of the equatorial Atlantic seems to contradict the basic postulate of the hypothesis—that warmer equatorial waters were responsible for increased precipitation. However, a similar cooling of the Pacific did not occur because Bering Strait is too narrow to permit much outflow of ice. Moreover, the strait was closed altogether during the low stands of sea level of the ice ages. Thus, there is no reason why there should not have been plenty of evaporation from the Pacific.

If so, the well-defined climatic zones of the Atlantic cores should be absent from cores taken in the Pacific. Actually this is the case; in the Pacific cores that we have examined so far, it is difficult to discern any zonation at all, and what faint zonation may be present seems to be in opposite phase with the zonation of the Atlantic.

We must admit that this evidence, which seems to fit the Simpson hypothesis so well, was a surprise to us. Until the evidence for two distinctly different kinds of interglacial climates had emerged from our complete record of the Pleistocene, we were repelled by the paradoxical appeal to more heat from the sun to explain the spread of continental glaciers. On the other hand, it is scarcely conceivable that glaciers could spread without increase in precipitation. But to expect a decrease in radiant energy from the sun to generate increased precipitation is worse than paradoxical; it is weak reasoning.

What climatic change will come next? Climate has changed repeatedly in the past; it is changing now; we know of nothing that can keep it from changing in the future, even the near future. Should a glacial advance on a scale at all comparable with that of the last ice age occur, most of the economically important lands of the world would vanish under ice. Thriving manufacturing centers, valuable agricultural lands, and important ore deposits would be buried and wholesale migrations of animals and people would be necessary. Thousands of feet of ice would cover the sites of New York, Berlin, and Moscow.

We have no reason to believe that the Pleistocene Epoch, an extraordinary interlude in the history of the earth, has come to an end. The onset of another ice age is a real probability, but when? At present any prediction lies in the realm of pure speculation. A definite answer to the question may be possible when the problem of the cause of the phenomena of the Pleistocene has been solved. Just possibly we are now one step closer to the solution of the problem.

15

GLIMPSES OF THE

REMOTE PAST

IN our search for a complete record of the Pleistocene in the sediments of the ocean basins, we have uncovered evidence of hitherto unrecognized processes. Among these are turbidity currents and local removal of layers of sediment by slumping or subsea landslides. In order to gain understanding of these processes and an appreciation of their importance in modifying the sedimentary record, we have studied many cores which contained no direct evidence of the chronology of the Pleistocene but which were full of information about oceanic processes, past and present. Some of these cores have led us into remoter times of earth history and have hinted things about the early Atlantic which are of much interest in their own right. They afford us glimpses of the conditions and processes that led to the ice ages, and therefore they have a bearing on the problem of the causation of the extraordinary conditions of the Pleistocene.

We have pointed out that slumping, by removing the late Pleisto-

cene cover, enabled us to core sediments deposited during the early
Pleistocene. We have described the first core taken during the first
cruise to the Mid-Atlantic Ridge, which contained sediment deposited some forty million years ago, during the dawn of Recent
time, the Eocene Epoch of the Cenozoic Era. Since then we have
found many other cores that contain depositional discontinuities.
Had we not studied these cores, it is possible that we would never
have sought for similar hiatuses within the Pleistocene section itself.
There, because of the uniformity of the sediment, they are anything
but obvious and can be recognized only by careful cross-correlation
of suites of cores. Thus, the occurrences of older sediments beneath
relatively thin covers of Pleistocene sediment suggested to us a way,
in fact at present the only way, of discovering the complete record
of the Pleistocene.

As a result, we were able to take a suite of cores of exceptional
interest on the sea floor around Bermuda. These contain fragments
of clams belonging to the genus *Inoceramus,* a group which lived
more than seventy million years ago during the Upper Cretaceous
period, near the close of the era of medieval life, the age of giant
reptiles. Paleontologists who have studied many occurrences of
these clams all over the world are in agreement that they lived
only in shallow water. Accordingly, their presence in sediments on
the Bermuda rise tells us that the enormous topographical feature
whose peak forms the islands dates back at least to the Upper
Cretaceous Period. Another core from a depth of about 1,500
meters off Bermuda contains pieces of an igneous rock with a
crystal texture as coarse as that of a granite, but of very different
mineral composition. Instead of the light minerals containing abundant silica, aluminum, sodium, and potassium which are characteristic of the granites commonly found on the continents, this rock is
composed of minerals in which heavier elements dominate, such as
iron and calcium. Its coarse texture shows that the molten rock,
or magma, from which it formed cooled very slowly; such slow
cooling with growth of large crystals can take place only under a
cover of sediment or other igneous rocks. Since the same rather
unusual minerals which occur in this igneous rock also occur as

detrital grains in one of the Bermuda limestones, we feel quite sure that some of the same coarse-grained rock must lie directly below the thin veneer of limestone which now forms the surface of the islands. In fact, it is very probable that some of this rock lies above sea level. Otherwise it is difficult to understand how the heavy mineral particles could have found their way into the sediment which later became a limestone.

These bits of information, put together, permit us to form a mental image of the primeval Bermuda. In our mind's eye we see a gloomy pile of dark volcanic cinders towering thousands of feet above the sea and probably of greater circumference than the present islands. At the core of this mass of cinders is the coarsely crystalline rock, slowly cooling—on the whole, a far more fitting place for Sycorax and Caliban than the charming islands that we see today. A present-day example of how Bermuda must have looked 100 million years ago is afforded by any one of the Cape Verde Islands on the other side of the Atlantic. However, as the millions of years rolled by, the perpetual gnawing of wave erosion gradually reduced the great cinder cone to a platform at sea level, except for a point or two, where the more resistant coarsely crystalline rock occurred. In the meantime, plants and animals in the warm and shallow water around the platform were secreting vast quantities of lime, much of it in the form of calcareous sand.

Various other examples of sediment of Upper Cretaceous age have been found in the Atlantic. One of particular interest was cored by the *Vema* on the Walvis Ridge twenty-three degrees south of the Equator and four hundred miles from the coast of Africa. The depth of water at the coring station was 4,025 meters. The Walvis Ridge starts at the African coast a short distance north of Walvis Bay and extends in a southwesterly direction a distance of almost two thousand miles to join the Mid-Atlantic Ridge at the island of Tristan da Cunha, a site of recent vulcanism. Seven meters of Pleistocene sediment overlie the Cretaceous sediment. The time interval represented by the discontinuity at the boundary between the Cretaceous and the Pleistocene sediments is on the order of 100 million years, and yet the two sediments are outwardly very similar. In both, the calcareous shells of single-celled animals, the planktonic foraminifera, are very abundant, but with the difference that all of the species in the Cretaceous sediment are now extinct. Many of these extinct species also occur in Upper Cretaceous rocks in Mexico, in Texas, and on the tops of seamounts on the other side of the world in the northwestern Pacific. This worldwide distribution of microscopic creatures without independent power of locomotion shows that by Upper Cretaceous time open seaways connected these widely separated parts of the world. Whether the oceans had already taken on their present outlines we cannot say until Upper Cretaceous sediment has been found in more broadly scattered sites in the ocean basins.

Not all discontinuities in the sedimentary record are due to slumping, however. Many, particularly those found on the tops of submarine volcanoes or seamounts, are due to the failure of normal sediment to accumulate during almost incredibly long periods of time. Almost the only kind of sediment which can reach seamounts far from the continents consists of extremely finely divided mineral particles wafted by oceanic currents from the continents and of the little shells of planktonic animals and plants which perpetually rain down from the upper layers of water. In recent years, oceanographers have become more and more aware of the importance of deep currents. These are not very swift. In fact, they are slow in comparison with turbidity currents, but they do possess enough energy to prevent the accumulation of almost all of the fine material which reaches the tops of seamounts and ridges. Currents of this kind are part of the great oceanic systems of circulation. They are radically different from turbidity currents; they are continuous at least over periods of thousands of years, and unlike turbidity currents, they are independent of the topography of the sea floor.

Photographs of the tops of seamounts at depths of a mile or more clearly show the traces of these currents. The pictures show the residual sand arranged in ripple marks quite similar to those formed on sand flats by a gentle current of the ebbing tide. Trails or drifts of loose sediment behind obstructions, such as cobbles dropped by drifting ice, provide evidence of a single direction of flow. Because of this unidirectional flow, an excess of fine sediment swept from the top of a seamount accumulates on the flank toward which the current flows, in the same way that a snow drift forms on the lee side of a house. Variations in amount of the excess of fine material from level to level in cores from stations near a seamount in the northwestern Atlantic suggest that the direction of the deep current sweeping the top of the mount has shifted from time to time, and that the shifts have coincided with the climatic changes of the late Pleistocene.

We have said that almost all sediment is continuously removed from the tops of seamounts. This is not quite true; an almost infinitesimal fraction of the material is coarse enough to resist deep current scour. It consists of the teeth of fish, coarse sand grains and small rock fragments rafted from shallow water by seaweeds torn from their moorings on the continental shelves, and such other odds and ends as the plates of certain kinds of barnacles which attach themselves to the drifting sargasso weed. Frequently these objects are coated with sooty-black manganese oxide, which accumulates very slowly as a chemical precipitate. Sometimes the manganese oxide forms nodules several centimeters in diameter, or it may form a continuous crust. As a rule, these residual deposits on the tops of seamounts are no more than about a foot thick. In their coarseness they are like some deposits laid down by turbidity currents; in every other respect they are as different as night from day. The nature of the particles, the presence of manganese oxide, and the absence of sorting by size of particles and of grading from coarse at the bottom to fine at the top clearly set them apart in a class by themselves. We call them winnowed sediments, in allusion to the winnowing effect of current scour.

All the samples of ancient sediments that have been cored or dredged from the tops of seamounts in the North and South Atlantic are similar in that they contain only the shells of microscopic organisms, most of which were of planktonic character. In no instance have we found any fossil suggesting that the tops of seamounts in the North and South Atlantic have ever been nearer to the surface of the ocean than they are now, that is, between 2,360 and 1,550 meters. In this respect, the Atlantic basins differ from the Pacific with its peculiar flat-topped seamounts known as guyots.

Guyots were discovered by Harry H. Hess, a Princeton University geologist, while he was in command of a naval vessel cruising in the Pacific during the war. They are distinguished from ordinary seamounts by their flat tops, which lie at depths varying between 750 and 1,000 meters. In plan they are roughly circular or elliptical. Hess almost certainly correctly attributed the flat tops to planation by wave erosion at some time in the past when the tops were at sea level. Since then, either sea level has risen all over the world by about a kilometer, or the floor of the Pacific on which the guyots stand must have sunk by the same amount. For some reason, Hess chose to develop the theory that the floor of the Pacific had remained stable and sea level had risen. However, incontrovertible evidence in the form of ancient marine sediments on the continents shows that the ocean basins have been filled to their brims ever since the dawn of life, some 600 million years ago. Accordingly, Hess was compelled to put the origin of the guyots back to an extremely early epoch of earth history when much of the water that now fills the ocean basins was still held beneath the surface of the earth.

This hypothesis was short-lived. Dredges dragged across the tops of guyots brought up the large fossil shells of clams which had lived during the Cretaceous Period, a mere hundred million years ago. Some of these belonged to a group known among paleontologists as the rudistids, and these creatures quite certainly could live only in shallow water. Obviously, planation of the tops of the guyots, and their subsequent drowning, had taken place at a fairly recent time as the chronology of geological events goes. Equally obviously, an enormous area of the floor of the Pacific had sunk by about a thousand meters since the end of Cretaceous time. Apparently the floor of the Pacific had not been so stable after all.

Actually, this evidence of subsidence of a large part of the floor of the Pacific intermeshes rather well with some other geological observations and conjectures which have been known for some time. One of these is the distribution of sedimentary rocks on the continents. Since the close of the Cretaceous Period, flooding of the continents has been progressively more and more restricted with each succeeding epoch. Now the margins of the oceans nearly coincide with the edges of the continental shelves, from which the continental masses drop off to abyssal depths. Such withdrawal of the shallow seas that flooded the continents can be explained only by supposing that at least some parts of the ocean basins were becoming deeper.

Even more pertinent to the problem was Charles Darwin's theory of the origin of coral atolls. More than a hundred years ago, during his famous voyage on the *Beagle,* young Darwin observed that most volcanic islands in the tropical Pacific were surrounded by fringing coral reefs. He reasoned that if such an island slowly sank, the corals would build upward and the surface of the reef would remain at or near sea level. Eventually, the central volcanic island would disappear below sea level, leaving a lagoon within a circular coral reef, in other words, an atoll. In recent years, deep drilling on certain atolls of the Pacific has proved that Darwin's theory of subsidence was quite correct.

Why did guyots not become atolls? Probably, local subsidence was too fast for the reef-building corals and other lime-secreting organisms. Once the top of a guyot had sunk below the depth to which light can reach, all lime-secreting plants and even the reef-building corals would die. Although corals are animals and do not depend on photosynthesis directly, they do so indirectly because of their vital dependence on microscopic algae which live within their tissues. Thus, a short period of rapid local sinking at the close of the Mesozoic Era deprived the guyots forever after of the privilege of becoming atolls.

In opposition to the theory of general subsidence, it has been claimed that the sinking of volcanic islands is a purely local effect due to the weight of the volcanic rocks, which cannot be supported by the underlying unconsolidated sediment. Perhaps this has contributed to the overall subsidence, but a little consideration of the evidence makes it clear that compression of the underlying sediment cannot account for all the subsidence. For one thing, the guyots must have been stable long enough for planation by wave erosion to occur, and the effect of planation was, if anything, to cause a decrease in the weight of the volcanic mass. And yet, after removal of some of the weight, the guyots must have sunk rapidly to a depth sufficient to drown the reef-building organisms. Furthermore, the islands that sank less rapidly received enormous loads of lime on their summits and flanks, yet they sank no deeper than their unloaded counterparts, the guyots. The really fatal objection is that on the average the total thickness of unconsolidated sediment in the Pacific is hardly more than 300 meters, yet we know that the guyots and atolls have sunk by several times that amount.

Although there are many seamounts in the Atlantic, none is a guyot. Their shapes give no evidence of planation by wave erosion. Cretaceous fossils have been found on some, but the forms are always such as could perfectly well have lived in water of the same depth as that which now covers the mounts. Bermuda provides supporting evidence of stability of the floor of the Atlantic. Although the eroded volcanic base is now completely covered by wind-blown calcareous deposits, drilling has shown that the base lies fairly close to the present surface, and the detrital particles of igneous rock in limestone strongly suggest that some parts of the base are even now above sea level.

However much the Atlantic and Pacific basins may differ in evidence of subsidence, they are very similar in some other interesting ways. In both oceans, old sediments and fossils have been found on seamounts and ridges where younger sediments have been removed by slumping or where, because of deep current scour, no additional sediments have been deposited. The ages of the sediments, on the evidence of the fossils, vary from one million to a hundred million years; nothing older has ever been found. Yet the remains of ancient life found in the widely spread marine sediment on the continents tell us that life has existed in the seas for six hundred million years. Can it be due to mere chance that as yet no one has found any trace of the earlier five sixths of the record of life in the oceans? Perhaps. But another peculiar characteristic of the sediments of the deep basins has a bearing on this question.

Two indispensable tools of the oceanographer are the echo sounder and the seismic profiler. We have told how sound waves were used to chart the Hudson Submarine Canyon. To measure the depth of water, the sound energy from an electrically generated "ping" suffices. When a more powerful sound wave is sent down, as by the explosion of a stick of dynamite just below the surface of the water, some of the energy passes through the interface between water and sediment, and down through the sediment, until it reaches a level of abrupt change in density and elastic properties such as occurs where unconsolidated sediment rests on hard rock. At such a discontinuity, some of the energy is reflected upward to the listening device on the ship, which records the time interval between the explosion and arrival of the reflected sound wave. From the known velocity of sound in unconsolidated sediment, one can calculate the thickness of the layer of sediment. In actual practice, everything is automatic except the detonation of the dynamite, and the machine draws a practically continuous profile of the bottom and the various levels of discontinuity below on a strip of moving paper.

Many profiles of this kind have been made; from these, geophysicists can make reliable estimates of the average thicknesses of unconsolidated sediment in the various oceans. In the Atlantic the thickness is in the order of about 750 meters; in the Pacific it is no more than 300 meters. In terms of time, these two thicknesses are probably just about equivalent. Investigators who have studied sedimentation in the Pacific believe that the average rate of accumulation there is only about one half what it is in the Atlantic. This is due to the much greater area of the Pacific, much of it far from sources of land-derived detritus, and to a bordering trench, particularly off the American continents, which traps turbidity currents and prevents the sediment-laden water from reaching far into the Pacific basin. It is hard to estimate how much time these average thicknesses represent. We have no right to assume that the rate of accumulation during the Pleistocene was the norm for the rest of geological time. The average rate has probably been lower because during vast intervals of time the continents have been low and featureless and even flooded by shallow seas, which impounded sediment and prevented it from reaching the ocean basins. Even so, we can make some reasonable guesses as to orders of magnitude.

If the ocean basins have been permanent, they have been receiving sediment for billions of years. We see at once that the thicknesses of sediment which have been measured cannot encompass such time spans. Let us see how deposition since the Cambrian Period, when the first highly organized animals appeared, corresponds to the thicknesses. The time elapsed, 600 million years, gives a rate of accumulation of a little more than one millimeter per thousand years. This seems incredibly slow when compared with the rate of twenty-five millimeters per thousand years in the Pleistocene. But when we divide the thickness of sediment in the Atlantic by the time since the beginning of the Upper Cretaceous Period, we get 7.5 millimeters per thousand years, which is of the right order of magnitude. Thus, two independent methods of investigation, geophysical and paleontological, yield consistent evidence which suggests that no sediment older than Upper Cretaceous time has been found in the ocean basins because there is none there to find.

This is a rather startling conclusion and does much violence to well-entrenched preconceptions concerning the geological interrelationship between continents and ocean basins. As we have seen, within the past twenty years Hess published his theory of the origin of guyots, a theory which implied an almost incredible stability of the floor of the Pacific since some time before the dawn of life. Following this static conception of the history of the ocean basins, we should expect to find a complete record of marine life from the very beginning in the sediment of the deep oceans. Vestigial thinking of this kind is probably responsible for the hope that samples from a Mohole in the Pacific or the Atlantic will provide us with such a record. We greatly hope that one, or better, several Moholes will be drilled in both oceans. They will yield information of much value and fascinating interest, but it is very unlikely that they will provide us with a long record of marine life. On the contrary, the record on the bottom of the oceans probably does not go back in time even so far as that which we have already found in the marine sedimentary rocks on the continents.

From the conception of extreme stability in the ocean basins, as implied by Hess's theory of the origin of guyots, we are now driven by the evidence found in the last fifteen years to a diametrically opposite view. The most active regions on the surface of the earth are, in fact, the ocean basins, and in spite of the abundant evidence on the continents of folding, fracturing, subsidence and upheaval, and intrusion and outpourings of molten rock, it is the continents which have been relatively passive and stable.

The paleontological and geophysical evidence tells us in clear enough language that some sort of drastic reorganization of the floors of the oceans must have taken place toward the end of the Lower Cretaceous Period. This may have taken the form of a series of invasions of the ocean floor by molten volcanic rock. Direct evidence of ancient submarine vulcanism is not hard to find. The Bermuda Islands rest on an enormous mass of volcanic rock old enough to have provided a home for Upper Cretaceous clams. Many seamounts in the Atlantic are known to be volcanic, and the same is true of that greatest of submarine mountain ranges, the Mid-Atlantic Ridge. In the Pacific there are guyots and atolls, with their volcanic bases. With so much evidence of vulcanism, it is easy to imagine that the pre-Cretaceous sediments were covered by sheets of lava, or altered beyond recognition by the heat and chemical effect of all this vulcanism. We can be sure that this volcanic transformation did not take place within the span of a few years; if it had, all marine life would have come to a sudden end as a gargantuan bouillabaisse of boiled fish. To avoid catastrophe of this sort, we need only be more liberal with time; we have plenty of it at our disposal! This interlude of intensive vulcanism could have dragged on for a million years or more, and yet still appear as a single event when viewed in the perspective of geological time, for we must remember that our precision in defining the beginning of the Upper Cretaceous Period is not nearly so good as one million years.

Whence came the energy and why should its effect have been concentrated at the beginning of the Upper Cretaceous? Radioactive heating was probably the source of energy. If heat was generated in the rocks beneath the oceans more rapidly than it could be removed by thermal conduction, the temperature of the rocks would rise. With rising temperature, they would become less dense and more mobile. This in turn would upset the gravitational stability of the ocean floor and at the same time would favor readjustment by lowering the viscosity of the material beneath the floor. Presumably, upward movement on a large scale began as the Lower Cretaceous Period was drawing to a close. From that time on, heat transfer took place by convection as well as conduction, and probably at a more rapid rate than it was being generated below. Eventually this should lead to a return to thermal equilibrium, at which time the ponderous engine will come to a halt. Judging from the number of active volcanoes in the ocean basins today, we doubt if the volcanic cycle has come to an end, though it would seem that the engine is turning over more slowly than formerly.

Can we infer from the existence of active volcanoes pouring out very fluid lava that there is somewhere below the surface of the earth a continuous layer of liquid rock? The answer is no; at least there is no layer at moderate depth which is liquid in the way that lavas are liquid. We can say this with assurance because seismologists through the study of earthquakes have found that the earth transmits a kind of elastic waves, known as shear waves, to a depth equal to about half its radius. In shear waves the motion of vibration is perpendicular to the direction in which the wave travels. Since liquids cannot transmit shear waves, it is evident that there is no continuous layer of liquid rock anywhere down to a depth equal to half the radius of the earth. Presumably the lava of volcanoes comes from relatively small isolated reservoirs of very hot liquid rock which may owe their existence to local release of pressure.

Nevertheless, material beneath the surface of the earth does flow, and on a global scale. The slow rise of the Scandinavian peninsula and the formerly heavily glaciated part of the North American continent is proof of this. The weight of the continental ice sheets was great enough to depress the land masses on which they rested, but the land masses could not sink without lateral displacement of underlying material. Between 11,000 and about 8,000 years ago the continental glaciers melted and the land surfaces where they had been began to rise. They are still rising at the rate of about one centimeter a year. Former, more rapid uplift is shown by old strandlines now hundreds of meters above sea level.

Antarctica affords evidence of similar vertical movement of a continental mass under the influence of a changing load of ice. Depression is shown by the depth of water on the continental shelf off Antarctica. The shelf, the belt of relatively shallow water which surrounds all continents, normally lies at a depth of about a hundred meters, but off Antarctica the depth is four hundred meters. Ancient raised beaches along the coast now standing a hundred meters above sea level indicate that some time ago, probably during the last ice age, when the icecap was thicker, the continent stood even lower than it does now. But the most significant feature for our purpose is a roughly circular pattern of rises lying about eighteen degrees from the coast of Antarctica. G. P. Woollard believes that this represents a compensating bulge in the crust caused by displacement of plastic material from the mantle below the depressed continent.

Further converging evidence is provided by many precise measurements of gravity in all parts of the world which show that large topographical features are in rough hydrostatic equilibrium with one another. The continents maintain their elevation above the floors of the ocean basins, not because of rigidity of the underlying rocks, but because they are composed of less dense material than that which forms the ocean basins. Scandinavia and eastern Canada are rising for the same reason that a ship rises as it discharges its cargo. Just as water must flow under the ship to make it rise, so must rock flow under a continent as it rises. In view of all this, we have no choice but to conclude that the material beneath the surface of the earth, which is capable of transmitting shear waves, is also capable of flowing. The answer to this seeming paradox turns on the time dimension and the nature of glasses.

A glass rod, which is highly elastic in response to short period stresses, will in the course of years change shape by flow. For example, if it is supported at both ends in a horizontal position, it will very slowly sag at the middle. Similarly, glassy rocks at high temperature and under great pressure can transmit earthquake waves traveling at velocities measured in kilometers a second and at the same time flow at rates of a few centimeters a year. Measured against the time scale of human history, this rate of flow is almost negligibly slow; in terms of the chronology of historical geology, it is torrentially fast. As such, it relegates the static conception of the ocean basins to everlasting limbo.

Earlier in this chapter, we attempted to explain the apparent absence of pre-Cretaceous sediment in the ocean basins on the basis of great upwellings of intensely heated material which burst through the ocean floors as lava. We envisioned vertical movement of the heated material by convection currents like those which one can plainly see when one heats a saucepan full of water containing some flakes of oatmeal.

By means of much the same mechanism, R. S. Dietz goes a step further. Instead of altering and hiding the older sediments, he would like to get rid of them altogether. In a recent paper he advances the hypothesis that the continents are a light scum floating on heavier rock which is in motion constantly maintained by thermal convection. He regards the ocean floor as crustless, in the sense that convection is effective to the very surface of the ocean floor. Heated glassy rock rises in the middles of the ocean basins, spreads laterally toward the continents, descends under them. This hypothesis gains plausibility by providing explanations for various otherwise puzzling features of the ocean basins. Running down the middle of the North and South Atlantic is an enormous submarine mountain range appropriately called the Mid-Atlantic Ridge. Throughout its sinuous course from north to south it remains very nearly halfway between the continents on both sides. A rift apparently due to tension follows its crest. The upwelling of hot glass along the middle of the Atlantic nicely explains the existence of the Mid-Atlantic Ridge as a topographical feature; it explains its position halfway between the continents; and the diverging streams of hot glass beneath the ridge provide an explanation for the tensional rift along the crest. Recent detailed charting of the Pacific and the Indian Ocean shows that ridges of somewhat more complex pattern also occur in those oceans. The hypothesis also takes care of the absence of older sediments in a satisfactory way. They are not only altered by intrusion and outpourings of volcanic rocks; they are also carried bodily along on the surface of the stream of hot glass toward the continents under which they are eventually swept.

The undersweeping implies downflow and the formation of trenches along the continental margins. In the Pacific we find just such marginal trenches; in the Atlantic, however, we find only one deep trench, the Puerto Rico Trench, which is not really marginal to a continent. But the apparent absence of marginal trenches in the Atlantic may be due to rapid filling by sediments transported by turbidity currents. For some reason, perhaps connected with topographical differences between the Atlantic and Pacific coasts, turbidity currents seem to have been most prevalent in the Atlantic.

For a long time the remarkably good fit between the Atlantic coasts of South America and of Africa has excited the imagination of geologists. About sixty years ago the Austrian geologist Eduard Suess succeeded in assembling the jigsaw puzzle of the continents into a single enormous land mass which he called Gondwanaland after a province in India. Later Alfred Wegener, a German meteorologist, went still further. In support of the theory that the continents had drifted apart, leaving the Atlantic basin in their wakes, he cited a remarkably large number of geological structures and occurrences of fossils and kinds of rocks which matched on both sides of the Atlantic. Since Wegener's death on the Greenland ice-cap during a scientific expedition, various other intriguing geological connections, particularly between South America and Africa, have been discovered. In spite of this evidence, the theory of continental drift gained few adherents, except among South African geologists. In the United States geologists for the most part have rejected it as being quite untenable. The objections to it most often cited are that no force deriving from the rotation of the earth is sufficiently powerful to move the continents; that to drift apart they would have to plow their way through the highly resistant rocks of the ocean floor, which is impossible because the continents are relatively weak and would break up in the process. Just why it was believed that the rocks of the floor of the oceans were highly resistant, in fact even stronger than those of the continents, is not clear. The idea was nothing more than a mere opinion unsupported by any direct evidence or valid theoretical considerations. But if not examined too closely, it served conveniently to refute the hypothesis of continental drift. At the same time the striking similarities in geological structure, fossils, and kinds of rocks, which pointed to a former connection between Africa and South America, were shrugged off as being due to mere coincidence.

However, in recent years a new kind of evidence has lent unexpected support to the hypothesis of continental drift. Most igneous and sedimentary rocks contain iron-bearing mineral particles which are weakly magnetized. For the most part, these little magnets are lined up in about the same direction and point to the position of the magnetic pole as it was at the time when the rock was formed. During the past ten years a large number of measurements of this so-called remanent magnetism have been made on rocks of all ages from widely scattered localities all over the world. The work on remanent magnetism is still in an early stage, and opinion regarding the interpretation of the findings is still rather fluid. Nevertheless, certain broad conclusions from the data already available are almost unavoidable. One is that during geological time the magnetic poles have shifted position very widely. This means that the geographical poles have also wandered about, and as widely; according to good geophysical theory, the magnetic poles always hover fairly closely about the geographical poles.

An even more exciting fact emerges when the data from different continents are compared. On the basis of the remanent magnetism of many rock samples of the same age from a single continent it is possible to determine, with fairly good agreement, the positions of the magnetic poles. But large discrepancies show up when the data from two or more continents are compared. To reconcile the discrepancies, it seems to be necessary to postulate that the continents have shifted about with respect to one another—in short, to admit that a certain amount of continental drift *has* taken place.

In the meantime, what has become of the supposedly irrefutable objections to continental drift? In the light of the new dynamic conception of the nature of the ocean basins, they vanish into thin air. It is not the continents which have had to plow through the resistant rocks of the ocean floor, impelled by some gratuitous force; it is the "resistant" rocks themselves which are moving, or flowing, as convection currents powered by radioactive heating. The whole thing is explicable in terms of well-known processes. On this mobile setting, drift of the continents becomes inevitable. This does not mean that the continents drifted in exactly the way Wegener supposed; in fact, almost certainly the timing and the courses followed by the continents were somewhat different from what he conceived. The important thing is rather that the principle of mobile ocean floors has been established; before we can work out the details of what happened, we will have to have more information.

Thus, in less than twenty years our thinking regarding the greatest features of the earth, the continents and ocean basins, has undergone a revolution. This must not be mistaken for a change in fashion, a mere swing of the pendulum; it has been an irreversible change brought about by the rapid expansion of our understanding of the dynamics of our planet, and this in turn has been possible because of the intensive exploration of the oceans during the past twenty years.

16

FUTURE DEVELOPMENTS

MODERN coring techniques have made it possible, with the piston
corer, to raise cores twenty-five meters long from areas of the deep
ocean floor where the sediment is relatively soft because of rapid accumulation, that is, accumulation at the rate of about twenty centimeters or more per thousand years. In areas where the sediment is
more compacted because it accumulated at the rate of about two
centimeters per thousand years, the length of the core is limited to
about fourteen meters. However, scientists and engineers in oceanographic institutions in the United States, the Soviet Union, Sweden,
and other countries are hard at work trying to develop coring apparatus capable of taking much longer cores. It is also possible that
core samples of the entire thickness of sediment of the ocean floor
may be recovered as a by-product of the Mohole Project.

The Mohole Project is a plan to drill a hole, 5,000 to 10,000
meters deep, through the crust beneath the oceans in order to explore the mantle. It will be an audacious attempt to plumb some

of the key mysteries of the interior of the earth and of the inner space beneath our feet, about which we know much less, in many respects, than we know about outer space. The Mohole Project will be the greatest, and very probably the most rewarding, geological venture ever carried out.

The intermediate stage of the project will make a major contribution to our knowledge of the history of the earth by providing a continuous series of cores of the entire sedimentary section at a number of places in both the Atlantic and the Pacific. These cores will give us access to an otherwise unobtainable record of the history of the ocean basins and the earth as a whole. Even a few preliminary holes deep enough to penetrate the complete sequence of oceanic sediments could hardly fail to add more to our knowledge of earth history than any other conceivable project in the field of earth sciences.

What do we know so far about the depths of the earth? Ever since man began to think, he has speculated about his cosmic home, his own particular planet. Until recently, however, he had only hypotheses based on scanty facts and speculative assumptions. The relatively limited scale of scientific research and the modest scale of technical probings until recently were in no way commensurate to the importance of the problem of studying the depths of the earth, which, as we see it, is comparable with the problem of the conquest of space. Astronomers detect light and receive radio signals from stars half a billion light-years away. In contrast, the opacity of the earth is such that probings by means of sound waves—or in the language of geophysicists, seismic waves —set in motion by explosions, do not exceed a depth of a few hundred kilometers. Automatic laboratories have reached Venus and the moon, but as yet man has penetrated only a little into the interior of the earth. So far, the deepest hole ever drilled, a well in west Texas, penetrated a little less than 8,000 meters of ancient marine sediments in search of deep-lying oil and gas deposits. Thus, the deepest drilling has penetrated only to a fraction more than 1/1,000 of the radius of the earth; the layer of the earth's crust from which samples of rocks have been obtained amounts to a thin film on the surface of our planet. On a globe representing the earth on the scale of 1:10,000,000, with a diameter of a little more than a meter, the thickness of this film would be less than one millimeter.

According to present-day conceptions, our planet consists of three concentric layers: the crust, the mantle, and the core. The earth can aptly be compared to a soft-boiled egg. The yolk is the earth's core; the mantle, its white; and the shell, its crust. The radius of the earth is about 4,000 miles, or 6,370 kilometers, and the core, or yolk, extends out from the center about 2,200 miles. The mantle, or white, occupies most of the remaining 1,800 miles. The crust, or shell, is relatively very thin; it varies between the extremes of a little less than three miles to more than forty miles in thickness. Moreover, this crust, which is the only part of the earth that we know from direct observation, is covered by oceans for over more than seventy percent of its surface.

From studies of the transmission of seismic waves, it has been learned that the earth's core is in large part a dense liquid. At least it behaves like a liquid; it does not transmit shear waves, that is, elastic waves in which the motion of the vibrating medium is perpendicular to the direction of travel of the wave itself. The core may perhaps be composed of molten nickel and iron, but the enveloping mantle, which constitutes more than eighty percent of the volume of the earth, is dense rock. The crust is separated from the mantle by the so-called Mohorovicic discontinuity, at which the velocity of earthquake waves changes abruptly from about six kilometers per second above to about eight below. Since it is known that the velocity of these waves depends on the density of the medium, it is evident that the material of the mantle must be denser than that of the crust. The nature and origin of the Mohorovicic discontinuity have been subjects of wide speculation. Some scientists hold that the mantle is largely or even entirely composed of a dense mineral called olivine, which is a silicate of magnesium and iron. But the abruptness of the change at the discontinuity is puzzling. This has prompted the conjecture that the change at the boundary is not chemical but rather a change of phase or physical state due to increase of temperature and pressure with depth. To reach the Mohorovicic discontinuity and obtain samples of the mysterious material below it is the primary objective of the Mohole Project; hence its name.

The earth's crust itself is roughly layered with respect to the velocities of earthquake waves. Thus, in theory, the crust just below the bottom of the ocean comprises a so-called "first layer," which consists of low-velocity, unconsolidated, or nearly unconsolidated, sediments varying from a few hundred meters to more than two kilometers in thickness. Below this a "second layer" is sometimes recognized. It is of small but variable thickness, and presumably consists of indurated sediments, volcanic rocks, or both. Lastly, there is a so-called "third layer," some five kilometers thick, which transmits earthquake waves at velocities averaging 6.7 kilometers per second. From this velocity, geophysicists reason that it may be composed of a kind of dense, igneous rock rich in iron, calcium, and magnesium, called diabase. Another substance that could satisfy the seismic velocities is the mineral serpentine, which is actually olivine—hypothetically the component of the mantle —combined with a certain amount of water and therefore of lower density. This implied systematic layering of the crust on the basis of seismic velocities, however, is much less clear-cut than the labeling might indicate. There are great variations in velocities from place to place, and the division into three layers may be in large part only the result of a very human but sometimes dangerous propensity to strain for the simple and systematic design in everything. Actually, in some places only two crustal layers can be recognized, and in other areas there seem to be four or more; and the velocities observed in individual layers are often quite variable.

A number of scientists believe that the mantle has had a decisive influence on the formation of the crust, the occurrence of ore deposits, and on the first appearance and the existence of the atmosphere and the oceans. This further emphasizes the importance of drilling through the earth's crust to the mantle.

Of no less importance is the question of the sources of energy of deep-seated processes. With increasing depth, the temperature of the earth rises by one degree Celsius for each five to thirty meters' depth in volcanic regions, and by the same amount for each thirty to a hundred meters on continental platforms and the so-called continental shields, the continental nuclei composed of the most ancient rocks. It has been estimated that the earth annually dissipates into outer space an amount of heat expressed in terms of ergs by a figure followed by twenty-seven zeroes. How can this tremendous expenditure of energy be maintained? Why has the interior of the earth not become cold after billions of years of loss of heat? Apparently, release of energy by radioactivity and by the gravitational compaction of matter compensates for loss of heat by radiation. The depths of the earth represent a kind of "geocosmos." It is known that at great altitudes untraviolet radiation from the sun knocks off the electrons from the outer shells of nitrogen and oxygen atoms. As a result, the air at high altitudes is continuously maintained at a high degree of ionization. In the depths of the earth, on the other hand, the tremendous pressure brings about deformation or crumbling together of the electron shells. At very great pressures the electron shells are destroyed altogether. Electrons lose their bonds with the atoms and form a kind of "electron gas." In the depths of the earth, atom structures must be in an unstable, plasma-like state, a condition of the greatest interest from the viewpoint of energetics.

In point of fact, hidden in the bowels of the earth are sources of energy which can be compared only with the possibilities of thermonuclear energy. The exploitation of this heat energy should not be thought of as a fantastic dream to be realized only in the world of science fiction; this energy has already been put to use in California, Italy, and Iceland. In industrial regions far from centers of recent volcanic activity, deep drilling will be necessary. To this end, the experience gained through the drilling of Moholes is invaluable. When ways to tap this deep thermal energy have become feasible, mankind will have at its disposal a source of power that will meet all its needs and make it possible to realize the most daring projects.

As a result of scientific probings of the great depths of the earth, we may hope to attain a better understanding of the mechanism of volcanoes and the causes of earthquakes, and, if we may not hope to control them, at least we may learn how to predict them. Other riddles which may be solved are the origin of the earth's magnetic field; why some parts of continents slowly rise, while others subside; whether the relative positions of the continents have changed during geological time; and whether the "figure" of the earth changes from time to time.

Because man's penetration into the depths of the earth has so far been so insignificant, our notions of the earth as a whole and even of its superficial integument, the crust, are extremely schematic. Science today has at its disposal considerably more data on the composition and development of cosmic matter, of the stars and stellar systems, than it has on the structure and development of our planet. The investigations of astrophysicists have to a great extent formed the basis of our present conception of the structure of matter; and these studies have already found application in the utilization of atomic energy and in flights into outer space.

The unexplored depths of the earth not only conceal the riddle of the origin and development of the thin layer of the earth's crust known to us, and the explanation of the laws that govern the concentration in this layer of deposits of useful minerals, but most probably they also conceal unknown riches and natural forces which could increase manyfold the productivity of human society. To penetrate into the depths of the earth is not merely the subject of a dream; it is an urgent and necessary next step in the progress of applied geology, for only from the depths of the earth can we meet the demands for ever greater quantities of the most varied kinds of minerals needed by a really vigorous industrial development.

The urgency of projects for study of the deep interior of the earth is due in large part to the fact that science has today admitted the crucial influence of the depths of the earth upon the processes that control the concentration and development of deposits of crude minerals. The activity in the interior of the earth is manifested in the form of volcanic and seismic phenomena, destructive earthquakes that in certain regions constitute a threat to centers of population and industry. The study of the deep interior of the earth will undoubtedly lead to discovery of new phenomena and properties of the earth and of terrestrial matter which may be just as important as the astrophysical data on outer space that not so long ago seemed far removed from the everyday needs of mankind but now promise to play such a great part in the future of science and in the practical, everyday world of man.

The countries with sufficiently well developed scientific resources have made a beginning in the study of the deep interior of the earth. The Soviet Union and the United States both have launched programs of deep drilling. Scientists in the Soviet Union feel that it is far better to drill on land than at sea; their work of probing the depths of the earth is developing on a broad front. Deep drilling has been discussed repeatedly by the leading scientists and engineers, and there seems to be unanimous support for the project, in combination with geological, geophysical, and geochemical investigations. The Russians consider it feasible to reach depths of ten to fifteen kilometers in the years immediately ahead. Drilling will take place initially in five general areas:

1. Deep depressions of platform regions. The aim is to penetrate and study the full thickness of the sedimentary layers that fill these deep depressions, which often contain gas and petroleum deposits, and determine how gas and petroleum are distributed. Also under study will be the physical states and ratios of gas, petroleum, and water under conditions of high temperature and pressure.

2. Regions of down-warped troughs, or geosynclines, filled with sediments deposited during the Paleozoic Era, between 600,000,000 and 230,000,000 years ago, which contain the first evidence of abundant and varied life. The objective is to learn more about the processes characteristic of the deeper zones.

3. The shield areas, the resistant and stable nuclei of the continents, within which occur the oldest known rocks. Study will concentrate on the base of the granite layer where it has not been subjected to subsequent transformations. Attempts will also be made in these areas to penetrate the basalt layer.

4. Regions characterized by a crust of the transitional type, where it may be possible to penetrate the basalt layer. Here an additional objective will be the study of the Conrad discontinuity, which lies above the Mohorovicic discontinuity and is defined by an abrupt increase in the velocity of seismic waves to about seven kilometers per second. This hole will also enable scientists to study processes in the basalt layer such as the formation of granites, the precipitation of metalliferous minerals, and the shifting of plastic material, which in turn causes vertical displacements at the earth's surface.

5. Regions of island arcs, such as the Aleutian Islands, where the crust is of the oceanic type. The aim is to penetrate to the Mohorovicic discontinuity and the upper mantle, in order to obtain evidence on the states of matter at high temperatures and under great pressures.

The Russian preparations for ultra-deep drilling are reported to consist of (1) intensive geophysical investigations by which choice of the most favorable sites for the holes may be made, (2) development of tools and apparatus needed for drilling and recovering samples, and (3) elaboration of geophysical and geochemical methods and instruments for study of the holes. Holes to a depth of 7,000 meters have already been drilled in the Caspian depression and on the Apsheron Peninsula in the Caspian Sea.

The American project to drill into the deep interior of the earth is called the Mohole Project. The name springs from the puzzling discontinuity between the mantle and the crust, called Mohorovicic discontinuity, or "Moho," in honor of its discoverer, a Yugoslav geophysicist, Andrija Mohorovičić. Thus, any deep hole projected to the mantle is called a Mohole. As yet no name has been chosen for the holes that will penetrate only the sedimentary section.

The existence of the earth's crust, as distinct from the deeper portions of the globe, was established in 1909 by Mohorovičić as a result of his study of records of nearby earthquakes. Seismometers, earthquake-recording devices, show the dual arrival of waves; Mohorovičić explained this phenomenon by the hypothetical presence at a depth of about sixty kilometers of an approximately horizontal surface below which the velocity of elastic waves traveling downward increases abruptly from 6.3 to 8 kilometers per second. Above the Moho lies the earth's crust; below it lies the upper part of the intermediate zone of the globe, the so-called upper mantle. The sharp definition of the Mohorovicic discontinuity, as determined by its effect on elastic waves generated by both nearby and remote earthquakes, makes it possible to utilize seismograms, the "letters" written by seismometers, to determine the thickness of the earth's crust. Although these determinations are not completely accurate, they have proven quite sufficient to establish remarkable differences in the thickness of the crust from place to place. Under regions of high mountains it is thickest, sometimes as much as sixty or even seventy-five kilometers. In contrast, its thickness under the oceans varies from seven to as little as three kilometers. This is why American scientists have chosen to make their attempt to reach the Mohorovicic discontinuity somewhere in an ocean basin. There the thickness of sediment and hard rock to be penetrated is very much less, but some extremely difficult technical problems arise. Drilling on land would put a heavy strain on methods already thoroughly familiar to the petroleum industry; these methods would probably require modification. But drilling at sea requires drastic innovations in drilling methods from the very start. Nothing like this has ever been done before.

At a minimum, holes will have to be drilled in depths of 4,000 to 6,000 meters of water, through some 4,000 to 6,000 meters of crustal rock. Moreover, one hole to the mantle may yield much important information, but one hole will be only a beginning. Many holes will have to be drilled in many places before we can reach any conclusions on the nature of the rocks in the mantle. A Mohole at sea will not only require a longer drill stem than has ever been used before; it will have to be used from a ship subject to the hazards of oceanic conditions—waves, currents, and storms. In addition, it will be necessary to cope with high temperatures and high pressures, as well as tough rock.

The Mohole Project presents a severe challenge to technology. Although the technological aspects of the project are secondary to the scientific, their implications for the future should not be overlooked. Development of a feasible method of drilling from a ship or floating platform in depths of water of several miles will eventually be of great economic value, if only to tap the pools of petroleum which very probably lie under the bottom of the deepest part of the Gulf of Mexico, beneath more than two miles of water.

The emphasis has been on reaching the Mohorovicic discontinuity, but the Mohole will probe into other phenomena as important as the discontinuity. For example, there is the fundamental problem of the origin or differentiation of continents and ocean basins. This in turn involves the hypothesis of continental drift, the permanence of continents and ocean basins, the possibility of contraction or expansion of the earth, even of alternating expansion and contraction. The Mohole may not provide all the answers, but it is a fairly obvious first step in the study of the ocean basins and what is under them.

The apparent thinness of sediment under the floors of the oceans is another tantalizing problem. According to seismic measurements, the thickness of sediment in the Atlantic is only about 800 meters, and in the Pacific it is even less. When calculations are made on the basis of conservative rates of sediment accumulation, we find that the time represented by these layers of sediment is only about enough to go back to the beginning of the Cretaceous Period. These thicknesses of sediment seem to account for somewhat less than one fifth of the time which has elapsed since the appearance of life. An additional hint that something happened in late Mesozoic time is the fact that although coring and sampling in both oceans have yielded many samples of Cretaceous and younger sediments, as yet no sediment older than Cretaceous has been found. Possible explanations come to mind; for example, that the ocean floors may have been flooded by great outpourings of lava. Or that some process of metamorphism may have altered the physical properties of pre-Cretaceous sediments in such a way as to make them unrecognizable by seismic methods. Continental drift is of no help because the thickness of sediment is severely limited in both oceans. Expansion of the earth could explain the youth of both oceans, but this implies a sudden and enormous expansion followed by near stability ever since, which is not easy to accept. One way, if not the only way, to find out what happened is to drill to the bottom of the sediment.

If, as the evidence indicates, an almost catastrophic reorganization of the major part of the surface of the earth took place fairly late in earth history, it is hardly likely that drilling in the ocean basins will provide us with a continuous record going back to the beginning of life. But we do have a basis for expecting a continuous record that will extend into the late Mesozoic, and the scientific value of this record would justify the drilling of a dozen Moholes. To obtain a continuous sedimentary record, however, it will be necessary to choose the drilling site with great care. We know from the study of many relatively short cores from the North and South Atlantic that discontinuous records, because of loss of some part by slumping, are to be found much more frequently than continuous records. The site ought to be either in the bottom of a basin or near the center of a broad, flat-topped rise. If the depth of the water at the site exceeds 5,000 meters, however, there is danger that the record will be seriously impaired by solution of calcareous organic remains.

The critical importance of the site suggests the desirability of drilling one Mohole at a site selected particularly for the purpose of reaching the Mohorovicic discontinuity and then drilling one or more non-Moholes at sites suitable for other objectives. Since the non-Moholes would not need to be so deep, they could be drilled at considerably less expense of time and money.

One area that would yield interesting results is the submarine delta of the Hudson Submarine Canyon. Another is the Sigsbee Deep in the Gulf of Mexico. In both, deposition by turbidity currents has been dominant during much of the Pleistocene Epoch. There is also evidence from piston cores taken in these areas that turbidity currents have been relatively infrequent during interglacials. If so, the Pleistocene sedimentary section in these areas ought to consist of zones dominated by graded layers of sand and silt, separated by zones dominated by clay containing the shells of planktonic foraminifera, the former corresponding to ice ages and the latter to interglacials. Many piston cores have been taken in both areas, but none has been long enough to reach foraminiferal clay representing the last interglacial, the Sangamon, presumably because deposition by turbidity currents during the last ice age was ten or more times faster than normal deep-sea deposition. The Mohole drilling equipment could do a good job here and probably in a very short time; it is hardly likely that the entire Pleistocene section in these areas is thicker than a few hundred meters. The Pleistocene record from these areas would be doubly valuable in that the climatic zones would be distinguishable not only by foraminifera, as in the record we have already established, but also by facies or lithology.

Deeper drilling at the intermediate stage, into the so-called "second" and "third" layers, would likewise be of scientific value even if it did not reach the Mohorovicic discontinuity. Are there really any consistently distinguishable "second" and "third" layers? Is the "second" layer perhaps a combination of indurated sediments and volcanic rocks? Have periodic outpourings of lava in the ocean areas hidden all the older oceanic sediments? Or have the older sediments been fragmented and resorbed into igneous rock by rising convection currents.

The direct measurements, in a borehole, of velocities, densities, and other physical and chemical properties of rocks deep in the earth should provide a much more reliable basis for conclusions about the constitution, history, and evolution of the earth than is possible from the present inferences based on indirect geophysical or geochemical interpretation, which may not be able adequately to take into consideration the effect of complex interrelations of these properties at high temperatures and high pressures under natural conditions deep in the earth. Such data may even have important bearing on conclusions on the character of bodies in space.

The first phase of the Mohole Project was carried out in the first quarter of 1961. Five holes were drilled off La Jolla, California, from the floating drilling vessel *Cuss I*, in water 950 meters deep, to a depth of as much 300 meters below the bottom of the ocean. Five additional holes were then drilled between Guadalupe Island and the coast of Baja California, in water 3,565 meters deep. These penetrated the subocean bottom to depths of as much as 180 meters. The drilling at the Guadalupe site penetrated about 170 meters of unconsolidated sediments before entering basalt. About 13 meters of basalt was penetrated in one of the holes.

All coring and logging was done through the drill pipe with the sand line or Schlumberger cable. Cores were taken by four types of barrels. The first type, a conventional punch barrel, was locked in the bit with the coring tube projecting about 1.5 meters below the bit; cores were taken by forcing the barrel into the sediments by the weight of the drill string. The second type of barrel was a hydraulic punch barrel, which locked into place above the bit and was forced three meters into the sediment by hydraulic pressure from the mud pumps. The third was a six-meter rotary barrel, and the fourth the turbo core barrel. The greatest recovery was made with the rotary barrel; it drilled nine meters into the sediments on each run, without circulation.

The sediment cores consisted for the most part of greenish-gray clays rich in siliceous and calcareous planktonic microfossils. The entire sedimentary section sampled is believed to be late Tertiary in age; the topmost section, of Pliocene age; and the sections directly above the basalt, late (or perhaps Middle) Miocene age.

One interesting physical property of the sediments was determined by direct measurement through the drilled holes: sound penetrated soft sediment at a rate of 1.6 kilometers per second. This is well below previous estimates of 2.2 kilometers per second and suggests that the layer of sediment on the floors of the ocean may be thinner than calculated.

Although the scientific results of the preliminary drilling phase of the Mohole Project do not seem to be of great importance, it is significant that the operation proved that a drilling ship could be held in position without anchors and that cores could be recovered and geophysical measurements made in holes drilled in the floor of the deep sea. No oceanic drilling has been carried out under the project since the conclusion of the Guadalupe drilling, in April 1961, however. In the light of the preliminary venture, it was decided that immediate attention should be given to the development of a more specialized vessel and more specialized drilling equipment to carry out deep oceanic drilling. The lessons learned in the preliminary drilling phase and the engineering developments it triggered now make it possible to construct and put into use a more advanced drilling vessel. With it, there is every likelihood that valuable scientific data can be gathered which will help to solve some of the puzzling problems in geology, geophysics, and oceanography.

It will be quite a long time, however, before a new drilling vessel is constructed, tested, and a hole is drilled into the mantle. It has been proposed, therefore, that another project be put into operation as soon as possible, with the objective of coring the ocean floor from a vessel of the type used in the preliminary drilling. This type of vessel is being used by the petroleum industry for conventional offshore drilling operations. The aim of the project would be to recover continuous cores of the total unconsolidated thickness of sediment on the ocean—which would yield important scientific data.

We have suggested a project that would not involve deep-sea drilling. Its aim would be to obtain a complete stratigraphical section of the Pliocene, and we believe it can be carried out by means of the conventional piston corer.

The Hudson Canyon, where it crosses the continental rise, provides a ready-made deep hole. The thickness of sediment exposed along the walls of the canyon is about 400 meters, and cores already taken from the walls of the canyon near the bottom are of Pliocene age. It is probable, therefore, that a complete section of Pleistocene and Pliocene sediments is exposed along the walls. To obtain a continuous section, it will be necessary to take hundreds of closely spaced cores. These can then be matched and, on the basis of overlapping, a complete stratigraphical section of the Pliocene, estimated to span a period of about 10,000,000 years, can be prepared. A number of problems that had stood in the way, such as the whys and wherefores of depositional processes, have been solved; methods of testing cores for continuity of accumulation have been worked out; precise and rapid methods of analyzing populations of planktonic foraminifera have been devised; and the complete stratigraphical section of the Pleistocene, with a complete chronology, has been pieced together. When this book is ready for publication, we will have started to attack the problems of the Pliocene, and also the problems of the causation of the ice ages and of the speciation of planktonic organisms during the Pleistocene. We will also take part in the drilling projects.

We stand on the threshold of a major scientific assault on our native planet, the earth. We have started ultra-deep drilling into the earth's mantle, on land and at sea; we are in process of drilling to recover a complete sequence of oceanic sediment and are attempting systematic coring of the walls of a submarine canyon to discover the complete stratigraphical section of the Pliocene. Even the relatively few completely new facts that will emerge will have great influence on the development of geology and the allied sciences and will make it possible all the sooner to roll back the curtain of obscurity from the structure and composition of our planet and the endogenous forces that govern it. The acceleration of these projects brings nearer the transition of contemporary geology to a qualitatively new stage—from a discipline devoted to study of the most superficial integument of our planet, to a science of the earth. This is no less vital than our forays into outer space. Indeed, a deeper understanding of the earth on which we live is essential for the further progress of human society.

The adventure into inner space has begun.

BIBLIOGRAPHY

Andrée, K.: "Geologie des Meeresbodens," in *Bodenbeschaffenheit, nutzbare Materialien am Meeresboden,* Vol. 2. Leipzig: Gebrüder Borntraeger; 1920.

Arrhenius, G.: *Sediment Cores from the East Pacific.* Reports of the Swedish Deep-Sea Expedition 1947–1948, Vol. V, Fasc. I. Göteborg: Elanders Boktryckeri Aktiebolag; 1952.

Bascom, W.: "The Mohole." *Scientific American,* Vol. 200, No. 4 (April 1959), pp. 41–9.

Boule, M., and Vallois, H. V.: *Fossil Men.* New York: The Dryden Press; 1957.

Bramlette, M. N., and Bradley, W. H.: *Geology and biology of North Atlantic deep-sea cores between Newfoundland and Ireland. Pt. 1. Lithology and geologic interpretations.* United States Geological Survey, Professional Paper 196 (1940), pp. 1–34.

Bramlette, M. N., and Riedel, W. R.: "Stratigraphic Value of Discoasters and Some Other Microfossils Related to Recent Coccolithophores." *Journal of Paleontology,* Vol. 28 (1954), pp. 385–403.

Broecker, W. S., and Farrand, W. R.,: "Radiocarbon age of the Two Creeks Forrest bed." *Geological Society of America Bulletin,* Vol. 74, No. 6 (June 1963), pp. 795–802.

Charlesworth, J. K.: *The Quaternary Era,* 2 vols. London: E. Arnold; 1957.

Coon, C. S.: *The Origin of Races.* New York: Alfred A. Knopf; 1962.

Curtis, G. H.: "A Clock for the Ages: Potassium-Argon." *National Geographic,* Vol. 120, No. 4 (October 1961), pp. 590–2.

Cushman, J. A., and Henbest, L. G.: *Geology and biology of North Atlantic deep-sea cores between Newfoundland and Ireland. Pt. 2. Foraminifera.* United States Geological Survey, Professional Paper 196 (1940), pp. 35–55.

Daly, R. A.: "Origin of Submarine Canyons." *American Journal of Science,* Vol. 27 (1936), pp. 401–20.

Dart, R. A.: *Adventures with the Missing Link*. New York: Viking Press;
    1961.

Darwin, C.: *The Origin of Species*. New York: Collier Books; 1962.

Emiliani, C.: "Pleistocene Temperatures." *Journal of Geology*, Vol. 63, No.
    6 (November 1955), pp. 538–78.

——: "Ancient Temperatures." *Scientific American*, Vol. 198, No. 2
    (February 1958), pp. 54–63.

Ericson, D. B.: "Coiling Direction of *Globigerina pachyderma* as a Climatic
    Index." *Science*, Vol. 130, No. 3369 (1959), pp. 219–20.

——: "Pleistocene Climatic Record in Some Deep-Sea Sediment Cores."
    Annals of the New York Academy of Sciences, Vol. 95, Article 1
    (October 1961), pp. 537–41.

——: "Cross-correlation of deep-sea sediment cores and determination of
    relative rates of sedimentation by micropaleontological techniques,"
    in Hill, M. N., ed.: *The Sea*. New York: John Wiley & Sons; 1963.

——, Ewing, M., and Heezen, B. C.: "Turbidity Currents and Sediments
    in the North Atlantic." *American Association of Petroleum Geologists
    Bulletin*, Vol. 36 (1952), pp. 489–511.

——, and Wollin, G.: *Sediment Deposition in Deep Atlantic*. Geological
    Society of America, Special Paper 62 (1955), pp. 205–20.

Ericson, D. B., Ewing, M., and Wollin, G.: "Pliocene-Pleistocene Boundary
    in Deep-Sea Sediment Cores." *Science*, Vol. 139, No. 3556 (1963),
    pp. 727–37.

——: "Sediment Cores from the Arctic and Subarctic Seas." *Science*, Vol.
    144, No. 3623 (1964), pp.   .

——: "The Pleistocene Epoch in Deep-Sea Sediments." *Science*, October
    1964.

——, and Heezen, B. C.: "Atlantic Deep-Sea Sediment Cores." *Geological
    Society of America Bulletin*, Vol. 72 (February 1961), pp. 193–286.

Ericson, D. B., and Wollin, G.: "Correlation of Six Cores from the Equa-
    torial Atlantic and Caribbean." *Deep-Sea Research*, Vol. 3 (January
    1956), pp. 104–25.

——: "Micropaleontological and Isotopic Determinations of Pleistocene
    Climates." *Micropaleontology*, Vol. 2, No. 3 (July 1956), pp.
    257–70.

——, and Wollin, J.: "Coiling Direction of *Globorotalia truncatulinoides*
    in Deep-Sea Cores." *Deep-Sea Research*, Vol. 2 (1954), pp. 152–8.

Flint, R. F.: *Glacial and Pleistocene Geology*. New York: John Wiley &
    Sons; 1957.

Hamilton, J. L.: *Sunken Islands of the Mid-Pacific Mountains*. Geological
    Society of America, Memoir 64 (1956).

Heezen, B. C., Tharp, M., and Ewing, M.: *The Floors of the Oceans. I. The North Atlantic.* Geological Society of America, Special Paper 65 (1959).

Hess, H. H.: *Drowned Ancient Islands of the Pacific Basin.* Washington: Smithsonian Institution. Report for 1947, pp. 281–300.

Hough, J. L.: "Pleistocene Climatic Record in Pacific Ocean Core Sample." *Journal of Geology,* Vol. 61, No. 3 (May 1953), pp. 252–62.

Kuenen, Ph. H.: *Marine Geology.* New York: John Wiley & Sons; 1950.

Kullenberg, B.: *Bottom Investigations. No. 2. Deep-Sea Coring.* Reports of the Swedish Deep-Sea Expedition 1947–1948, Vol. IV, Fasc. I. Göteborg: Elanders Boktryckeri Aktiebolag; 1955.

Leakey, L. S. B.: "Exploring 1,750,000 Years into Man's Past." *National Geographic,* Vol. 120, No. 4 (October 1961), pp. 564–89.

———, and Leakey, M. D.: "Recent Discoveries of Fossil Hominids in Tanganyika: at Olduvai and Near Lake Natron." *Nature,* Vol. 202, No. 4927 (1964), pp. 5–7.

Öpik, E. J.: "Climate and the Changing Sun." *Scientific American,* Vol. 198, No. 6 (June 1958), pp. 85–92.

Ovey, C. D.: "On the Interpretation of Climatic Variations as Revealed by a Study of Samples from an Equatorial Atlantic Deep-Sea Core," in *Centenary Symposium on Climatic Change.* Royal Meteorological Society, Centenary Proc. (1950), pp. 211–15.

Pettersson, H.: *The Ocean Floor.* New Haven: Yale University Press; 1954.

———: *Westward Ho with the Albatross.* New York: E. P. Dutton & Co.; 1952.

Phleger, F. B: "Vertical Distribution of Pelagic Foraminifera." *American Journal of Science,* Vol. 243 (1945), pp. 377–83.

———, Parker, F. L., and Peirson, J. F.: *Sediment Cores from the North Atlantic Ocean. No. 1. North Atlantic Foraminifera.* Reports of the Swedish Deep-Sea Expedition 1947–1948, Vol. VII, Fasc. I. Göteborg: Elanders Boktryckeri Aktiebolag; 1953.

Revelle, R. R., Bramlette, M. N., Arrhenius, G., and Goldberg, E. D.: "Pelagic Sediments of the Pacific," in Poldervaart, A., ed.: *Crust of the Earth.* Geological Society of America, Special Paper 62 (1955), pp. 221–36.

Rosholt, J. N., Emiliani, C., Geiss, J., Koczy, F. F., and Wangersky, P. J.: "Absolute Dating of Deep-Sea Cores by the Pa^{231}/Th^{230} Method." *Journal of Geology,* Vol. 69, No. 2 (March 1961), pp. 162–85.

Schott, W.: "Rate of Sedimentation of Recent Marine Sediments," Trask, P. D., ed.: *Recent Marine Sediments.* Tulsa: American Association of Petroleum Geologists; 1939.

Shapley, H., ed.: *Climatic Change*. Cambridge: Harvard University Press; 1953.

Shepard, F. P.: *Transportation of Sand into Deep Water*. Society of Economic Paleontologists and Mineralogists, Special Publication No. 2 (1951).

————: *Submarine Geology*. Second edition. New York: Harper and Row; 1963.

Simpson, G. C.: "Ice Ages." *Nature,* Vol. 141, No. 3570 (1938), pp. 591–8.

Sinnott, E. W., Dunn, L. C., and Dobzhansky, T.: *Principles of Genetics*. Fifth edition. New York: McGraw-Hill Book Company, Inc.; 1958.

Sverdrup, H. U., Fleming, R., and Johnson, M. W.: *The Oceans*. New York: Prentice-Hall, Inc.; 1942.

Wilson, J. T.: "Continental Drift." *Scientific American,* Vol. 208, No. 4 (April 1963), pp. 86–100.

Wiseman, J. D. H.: "The Determination and Significance of Past Temperature Changes in the Upper Layer of the Equatorial Atlantic Ocean." *Proceedings of the Royal Society, A*. Vol. 222 (1954), pp. 296–323.

Woollard, G. P.: "The Land of the Antarctic." *Scientific American,* Vol. 207, No. 3 (September 1962), pp. 151–66.

Zeuner, F. E.: *The Pleistocene. Its climate, chronology and faunal successions*. London: Bernard Quaritch; 1945.

————: *Dating the Past*. Second Edition. London: Methuen & Co.; 1950.

"History Layer by Layer." A film about the study of deep-sea sediment cores at the Lamont Geological Observatory. Produced by Robert E. Dierbeck of United States Productions. New York, 1964.

INDEX

A Note on the Type

THE TEXT of this book was set on the Linotype in a face called *Times Roman,* designed by STANLEY MORISON for *The Times* (London), and first introduced by that newspaper in 1932.

Among typographers and designers of the twentieth century, Stanley Morison has been a strong forming influence, as typographical advisor to the English Monotype Corporation, as a director of two distinguished English publishing houses, and as a writer of sensibility, erudition, and keen practical sense.

Composed, printed, and bound by
The Haddon Craftsmen, Scranton, Pa.
Typography and binding design by
VINCENT TORRE

A Note on the Authors

DAVID B. ERICSON

Senior Research Scientist at the Lamont Geological Observatory, was born in New York City and received his B.S. at M.I.T. and his M.S. in geology and paleontology at the California Institute of Technology. Until 1938 Mr. Ericson worked as geologist for various oil companies and served as petroleum geologist for the Turkish government for two years. Subsequently he was Assistant State Geologist for the Florida Geology Survey and Marine Geologist at the Woods Hole Oceanographic Institution before taking up his present post in 1947. He is Vice President for Oceanography of the Seventh Congress of the International Association for Quaternary Research in 1965.

GOESTA WOLLIN

born in Sweden and educated at the University of Lund and at Columbia University, was formerly Research Assistant at Lamont. He has continued to collaborate in the Observatory's projects while carrying on his own career in mental health and social work. He was an Intelligence officer and paratrooper in the 82nd Airborne Division of the U.S. Army from 1943 to 1945 and entered the field of journalism after the war. He had had two novels published before joining the Lamont group in 1949. Mr. Wollin is married and he and his wife have one daughter.